Algrove Publishing Limited
1090 Morrison Drive
Ottawa, Ontario
Canada K2H 1C2

National Library of Canada Cataloguing in Publication Data

Main entry under title:

    Popular mechanics shop notes for ...

(Classic reprint series)
Includes indexes.
Originally published: Chicago : Popular Mechanics Co., 1905-
"Compiled from the "Shop notes" department of Popular
        mechanics magazine, and "Written so you can understand
        it"; tells easy ways to do hard things" --Added t.p., v. 1.
Cover title.
Contents: v. 25. 1929.
ISBN 1-894572-31-9 (v. 25)

    1. Do-it-yourself work. 2. Industrial arts. 3. Bricolage.
4. Métiers. I. Title: Shop notes for... . II. Series: Classic
reprint series (Ottawa, Ont.)

TJ1160.P66 1999   600   C99-900763-7

Printed in Canada
#10701

Publisher's Note

Virtually every woodworking magazine in the English-speaking world has a shop notes section and has published an accumulation of them in book form. This was all started in 1905 with the first annual issue of *Popular Mechanics Shop Notes*, a compilation of advice on jigs, fixtures, methods of work, processes and projects. The earlier issues focussed primarily on metalworking, but with tips for a variety of other trades liberally sprinkled throughout. As years went by, the contents shifted more and more to woodworking and handyman projects. Each book is profusely illustrated. The line drawings of the earlier issues were supplanted by superb engravings until photographs started to creep in during the 1920s. Each year has its charm but all issues share the attribute of being clear, concise and widely informative.

Leonard G. Lee, Publisher
Ottawa
September, 1999

WARNING

This is a reprint of a book compiled in the early 1900s. The book describes what was recommended to be done in accordance with the knowledge of the day.

It would be advisable to treat all corrosive, explosive and toxic materials with much greater caution than is indicated here, particularly any materials that come in contact with the body.

Similarly, some of the recommended projects were dangerous then and remain so now. All of this material should be regarded with a judicious eye and necessary precautions taken.

POPULAR MECHANICS

SHOP NOTES

FOR 1929

VOLUME XXV

WITH 400 ILLUSTRATIONS

————

POPULAR MECHANICS PRESS
CHICAGO

THE wide range of subjects covered in this 1929 issue of Shop Notes is indicated by the following partial list. Most readers will probably be interested in some of these, and many will derive benefit from all the 347 articles.

Complete Index, Page 201

Shop Notes

Insulating the Hot-Water Tank

By E. E. SCOTT

WHY place a radiator in the cellar? That is just what you do when you permit the plumbing contractor to install the hot-water tank in your new house, without covering it to prevent loss of heat. The usual 40-gal. dwelling-house tank will radiate sufficient heat to keep a 10 by 12-ft. room comfortably warm. In so doing, it causes the temperature of the water in the tank to drop about 20° below that at which it enters the tank. Furthermore this heat is not needed in the basement as the heater itself will radiate, unavoidably, sufficient warmth to keep that part of the house comfortable.

If you would have more and hotter water and save some fuel besides, cover the tank with as-bestos cement. But, you ask, how can it be made to stick to such a smooth surface as that of a galvanized-iron water tank? First, buy sufficient wire window screening to cover the tank completely except for the top and bottom. Bind this screening around the tank with bare-copper or soft-iron wire of about No. 18 gauge and

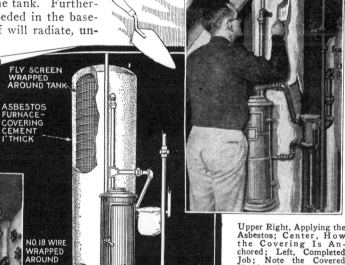

Upper Right, Applying the Asbestos; Center, How the Covering Is Anchored; Left, Completed Job; Note the Covered Heating Coil between the Tank and Boiler

draw the wire up as tightly as possible. Next purchase about 30 lb. asbestos "furnace-covering cement" from a hardware-supply house or plumbing shop; this should cost about five cents per pound when bought in bulk. Make a paste by mixing this material with

1

water. The consistency should be such that, when a little of the paste is thrown at the screen-covered tank, it will stick. Apply the paste with a masons' trowel; the quality obtainable at a five and ten-cent store will be satisfactory.

The first coat is known as the skin coat and should be smoothed on to a depth of about ¼ in. and allowed to set about 24 hours, until it dries white and hard. Add layers of the cement until a covering about ¾ in. in thickness is obtained. The upper half of the tank should, however, be covered a little more heavily than the lower as the hottest water is always at the top. This is also desirable because, frequently, only the upper portion of the tank contains hot water, due to a low fire or to the water having been drawn off. The thickness of the coating can be determined by sticking a pin through the asbestos to the tank. The rounded top of the tank should also be covered to a depth of 1 in. or more.

Considerable care must be expended on the finish coat. A molders' slick makes the best smoothing tool, although a large spoon, flattened somewhat on the bottom, will do. Cover only about 1 ft. at a time, and smooth it carefully before putting on more. The work can be stopped at any time, as the new wet cement will make a perfect joint with a completely dried section. In order to make the finished surface as smooth as possible, a second smoothing with the slick should be given after the cement has dried for about one-half hour. If sufficient care is taken, a smooth eggshell gloss will result, which will not only shed dust but will also permit only the very minimum amount of radiation.

Many hot-water tanks used in connection with home steam-heating

plants are heated by an external copper coil which is so connected that it is completely surrounded by hot water from the boiler. This heater is always at nearly the temperature of boiling water and should consequently be covered with an extra-heavy coating of cement, about 1½ in.

The first layer should be quite thin, ⅛ in. or so, as a heavier application will drop off in patches due to the smaller radius and sharper angles of the heater. As the piping between the heater, boiler and tank presents only a small amount of radiating surface, it may simply be painted black with stovepipe enamel. The gas or separate heater used during the summer may also be improved in appearance, while it is standing idle, with a coat of the black enamel.

Double Wheels Conquer Soft Dirt

By bolting a complete extra wheel and tire to the regular rear wheels of his Ford cars, a large landowner in the peat-sediment delta of the San Joaquin river in California has solved a difficult traction problem. The soil is of the peculiar ashy, springy type characteristic of reclaimed peat areas, and affords little traction to the ordinary small single tire. The ranch foremen and mechanics must travel from field to field, often when cultivation is going on, and there is no time to make roads. With these double wheels a Ford can go anywhere on the ranch, even across a freshly plowed field. The photo shows how the extra wheel is attached by means of blocks of wood, through which are driven bolts, held in place by iron strips on both sides. The work was done in the ranch shop. —Logan Studio, Stockton, Calif.

Extra Rear Wheel on Ford Permits It to Cross Freshly Plowed Soft Land

Pivoted Containers for Vegetables in Grocery Store Make It an Easy Task to Transfer Them into Peck and Other Measures or to Bags

Handy Vegetable Containers for Stores

In grocery stores, clerks usually have to lift a whole basket of potatoes, apples or vegetables when transferring them into a peck measure or bag. This practice is more or less difficult and inconvenient, and can be entirely eliminated by pivoting the containers as shown in the illustration. It is advisable to use half sections of small barrels or large kegs for this purpose. Each one is securely strengthened and two 1-in. holes are drilled directly opposite each other through the side, so that the container can be slipped over a suitable length of pipe. The ends of this pipe are slipped through tees, provided on the ends of vertical standards, as indicated, the latter being securely bolted to the floor. The containers are filled, and it is an easy matter to fill either measures or bags by tilting the proper container to one side.

Steel Wool as Aluminum-Ware Cleaner

It takes little trouble to keep aluminum pots and pans shining if they are cleaned frequently with steel wool, water, and a nonalkaline soap. Use a very fine grade of the wool, and give the utensils a few rubs frequently, rather than attempt to clean them only occasionally, when they have become more soiled.—L. P. Langan, Denver, Colo.

A Timesaver for the Draftsman

Draftsmen who make electrical diagrams find that the drawing of a large number of resistance symbols is a rather irksome task. If slots are cut in a 30°-60° triangle, as shown in the drawing, the task becomes simply one of working between two previously established guide lines.—Reuben Jensen, Silverton, Oregon.

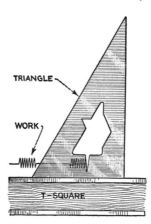

ened just enough to permit the wagon to be drawn slowly toward the saw frame. When the wires have been twisted enough, the belt is thrown and a block of wood is held against the fly wheel to prevent too much back spin. Sometimes long pieces of cable, 100 to 200 ft., are twisted at one time and are later cut up into smaller lengths of proper size.—Dale R. Van Horn, Walton, Nebr.

The Farm Saw Frame Can Be Put to Many Other Uses

Uses for the Farm Saw Frame

A Nebraska power farmer, who employs a large circular saw each winter for getting stove wood in shape, finds other uses for the machine. During the haying season he removes the saw and puts the grindstone in its place. Of course, the drive shaft is turned at low speed, about 150 r.p.m., by putting the belt onto a 4-in. pulley on the 4-hp. engine which is used to drive it. Another use to which the saw frame is put is for twisting cable for fence-corner braces. The frame is braced against end strain and the several strands are attached to the shaft. The other ends of the wires are fastened to the rear end of a heavy farm wagon. As the wires are twisted together, the over-all length is reduced. A man stands in the wagon with his hand on the brake and as the tension grows stiff, the brake is loos-

Effective Tool for Stirring Paint

The secret of stirring up paint to its best consistency is to churn the contents of the can thoroughly so that all the ingredients are completely mixed. This cannot be done with a stick except by long patient effort. A device that will do the trick in a much shorter time can quickly be made from a short length of stiff wire cable. Wrap some cloth around one end for a handle. Then open the strands near the bottom and bow them out in the form of a hollow ball, as shown in the drawing. Such a stirring rod will pick up all the solid matter at the bottom of the can, and the separated strands will churn it into a good mixture.—L. B. Robbins, Harwich, Massachusetts.

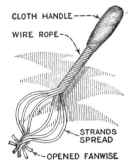

CLOTH HANDLE
WIRE ROPE
STRANDS SPREAD
OPENED FANWISE

¶A cork can be made to do the work of a glass stopper by placing it in a metal vessel and boiling it in vaseline; when dry, it is acid-resistant, unaffected by jamming it into a bottle, and will last indefinitely.

Continuous Fertilizer for the Garden

In many locations, especially in the cities, small garden spots need a great deal of fertilizing to make plants and flowers grow successfully. Take an old lime barrel or a metal can and clean it out well with water. It should be perforated with ½-in. holes along the sides and bottom, and is then half filled with some good fertilizer. Pour in water enough to fill the barrel. The fertilizer should be churned up every day. It has been found that the most stubborn soil conditions have been corrected in this way so that almost anything could be made to grow.—L. H. Georger, Buffalo, N. Y.

Pliers Have Stop for Bending Wire

Soft wire up to ⅛ in. in diameter can be most conveniently bent with the aid of a pair of pliers and a simple stop piece, clamped in place as shown in the drawing. As an example of what can be done with this device, a number of wire squares can be made exactly the same size. The stop is made and attached in a few moments and the whole batch of pieces finished quickly. A length of strip metal is bent at right angles at both ends and clamped to the side of one of the plier jaws. To make a right-angle bend, push the wire tip to the stop and bend it close over the other jaw.

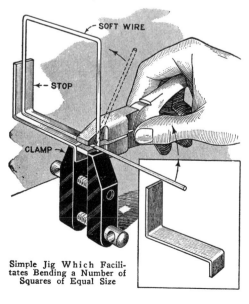

Simple Jig Which Facilitates Bending a Number of Squares of Equal Size

Cloth Attached to Draftsman's T-Square Prevents Drawings from Being Soiled

Protecting Drawings from Being Soiled

Draftsmen making sketches and pencil plans will find that a cloth fastened to the T-square with thumbtacks, as shown in the illustration, is of considerable service in protecting drawings from being soiled. The cloth does not interfere with the work and covers the section of the drawing not being worked on, permitting the draftsman to rest his arms on it without any risk of smudging the work.

Using Sandpaper in Plane

For sandpapering a smooth surface where it is necessary to keep the paper absolutely flat so that no hollow places will be rubbed into the surface, a common plane can be used to advantage. Remove the blade and cut a strip of sandpaper sufficiently narrow to fit through the slot in the plane, then double it over so that it will remain fixed under the clamp that is used to hold the blade in position. The free end of the paper can be brought around under the plane and up over the front to be held down by the hand grasping the knob in front. By pushing and pulling the plane over the surface it can be sanded flat and with the least exertion.

Machine to Lap Crankcases

Crankcases have not been lapped by hand in the plant of the Marmon Motor

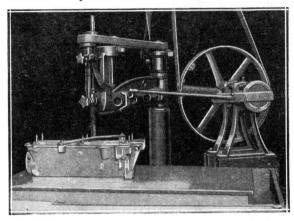

Old Radial Drill Press Converted into a Good Machine for Lapping Auto Crankcases

Car company at Indiànapolis since J. W. Anderson, mechanical engineer of the company, built, at a very low cost, a machine that does the work better, and saves 47 cents on the cost of each crankcase. A discarded radial drill press, reclaimed from the junk heap, is the principal part of the apparatus. The crankcase is fastened to a rotating vertical arm of the press and is given a supplemental to-and-fro movement by an eccentrically driven shaft. Ground glass was formerly used as the lapping compound. Worn-out sand from sand-blasting machines has replaced the ground glass. Mixed with coal oil, this sand has been found more satisfactory than the ground glass.

Piston-Ring Compressor

In the absence of a regular piston-ring compressor, an excellent substitute can be

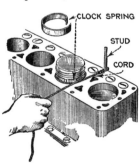

made from a piece of ½-in. clock spring, about an inch longer than the circumference of the ring, and a piece of stout cord. Insert the piston in the cylinder as far as the expanded ring will permit, fit the clock spring around the first ring to be inserted, anchor the cord to a stud or other fitting, which will enable it to lie flat on top of the cylinder block, wrap it once around the clock spring and pull it tight. As a result the ring will be evenly and positively compressed and the first ring will slide into the cylinder. Loosen the cord, remove the spring and repeat the operation for the other rings.

Double Cock Handle

A method of connecting two cocks so that one handle can be used to control both is shown in the accompanying drawing. This idea is being successfully used in connection with filling an inclosed tank with the correct amount of liquid required to make a mixture used in the printing business. The inlet cock is attached to the tank upside down, at the top, and the outlet in an upright position at the bottom. The handle is a piece of flat steel bent at right angles at both ends with square holes to fit over the squares on the plugs. Sockets are brazed to the tank to receive the cocks, one of these being brazed in place with the wrench assembled. When this is

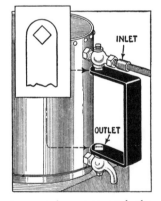

done, one faucet must be open and the other shut. Thus, if the inlet is open the tank will be filled, and when the outlet is open the inlet is automatically closed. As soon as the tank is emptied the outlet is closed, which automatically opens the inlet again, filling the tank ready for the next measure.—Harry Moore, Montreal, Can.

¶Graphite should never be used on an engine timer as it may cause short-circuiting of the current.

Packing for Ford Window Glass

Older models of Ford closed cars had a metal frame on the glass windows. It was padded with cloth on the sides, but was merely a metal channel along the lower side of the glass. The frame was filled on both sides of the glass with some sort of wax. This is hard to find when the glass must be replaced, and if not used, the glass vibrates along the lower edge. Also, during a rain, water is likely to run into the channel and under the glass, where it will be thrown into the car by the movement of the glass. Cork strips, which may be cut from gasket material and forced down edgewise beside the glass into the frame, make good packing. The strips should be coated with shellac on both sides to keep them in place. The upper edge of the strips should be painted with black enamel, using a small brush. This is done to keep the gaskets dry, as the glue that binds the cork will be dissolved if it becomes wet.—E. T. Gunderson, Jr., Humboldt, Iowa.

Help for Drilling Vertical Holes

A mechanic who does not have access to a drill press, but is required to drill a perfectly vertical hole with an ordinary hand or breast drill, will appreciate the kink shown in the drawing. A circular level, such as used on cameras, is attached to the drill frame by means of a sheet-metal clamp. One ring of the clamp fits around the frame of the drill, preferably below the driving wheel, while the ring to 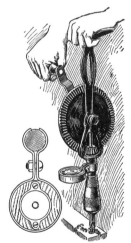 which the level is attached is made the same diameter as the level, and has a wooden disk inserted in it so that the level may be screwed on it as indicated. The clamp is about ⅜ in. in width.—W. J. Edmonds, Jr., Whitehall, N. Y.

Reading Glass, Inserted in the End of a Flexible Tube of Desk Lamp, Helps Letterer

Reading Glass for Draftsmen

I had to do quite a bit of fine lettering in my high-school work and, as I worked at night, this caused a strain on my eyes. I took a lamp shade, which was an adjustable one of the hollow-tube kind, unscrewed the lamp socket, and withdrew the electric cord. Then I bought a 5-in. reading glass and whittled the wooden handle down until it fitted snugly into the end of the hose. In use, the glass is arranged directly over the work, as shown in the drawing. I showed this scheme to our drawing instructor and he has had one fixed up for himself.—Harry Lampert, Los Angeles, Calif.

Easy Way to Fill Furnace Water Pan

On pipeless furnaces the water pan is often difficult to get at. The trouble was overcome in one case by filling the pan from the register in the floor rather than from the cramped and inconvenient position in the basement. An old gasoline-stove tank was used as a funnel and the pipe attached to it was extended into the water pan. A large-sized funnel can be substituted if desired, and a length of copper tubing used instead of the pipe, the tubing being soldered to the funnel.

Improvised Hangers Hold Eave Troughs in Position While Attaching Regular Hangers

be carried up the ladder and balanced in place with one hand while the other wields the hammer to drive the hook point through the loop and into the shingles. The trough being thus quickly and easily supported, the workman is free to move his ladder back and forth to fasten the remaining hangers, and the work is completed.—G. E. Hendrickson. Argyle, Wis.

Rubber Tips to Keep Finger Nails Clean

Having trouble to prevent ink from getting under the cuticle of his nails, and not caring to wear rubber gloves all the time, a printer thought of a plan for keeping his nails clean without using gloves. He took a pair of rubber gloves, cut the finger ends off about 1 in. and put the tips over his fingers, which effectively avoided the trouble.—G. R. Dement, Buffalo, N. Y.

Commutator Tool

One of the most frequent causes of trouble on direct-current motors, particularly those having undercut commutators, is short circuits between commutator bars. Serious breakdowns in the commutators or windings of the armature can be prevented if the trouble is discovered in time, by digging out the carbonized mass between bars down to the clean mica. Tools useful for this purpose can be cheaply made from pieces of old hacksaw blades. The blades should vary in thickness to take care of mica segments of different widths, and a point of the desired shape is ground on the broken end. A number of tools with differently shaped points should be made, to suit the work of various types of motors. After the desired

shape and edge have been formed on the blades, they should be hinged together by passing a rivet through the hole in the end of each and turning the head over with a hammer. This arrangement makes a very serviceable tool for the electrician and mechanics who find need of differently shaped tools of this type. It also provides a better grip than separate blades.

Combination Eave-Trough Hanger

Tinsmiths, when handling eave troughs, often find it inconvenient to fasten the first hanger onto the edge of the roof, as one must hold the long section of the trough, place the nail and manipulate the hammer, all while maintaining a safe position on the ladder or scaffold. A Wisconsin tinsmith simplified the labor and eliminated much of the attendant danger by altering a number of common wire hangers in the manner shown. As not more than three or four of these are necessary on the average job, they are well worth the little trouble required to make them. Extra-long hangers are used for this purpose, the wire being cut diagonally at the loop end to provide a sharp point on the hook. One of the severed ends is bent in the form of a loop while the other is hooked so that the point centers within the loop. When the trough has been soldered, on the ground, the altered hanger is placed as near the middle of the trough as possible and bent to the angle of the eaves. The trough may then

Making the Old Pump New

By L. B. ROBBINS

WHEN a pump commences to gurgle, suck and whistle at each stroke of the handle you may feel assured that something is wrong. Either the leathers are worn out or some air leak has developed, in the pump castings or in the pipe line above or below ground. In the majority of cases this will be found to be due to worn leathers.

For maximum efficiency, a pump depends upon a vacuum being created in the cylinder at each upstroke of the plunger. If air leaks past, this vacuum is destroyed and water will refuse to rise in the pipe. It is then that pumping water becomes a soul-searing and back-breaking job.

Now, it doesn't take a great deal of work to transform a leaky pump that requires 75 strokes to the bucket to one that will lift the same amount of water in 25 strokes

because so many pumps can be fitted with standard-size factory-cut leathers. It is simply a matter of taking the pump apart, inserting the new leathers and then reassembling as before.

There are essentially two types of dwelling-house pumps; the pitcher pump and the force pump. The former is found everywhere, and consists simply of an open-ended metal cylinder in which works a plunger with a lifting valve in the center. Between the bottom end of the cylinder and the pipe there is another valve, or deck leather. As the plunger is pushed down, the deck-leather valve closes and the plunger valve opens, thus allowing any water above the deck leather to pass through the plunger instead of being forced down into the well. When the plunger rises, the water thus brought over

Above, the Plunger Spider; Upper Right, Form of Deck Leather and Weight; Center, Removing the Cylinder

or less. In the majority of cases the trouble will be located in defective leathers. Nowadays it is a comparatively simple matter to change leathers,

it is raised higher and the suction below it lifts the deck-leather valve, and water in the pipe rises for the next stroke. In this way a more or less continuous stream of water is lifted from the depths and flows from the top of the cylinder through the open spout or "pitcher" lip. Varied forms of the pitcher pump exist, but the essentials of operation are identical.

The force pump makes use of the same principle, but the cylinder is entirely closed and the lifted water is directed into a closed chamber called the air dome. In there it comes into contact with a body of air which after compression by the in-flowing water, forces the water in a continuous and steady stream to a considerable distance or height. The compressed air forms a wonderfully powerful cushion and in this manner creates an internal pressure very useful in filling overhead tanks or projecting the pumped water along a rising pipe line.

Deep-well pumps are essentially the same as the simple shallow-well pumps except the pumping cylinder may be separated many feet from the pump body. This is because the plunger can only operate at a maximum of about 28 ft. above water level. Therefore, for a 50-ft. well, the cylinder must be placed in a pit or driven to within at least 28 ft. of the water level, and the plunger operated from above ground by a long rod running down through the pipe to the plunger rod in the cylinder.

The leathering of any of these types of pumps is essentially the same. Where the entire pump is above ground, the job is simple. If one or more cylinders are below ground the job becomes more difficult. But the leathering job remains the same; the plunger and the deck leather must be renewed.

The first thing to do with a shallow-well pump is to trip the water out by forcing the plunger down until you hear a sucking noise and the water drops back into the well. Then loosen the bolts holding the cylinder and the base casting together and lift the cylinder off. This exposes the deck leather, shown clearly in the photograph illustrating this operation. The drawing on page 9 also shows the shape of a typical deck leather and its component parts. It consists of a circular ring of stiff leather inside of which is a round

leather disk attached to the ring at one side. The open space between is horseshoe-shaped and permits the passage of water. A weight fastened to the disk helps to force it in place over the deck opening and thus make it a quicker-operating and tighter-fitting valve.

Remove this leather carefully so as not to score the metal deck or seat. If it is hard or cracked it should be discarded and a new leather provided. Remove the clapper weight by taking out the retaining screw in the center. Fit this on the new leather in its proper position, which is with the raised lug over the hinge. If no ready-cut leather can be obtained, a suitable one can be cut from a piece of $\frac{1}{8}$-in. oak-tanned stock by placing the old one over it as a pattern and marking around it with a pencil. Then cut the new one out with a sharp knife and fit the clapper weight to it. If the old leather is beyond use as a pattern, place the new piece of leather over the deck and tap it gently but firmly with the ball end of a ball-peen hammer around the outside edge and the edge of the pipe opening. When removed, the markings of the metal edges will be plainly visible and can be followed with the cutting knife.

Before the new deck leather is placed in position, wipe the deck clean of any dirt or grit. If any slight bits of nicked metal exist along the surface, smooth them off with a fine emery stone. Soak the new leather in water an hour or two to thoroughly soften it and then lay it carefully on the deck, still wet, placing the weight uppermost. When in the proper position, place the cylinder carefully upon it so as not to disturb its position, reinsert the bolts and take up on them slowly and evenly until the leather is firmly clamped in position. Use care in taking up on these bolts, taking a part of a turn on each one at a time. This will compress the leather evenly and also prevent clamping down one side before the other, and thus insure even pressure and eliminate chances of cracking the casting from uneven pressure on either side.

On deep-well pumps the cylinder must, of course, be removed from the pipe line before the packing can be accomplished. If it is in a pit, it is only a matter of removing the pipe from above and the sections of wooden plunger rod, and then releasing the cylinder from its base. Otherwise it must be pulled up with a pump puller and raised above ground until it can be dismantled. In any case the method of replacing is essentially as previously described for a simple above-ground pump.

Most plungers are constructed similar

Center, Soaking Deck and Cup Leathers; Below, Forming New Cup Leather

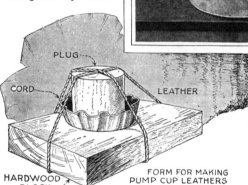

PLUG

CORD

LEATHER

HARDWOOD BLOCK

FORM FOR MAKING PUMP CUP LEATHERS

to the one shown in the photographs. To releather, clamp the spider carefully but firmly in a vise and then turn off the plunger end which threads onto the spider. The old leather can then be removed. If the retaining nut turns off hard, be especially careful in removing so as not to strain the spider to the cracking point. Turn it up a bit and then in the opposite direction until it will start. Sometimes a tap with a cold chisel in one of the notches will serve to start it. For general use a large pipe wrench is best suited for this job although there are special spanners that come with some makes of pumps for this purpose.

When disassembled, clean the threads on the spider and retaining nut and graphite them. Then slip the new cup leather in position, replace the nut and take up on it until the leather is held firmly in posi-

tion, using care, of course, with this procedure. If a ready-cut cup leather cannot be procured, here is an excellent method of making one at home, using ⅛-in. oak-tanned leather as material. Put the leather to soak in water for at least 24 hours while making the former, herein described.

Using an expansion bit, bore a hole in the center of a hardwood block ¼ in. larger than the diameter of the plunger, and 1½ in. deep. Then fashion a round plug of hardwood just the diameter of the plunger and about 3 or 4 in. long. Thoroughly oil both pieces, provide some strong cord and have a large bench vise handy. When the leather is sufficiently pliable, place it over the hole in the block and then place the plug end upon it directly over the hole. Carefully turn the entire assembly on its side and place between the vise jaws. Then slowly turn up on the vise and push the plug into the hole, carrying the leather with it. Work very slowly so the leather will stretch over the plug during the process. When the bottom of the hole has been reached, leave the job alone until the leather has thoroughly dried out or, if the vise must be used for other purposes, tie block and plug together with the cord, as shown in drawing and set aside to dry.

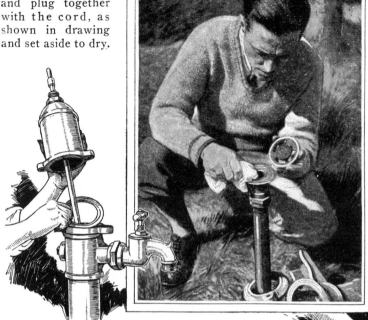

Left, Replacing Air-Dome Gasket; Center, Wiping Off Deck-Leather Seat; Right, Tightening Down Cylinder

marked out, as previously mentioned, with a ball-peen hammer. Leather gaskets are best, but for this purpose a thinner stock can be used than for the section leathers.

After the pump has been releathered and assembled a few days, it will be wise to go over all bolts and take up adjustments. New leather is flexible

When the leather is bone-dry, take off the cord, pull out the plug, and a nicely formed cup leather will be the result. Trim off the edges with a sharp knife, bevel the top edge on the inside, and then cut a round hole in the bottom to fit snugly around the retaining nut of the plunger.

With the new leather on the plunger, soak it in water again until softened and then insert in the pump cylinder and push down until the top of the rod can be again connected to the pump handle. It is also a good plan, with unlined cylinders, to wipe out the inside with very fine emery paper to remove any rust coating that may have formed through the years. This rough surface is particularly hard on leathers and wears them out before their time. Keep the cylinder walls clean and bright and the leathers will last much longer than would otherwise be the case.

The air domes on force pumps are usually provided with leather gaskets between them and the cylinder connection. When these grow hard they should be renewed. They can be cut from leather or sheet rubber, using the old one as a pattern, or

and it will probably be found that a turn or two can be taken up on all adjustments as the leather compresses. This will insure an air-tight job and give a positive vacuum in the cylinder. The plunger will, of course, have to be removed and the retaining nut turned up in the vise as before. If the cup leather has swollen too much and it works unduly hard, shave off a little from the edges with a safety-razor blade.

Now with the pump newly releathered, it should hold water indefinitely. If the water still persists in dropping back and the pump needs priming each time it is used, you may feel absolutely sure the leak is in the mechanical end of the affair. Go over all connections to see that they are drawn up tight. Inspect the castings and pipe sections above ground for cracks or leaky couplings. If possible, grab the pump base with a large pipe wrench and turn clockwise, rotating the entire pipe line and strainer point in the ground. This will take up any loose threads that may have developed, due to threads corroding over a long period of time. Do not, however, turn the pipe backward, as threads will undoubtedly be loosened and you will be worse off than before. In making up new connections, always use plenty of lead in the joints and turn them well home, and leaky joints will be practically impossible. By attending to this while sinking a well and assembling a pump, about the only trouble that can develop will be cracked parts due to freezing or overstrain in assembling, or faulty leathers. Other things being equal, water should flow freely always.

Accurate Perpendiculars with a 2-Ft. Rule

The 2-ft. rule is the faithful standby of the rough-and-ready draftsman who makes sketches on the job. To draw a fairly accurate perpendicular to a line not parallel with an edge of the sheet or pad is not so easy to do but often necessary to the correctness of a sketch. The photo shows how a perpendicular can be drawn which will be about as correct as any circumstance will require. Lay the rule down along the line, then lay a dollar or washer on one side of the circular middle-joint hinge of the rule, and touching it, and scribe an arc. Place the dollar on the other side and scribe another. Draw a line through the two points where the arcs intersect. This line will be perpendicular and as correct as necessary.

How to Draw a Perpendicular to a Horizontal Line with an Ordinary 2-Ft. Rule

Handy Dolly, Which Can Be Swung in Any Direction, Made from Old Roller Skates

Dolly for Handling Baled Hay

When any great number of bales of hay have to be moved across the floor it becomes a heavy and tiresome task. To alleviate some of this work a dolly, as shown in the illustration, can easily be made from odds and ends. Build a small plank platform of short boards and cleat them solidly from underneath with similar stout boards. Make it about the size of a bale of hay. Fasten four roller-bearings casters, one to each corner, or four wheels removed from a pair of old roller skates. In the latter case, see that the wheels are pivoted so that they will turn in any direction.— L. B. Robbins, Harwich, Mass.

Drilling Chilled Cast Iron

Iron castings, made in chilled molds, are frequently too hard to drill. Even high-speed drills and turpentine will fail to break through the surface of the casting. The trouble can, however, be remedied in the following way: Place a lump of sulphur on the spot to be drilled and slowly bring the casting to a red heat, then allow it to cool off. This will soften the spot so that the drill will cut it readily.—G. A. Luers, Washington, D. C.

Easy Method of Removing a Driven Well Pipe from the Ground

Pulling a Driven Well Pipe

It was desired to salvage the driven pipe of an old well. Usually a driven pipe is abandoned because of the difficulty connected with its removal, but in this case the task was simplified considerably and the pipe was removed without much difficulty. A post was set about 2 ft. on one side of the pipe, the top being about 4 ft. from the ground. The crosspiece, a length of 4 by 6-in. wood, was fastened to the post at one end and at the other end it was set on a screw jack, properly supported. A chain was fastened to the crosspiece in the center, and to the pipe, on which a cap was screwed. First the jack was turned up until the chain was tight. The pipe was then struck a few light blows with a sledge while the jack pressure was being increased. In this way, combining pipe vibration with a constant pull, the pipe was readily pulled out.

Softening Hard Leather Belting

I had some old leather belting that had not been used for several years. To my knowledge it had been around the shop for over 30 years. Needing some belting I was forced to make use of this old piece, which was made soft and pliable in the fol-

lowing way: I filled a tub with boiling water and poured in about a gallon of old engine oil, which floated on top of the water. I dipped the belting to the bottom of the tub and allowed it to soak a few moments. Then I lifted it slowly through the layer of oil and repeated the operation several times. Within 15 min. the leather was as soft and pliable as though it had just been removed from a machine. The boiling water had opened up the pores of the leather and on removing it from the water, the hot oil had penetrated the pores and completely filled them. The belt is still in use after some years and is apparently good for many more.—L. B. Robbins, Harwich, Mass.

Improvised Electric Crucible

A small crucible that can be used for melting chemicals and soft metals can readily be constructed, using only a porcelain lamp socket and the element of an electric heater. The socket is mounted on a small base of marble, slate or bakelite, about 6 in. square. The heating element is screwed into this socket. The heater should be of the kind that is shaped like a cup, which is mostly used in reflecting heaters. A small clay crucible is easily slipped into this cup-shaped opening. If no crucible is available, a clay pipe with the stem broken off and the hole plugged will do. A length of lampcord and plug is connected to the socket and plugged with this outfit in a few minutes. It can be placed in a metal box or case

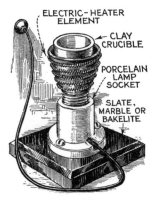

ELECTRIC-HEATER ELEMENT

CLAY CRUCIBLE

PORCELAIN LAMP SOCKET

SLATE, MARBLE OR BAKELITE

so that the heat will not be dissipated into the surrounding air, although this is not absolutely necessary. For melting lead and soft metals, such an improvised crucible is convenient. as a cupful of scrap lead will melt in less than half a minute.—Herman R. Wallin, Brooklyn, N. Y.

How to Build a Dumb-Waiter

By ERIC B. ROBERTS

AMATEUR knowledge of carpentry is all that is necessary to build the dumb-waiter described in this article and shown in the illustrations. The first step is to choose a location where a vertical drop to the basement will meet with no obstructions. After the location has been determined, the shaft is built from the ceiling of the first story to the basement floor. The frame of the shaft consists of 2 by 4-in. material; in the kitchen this is boxed in with 1-in. stock on the inside and lathed on the outside preparatory to plastering. If desired, wallboard can be used on the outside. The basement section of the shaft is also boarded up tightly. A neat paneled door should be provided for the kitchen outlet of the waiter, but a simple board door will suffice in the basement. A wooden floor is provided at the bottom of the shaft and four holes are

drilled in the floor to hold old auto-valve springs in a vertical position to absorb the shock of the lift when it is lowered rapidly.

After the shaft has been finished, the rails or guides for the lift are fastened on the inside, leaving out a short section to permit the insertion of the lift, after which the omitted guide section also may be fastened in place. Lengths of ¾-in. wood may be used for making the guides. Next, the lift should be made. For the average household it should weigh about 65 lb., so that it will carry a load of from 5 to 20 lb. The counterweight, which consists of scrap lead, iron, etc., must be between 5 and 10 lb. heavier than the empty waiter, to allow for the additional load. To obtain the above-mentioned weights, I

A Handy Kitchen Dumb-Waiter Can Readily Be Built by Any Home Owner with the Aid of a Few Tools, and the Slight Cost of the Installation Will Be Compensated For by the Convenience It Affords

15

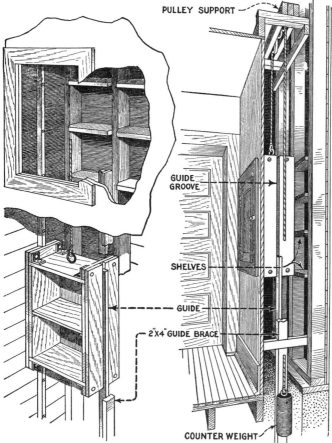

a position where it can do no damage if it falls. The pulleys need be of no special size; anything from 2 to 7 or 8 in. will do. They must, however, be of the grooved type and able to retain a ⅜-in. rope. Lengths of pipe or rod make good axles. I used one 2-in. and two 4-in. pulleys, the rope passing over the large ones and under the small one to provide the necessary friction to hold the waiter steady at the top or bottom, yet allow it to move freely when pulled up or let down. Ordinary sash cord is well suited for use in a dumb-waiter.

Constructional Details of the Dumb-Waiter, Showing the Shaft, Lift and the Counterweight, and the Method of Assembly

placed the materials used for making the lift on one end of a plank, pivoted in the center, to balance the counterweight on the other end. When both weights were equal, I added about 8 lb. to the counterweight. Then I proceeded to build the lift, which was made with double sides, top and bottom in order to make it solid and heavy. Ordinary 1 by 6-in. lumber was used. Angle iron may be used to add weight and rigidity but it must be remembered that no additional material must be used besides that which was balanced with the counterweight. Between the two boards forming the side, a groove is left for the guide, on each side. The pulley assembly is then made. It must be carefully calculated where the ropes and weights are to hang in order to be sure that they clear the lift while in motion or at rest, and the weight must be hung in

Copper Pipe Aids in Coiling Wire

Coiling wire for springs, electrical coils or for binding purposes, is accomplished usually with some means to restrain the wire and keep it under tension. Leather and wood will serve for holding the wire under tension while it is fed on a lathe mandrel at a slow speed. A new means, differing from any of the customary practices, is shown in the attached drawing, and consists of a short length of small copper pipe, with abrupt bends, which restrains the wire and maintains sufficient friction to insure tightly wound coils, in spite of the fact that the operation is rapid and the wire tension uniform.

Renovating Copper-Asbestos Gaskets

When the cylinder head of a car is removed for valve grinding and carbon removal, the gasket is frequently bent, dented or otherwise mutilated. Efforts to straighten it are not often successful, because the copper is usually brittle and hardened from use. This is also the case with the copper-asbestos gaskets used for the water connections, manifolds and valve seats. If installed with sharp bends and kinks in them, they are almost certain to leak. To renew the old gaskets, they are placed in the flame of a gas heater until they are quite red and then plunged in cold water. The copper is made plastic by this treatment, and, when the gasket is bolted down, it spreads and makes a tight seal.

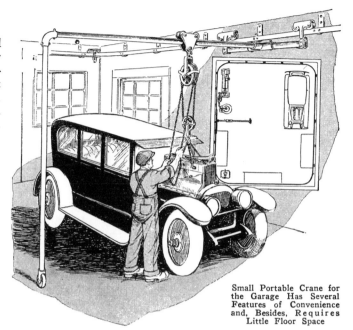

Small Portable Crane for the Garage Has Several Features of Convenience and, Besides, Requires Little Floor Space

Small Crane for the Garage

The crane shown in the accompanying drawing has a wide range of travel and is capable of transferring heavy units from the bench to the machines and to the several cars being repaired. It uses the same track as employed to support the hanging doors at the front of the garage. The provision of such a track around the four walls, is the main support for the crane. A double hanger with swivel rollers allows the crane to travel along the continuous runway. The corners are traversed on a curved track, similar to the track on which the door is supported when swung from the front to the side. A cross rail extends from these hangers and rests on a vertical support of pipe, provided with a fixed roller at the bottom. The hoist is carried by a trolley on the cross rail, which permits placing the hoist directly above the load. While every advantage of a crane is provided, the single leg, reaching to the floor, does not encroach on the available floor space, as is usually the case with four-legged portable cranes.

Vulcanizing Inner Tubes

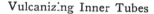

In vulcanizing small patches on inner tubes with an electric or gasoline vulcanizer, a Wisconsin repairman claims that the portion of the tube covered by the patch is apt to become overcooked or burned, and thereby weakened. To overcome this trouble, he uses four strips of asbestos paper over the tube, as shown in the illustration, leaving only the patch exposed to the full heat of the vulcanizing plate.

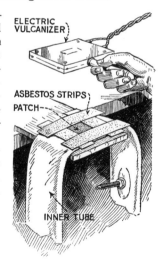

ELECTRIC VULCANIZER

ASBESTOS STRIPS

PATCH

INNER TUBE

¶Insert a scratch awl in common hard soap for hardening, and it will need no drawing after the plunge.

Unscrewing Thin Tubing

When unscrewing thin tubing, there is a decided tendency for it to close under the wrench grip, especially at the open ends. To prevent damaging the pipe, the method

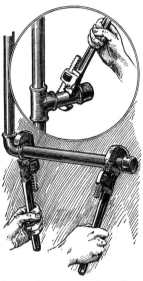

of protecting it shown in the illustration, has been found effective. It consists in screwing a pipe cap on the end of the pipe and gripping it as close to the cap as possible. Also in the removal of close nipples, this procedure is useful. The cap stiffens the nipple so that it can be removed easily, regardless of the tendency of the pipe-joint compound to hold it tight.—G. A. Luers, Washington, District of Columbia.

Better Potato Plants

By placing a 4-in. layer of sawdust on top of his hotbed, a Mississippi farmer produced potato plants with much longer roots than usual, which made them more desirable than short-rooted plants. In making the hotbed, he first dug a hole to a depth of about 12 in. In the bottom of this he placed a 6-in. layer of barnyard manure, covering it with a layer of soil, about 5 or 6 in. thick. On top of this he placed the potatoes to be sprouted, pressing them into the earth and covering them with a thin layer of soil. A 4-in. layer of sawdust was then applied. Some 6-in. planks, held in position by stakes, prevented the sawdust from being washed away. This hotbed was not covered with glass. Besides producing long roots on potato plants, the sawdust helps to retain moisture. Potatoes should not come in contact with manure because the latter is likely to transmit certain diseases to the former, causing the potatoes produced to be defective.—Bunyan Kennedy, McCool, Mississippi.

How to Mend Aluminum with Zinc

Holes in aluminum vessels can be mended by the following method: Paste a piece of strong paper over the hole on the inside, using shellac as an adhesive. Have the surface of the aluminum very clean by sandpapering it well. Pack the vessel with sand to hold the paper in position securely. Now take some clean zinc, melt it, clean off all the dross and pour the zinc over the hole from the outside. It will stick to aluminum, and can be finished with a file and sandpaper. We have mended canteens, hot-water bottles, kettles, pans, etc., by this simple method. If you wish to solder anything to aluminum, first coat the aluminum with melted zinc poured on, then solder to the zinc surface, using common solder and a good flux.—Robert C. Knox, Santa Barbara, Calif.

Saw Case for the Tool Chest

A number of saws are generally carried in a well-equipped tool chest, and protection for the teeth is not always easy

CASE FOR BACKED MITRE SAW

TAPE
PREPARED ROOFING

CASE FOR SAW BLADES

to provide. One carpenter uses a novel saw holder, which occupies little space and holds several blades for the detachable handle. Separate cases are used for miter and other attached-handle and backed saws. Such holders are made of pieces of prepared roofing, such as comes in rolls, using a kind which does not contain crushed stone or anything injurious to the saw teeth. After cutting and forming it to the shape of the saw, a few turns of friction tape hold everything firmly, and the case may be tossed into the tool chest without risk of damaging the saws.

Shop Notes

How to Burn Coke in Stove or Furnace

By J. S. HAGANS

MANY householders have been attracted to the use of coke for heating at one time or another, because of its merits of cleanliness, minimum ash, smokelessness and other considerations, only to abandon the fuel in disgust because the results were not what they had expected. In practically every such case, the trouble was not due to the fuel, but to unfamiliarity with the proper method of handling it, and to improper management of the furnace or stove in which it was used.

In the first place, there are several sizes of coke, just as there are of coal, and, for greatest economy and service, the size must be suited to the kind of heating apparatus it is to be used in; the ordinary sizes are: mixed egg and stove, for furnaces,

steam and hot-water boilers with very large fireboxes; stove (range) size, for furnaces, steam and water boilers, such as form the heating equipment in the aver-

CHECK DAMPER

FURNACE FILLED WITH COKE

FIRE-DOOR DAMPER

1" TO 2" LAYER OF ASHES ON GRATE BARS

ASHPIT DAMPER

ASHPIT CLEAN

FIG. 1

age six to ten-room house; No. 1 nut, for small furnaces, boilers and open grates; No. 2 nut, for stoves and ranges, base burners, hot-water heaters and magazine-feed boilers and furnaces.

For use in furnaces, steam and hot-water boilers, after the fire is kindled fill the firepot with coke and close the fire-door and smoke-pipe dampers. Open the check damper (Fig. 1) and regulate the draft with the ashpit damper. It may be necessary, in some cases, to keep the smokepipe (twist) damper slightly open, but this is easily determined by experiment. When preparing the fire for the night, stir with the poker and open the drafts until the fire is burning brightly. Fill with coke and close the twist or smoke-pipe damper; open the fire-door and check dampers and, if necessary, open the ashpit damper slightly. Usually this damper can be kept closed.

In the morning the fire should be shaken only until the first red sparks appear in the ashpit. If the fire is low, don't shake it; stir it up from the top with the poker, throw on a few shovelfuls of coke and turn on the draft. When the fire is going well, fill the firepot with coke and regulate the drafts as before, or according to weather conditions. Should the fire occasionally go out, it is not necessary to dump it; dig a hole in the front of the coke and rekindle.

It is usually desirable to protect the bars of the furnace grate from the intense heat of the fire by allowing a layer of ashes to accumulate on the bars. In mild weather the thickness of this layer can be increased. Always keep the firepot full, since a thick fire, burning slowly, will generate more heat than a thin fire burning fast, and don't shake the fire more than once a day, preferably in the morning, except in severe weather, or when heat is required in a hurry.

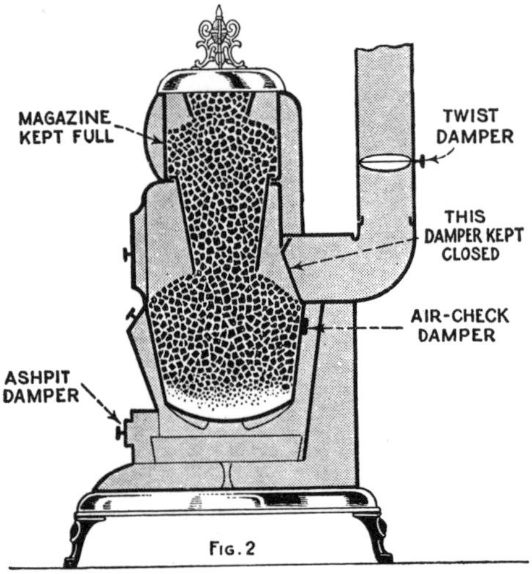

When burning coke in a base burner or magazine-type of stove (Fig. 2), kindle in the usual way, then fill the magazine with coke. When well started, close the twist damper and regulate with the check, fire-door and ashpit dampers. A little experience will demonstrate that less draft is required with coke than with most other fuels. At night, open the fire door and poke so as to cover the fire with fresh coke from the magazine. Fill the magazine and regulate the drafts, and there will be a good fire in the morning. In the morning, shake gently until the first red sparks appear in the ashpit, after opening the drafts. When the fire has started nicely, close the smokepipe damper as before, and regulate with check, ashpit and fire-door dampers. If the fire does not burn evenly or freely, poke it.

To get good results with coke it is only necessary to experiment a little with the stove or furnace, basing the experiments on the foregoing hints. This is true not only with coke, but with every other fuel used for house heating; the heat units are there, and it is only a matter of determining how to get most of them into useful heat at the lowest cost, and to keep as many as possible from going up the chimney without performing their share in heating the house.

MAGAZINE KEPT FULL

TWIST DAMPER

THIS DAMPER KEPT CLOSED

AIR-CHECK DAMPER

ASHPIT DAMPER

Fig. 2

Snow Packs for Honey Bees

Putting bees in a snow pack out of doors has been found to be an ideal way to bring them safely through northern winters. Cases large enough to hold two hives, with space of 4 to 6 in. to spare, were built of boards and set out in the woods. In the late fall, hives were put in these and packed all around with dead leaves, with a foot or more of dead leaves on top. The cases were set facing east, to protect them from northwest winds. The leaves were

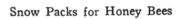

sufficient to keep the bees warm until snow came; then piles of snow on top and all around the cases served as a warm pack for the bees. Wintered in this way, they were found to come out in the spring in fine, hardy shape.

Drilling Holes in Lead

Every machinist knows what a difficult task it is to drill lead accurately. Large jobs cause considerable trouble, due to heated drills, which tend to stick, large burrs which form about the edges of the holes, and crawling chips, which tend to enlarge holes. The usual water lubricants, drilling compounds, kerosene, etc., are useless in such cases, but the use of good lard oil appears to be the solution for the problem. Use plenty of the oil and lift the drill out often during the drilling in order to clear the chips. A drill speed of between 800 and 1,000 r.p.m. has been found to give the best results.

Rest for Grinding Drills

I have had occasion to have a number of drills sharpened in small shops, and was surprised to note that in no case was the grinder operator supplied with any rest for holding the drill while doing the job. This method of sharpening a drill does not give an even bevel to the point and therefore the cutting is not performed by the entire surface of the point as it should be. In some instances there is but one edge cutting, the second having been ground down more than the first. I suggested the use of an ordinary rest having two V-grooves filed in the top at the proper angle to the surface of the emery wheel. A drill is placed in one of the grooves, and it can then be turned around while grinding, with assurance of having the correct cutting angle on the end.—Harry E. Gifford, Medford, Mass.

GROOVES IN REST

Auto-Wheel Spoke and Piece of Steel Plate Make Tool for Removing Mortar from Bricks

Chopping Mortar from Old Bricks

There are hundreds of brick buildings being torn down every year and contractors often try to salvage as much of the old bricks as possible. The photo shows a workman who made a brick hatchet out of a short auto-wheel spoke and a piece of ⅛ by 8-in. steel plate. The handle is split on the end for the blade and two screws hold the latter securely. This is a handy tool for chopping the mortar from the bricks and prying them apart. —Carlton Groat, The Dalles, Oreg.

How to Keep a Drawing Clean

Moving a T-square up and down on a drawing board over a sheet of paper tends to smudge the drawing. To prevent this from occurring, tie a length of string on each end of the board from top to bottom and the T-square will ride on them without touching the drawing.

The Farm Tractor Will Pay for Itself in a Short Time by Using It as a Power Plant for Various Purposes

Tractor Used to Sharpen Harrow Disks

Two years ago I purchased a harrow-disk sharpener. It was one of those arrangements in which you turn the harrow on its back, clamp a crank to one end of the shaft that holds the disks together, and, while one person turns the crank, another holds the sharpener against the disks. However, the job was not entirely satisfactory because of the lack of steady power delivered by the crank operator. Believing that a tractor could be used for this purpose, I made a device that coupled the harrow shaft to the tractor wheel directly, the coupling device consisting of a 3-ft. steel bar, 2 in. wide

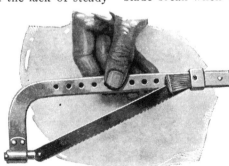

Method of Using a Broken Hacksaw Blade

and ½ in. thick, bent as indicated in the detail and having a link attached at the center with two bolts for clamping it securely to the end of the disk shaft. Set the disk assembly on a heavy stand.—Geo. G. McVicker, North Bend, Nebr.

When Your Last Saw Blade Breaks

Did you ever have the only hacksaw blade break when working on a job away from the shop and where another blade was not available? Even if broken near the center, a blade can still be used. Dismantle the frame, and insert the broken end of the blade in the loose frame eye, wedging it with a bit of wood, as shown in the photo on the opposite page. If the blade is not used too strenuously small cuts can be made with it.

Repair on Gasoline-Tank Clamp

The bar that holds down the square gasoline tank on the older-model Ford coupes is held at the outer end by a wood screw, driven into the turtle-back frame. This screw often works loose and drops out, allowing the tank to vibrate on its supports. As the screw extends nearly through the wood frame, a longer wood screw cannot be used. A good repair can be made by using a small bolt through the turtle-back frame with the head on the outside. As the hole is directly above the tank, it is not easily drilled from the inside, though it can be done with a ratchet brace. A sharp-pointed punch can be driven through from the inside until a small dent is made in the metal on the outside of the turtle back. A hole for the through bolt is then drilled from the outside. A carriage bolt is good for this use and makes a neat finish on the outside. A bolt taken from a front-spring rebound clip is the right size.

Keeping the Marking Brush Clean

The handle of a long marking brush is a hard thing to keep clean and free from paint in the average paint pot. Take a short piece of heavy hose, about 1½ in. to 2 in. long, and cut a deep angular groove in the top of it, as shown, to hold the handle of the brush. Split the lower end of the hose to fit snugly over the rim or edge of the pot. The brush handle is thus held away from the edge and will not get dirty or caked, nor roll around when the pot is moved.—Frank W. Bentley, Jr., Missouri Valley, Iowa.

¶A section of an old inner tube, with one end cemented shut, makes a handy water pail for the motorist.

A Safe Folding Ladder

It is not uncommon for building workers to nail together rough, temporary ladders

Folding Ladder Which Locks Securely to Provide Safety for the Worker

to suit their own requirements. For example, there are many occasions during building construction where a ladder is needed in some particular part but it is impossible to reach it because of narrow passages and sharp turns. In cases like this a folding ladder can be made up out of materials found about the job. Instead of nailing the steps to two long uprights as usual, make the ladder in two halves and join them together with two stout hinges. Thus the ladder can be folded double, making it easy to pass it through places where a solid ladder would not go. However, such a ladder might be dangerous in use and therefore locking arms are provided to make it safe. These consist of two wood strips nailed to each side and two wood arms hinged to each side. When the arms are dropped, the ladder is locked and they must be lifted again before the ladder can be folded.—Harry Moore, Montreal, Can.

Convenient Truck Which May Be Made Stationary by Lowering the Legs

Truck Aids Moving Heavy Iron Machinery

The truck shown in the photo is constructed so that, by the use of a lever on the end, the guide wheel may be raised or lowered. When lowered, the truck rests on the two iron legs and becomes stationary. It is used for moving heavy iron machinery, but would also make a good portable bench.

Practical Improvised Surface Gauge

Many leveling or setting-up jobs encountered away from the shop can be done with an improvised surface gauge of the kind shown in the photo. The needle is simply a piece of wire forced through a heavy cork, which in turn is pushed down over the oilcan spout. The needle is easily moved up or down, yet it is firmly held by the cork. Of course, the tool cannot be relied upon for extreme accuracy, but it gives quick-

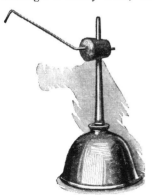

er and better results than the practice of attempting close work with a rule.

Sewers Plugged with Old Auto Inner Tubes

Old auto inner tubes are being used by plumbers and city sewer repairmen for plugging up sewer pipes while making repairs on them. Many tubes are ordinarily thrown away, due to a bad blowout, although the rest of the tube is in good condition. The good section of the tube is cut off and the ends vulcanized to make it air-tight. If the valve is on the discarded section it should be removed and attached to the vulcanized section. Balloon tubes are the best kind to use. While the workmen are engaged in repairing a break in the sewer, the inner tube is inserted in the end of the pipe and is pumped up with air, forming a "plug," which effectively holds back water and sewage while the repair is being made. This method has been successfully used on pipes up to 30 in. in diameter. Small inner tubes can be used for smaller pipes.

Pin Attached to a Measuring Tape

When one is obliged to use a 50 or 100-ft. measuring tape alone, it is more or less of an awkward job. A nail and a rock are about the only means of holding the ring at the end of the tape in position for running the tape, and even

HARDENED-STEEL POINT

these anchors are not always secure. A real-estate man used the pin shown in the accompanying drawing. A piece of flat steel was ground down to the form of a letter "L," with the longer portion $1\frac{1}{2}$ in. long. This was sharpened to a point and hardened. A hole was drilled in the elbow and the short end rounded. The ring at the end of the rope was opened, slipped through the hole in the pin and closed, after which the butting ends were soldered together. With the aid of this pin, the tape can be held at any point on a tree, building or wood surface.—L. B. Robbins, Harwich, Mass.

YOU CAN MAKE THIS COLONIAL SPINNING WHEEL

BY E·M·LOVE

SAVE in remote country districts, spinning has passed from the realm of household arts, outdistanced by machines that multiply hand labor a thousand fold. Yet an air of romance still clings to distaff and spindle, and the spinning wheel, celebrated in song and legend, takes its place in the modern home as a quaint reminder of an ancient craft and an example of early American furniture. Few people are fortunate enough to own a colonial wheel, but any handy man can make an excellent copy by following this article.

Most common hardwoods are suitable for material. Maple is perhaps the most desirable for the turned work, and oak or ash for the base, treadle and pitman. Glue up the wheel rim as a square frame from stock 1½ by 4¼ in. in the rough, the four pieces being 16 in. long. The ends are cut to an angle of 45°, as in Fig. 1.

Smooth one side and one edge of each piece for working faces, and gauge the ends with two lines, one ⅜ in. from the face; the other ⅞ in., for the sides of the tenons and mortises. Shoulder lines, 9½ in. apart, are scored with a knife square across the faces of the tenoned pieces, while pencil lines across the others limit the depth of the mortises. Rip the ends with the saw, splitting the line and cutting in the waste wood. Crosscut the shoulders, and chisel the mortise bottoms from both edges. Try for fit, apply glue liberally to all joining surfaces, and clamp up. Small clamps across the thickness of the joints will prevent wedging open. Set aside to dry until the turned work is done.

Rip 1½-in. strips from 1½-in. stock for larger spindles, and punch the centers of the ends with a nail. The photo below Fig. 1 shows a crude lathe driven by a washing-machine motor. The headstock is a piece of 2 by 4-in. wood, notched at one end to fit over the edge of another length of 2-in. material, to which it is nailed. A 16-in. spike, driven through the center 4 in. above the bed, forms a turning

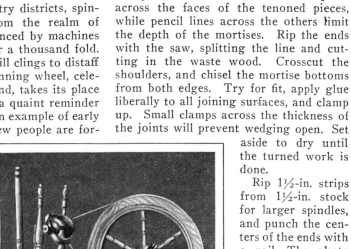

center. The tailstock is like it, but left loose. The tool rest is a board of suitable width clamped in the vise. The spindle, drilled to fit the centers, and roughly rounded on one end to serve as a pulley, determines the distance between head and tailstocks. These, when clamped to the tool rest, form a rigid assembly.

Bore a piece of hardwood to fit the motor shaft or collar, turning it to a groove diameter of 2½ in. Over this drive pulley, pass a round leather belt, or, lacking this, a piece of carpenters' chalk line woven into a chain stitch and knotted together for a splice.

If a motor is not available, tie a 2-ft. length of inner tube to the ceiling for a return spring, with the belt tied to the lower end. Loop the belt around the spindle, attaching it to a 1 by 4-in. treadle, 3 ft. long and hinged to the floor at one end by two spikes driven through ¼-in. holes. With a little practice, very good turning can be done on this primitive lathe.

The average amateur has no turning tools, so shift must be made with common chisels. Sharpen a gouge to a razor edge. Fix the rest a little above center. Lay the gouge on it, holding it level with the left hand close to the rest and steadying the handle with the right. Point the blade and incline its diameter somewhat in the direction of motion, taking a cut from one end to the other of the stick. A little practice will show how heavy a cut can be made without slipping the belt. Rough the spindle to the largest diameter.

Figures 3 and 5 illustrate the legs. Cut the stock 1½ in. longer than the finished length, to allow for the pulley. Lubricate the centers with hard oil. When roughed to roundness, lay a rule on the rest, marking the divisions with a pencil while the piece turns. Work out the slender parts with the gouge to the finished diameter. If the tool is held well on edge in making the large coves, a shearing cut is obtained. Scrape the cylindrical portions with a ¼-in. chisel, holding it on edge to cut the shoulders and finishing with the blade held flat. For the beads, use the corner of the gouge, tipping the tool on edge as it nears the root depth. Cut the ⅛-in. coves with the tip of a rat-tail file. When the whole leg is shaped, smooth well with sandpaper. Lastly, cut to length.

Turn the two wheel supports, Fig. 2, in the same way. Rip the upper end of each through the diameter to a depth of 2⅛ in. Parallel to this, ³⁄₁₆ in. from it on either side, make two other cuts. Bore the bottom with a ⅜-in. bit, as in another photo. File the slots smooth.

Figure 4 details the spindle crossarm, which fits over the tapered nut above the turned base, carrying the two spindle supports. The smallest coves are lines made with a three-cornered file. Centering 1⅛ in. from the left shoulder, bore a ¼-in. hole, ⅛ in. deep. Bore through the diameter with a ½-in. bit, and with a ¼-in. chisel and round file taper the small hole to meet the large upper one. Another hole, centering 8½ in. from it, is bored and tapered parallel to it. A third hole, tapering from ⅝ in. above to ¾ in. below, centers 2½ in. from the first, inclining at the rate of 3⅜ in. horizontally with a vertical rise of 6 in. Clamp the piece in a vise with the end holes properly inclined, as determined by a straight stick thrust through and compared with a square held upright on the bench. The bit can then be held vertical in the usual manner.

Figure 6 shows a mortise, ¼ by 1 in., in each spindle support, receiving a sole-leather spindle bearing. One leather is pierced with a ⅜-in. hole, while the other, carrying the tapered end of the spindle, is ³⁄₁₆ in. Glue these in. Turn the tapers to such a diameter that the lower ends, solidly seated, project ¼ in. below the crossarm. Fig. 7 illustrates the distaff support. Four and one-eighth inches from the lower end, a ½-in. hole, 1 in. deep, carries the distaff crossarm, also detailed in Fig. 7. A ½-in. hole, 1 in. deep, centered on the cylindrical part of the crossarm, receives the distaff.

For tightening the belt, a screw, shown in Fig. 8, must be made. If an old wood clamp is available, the screw and nut may be turned from it; but if not, turn the screw from 1½-in. stock, with the threaded part ¾ in. in diameter. The end bearing is ½ in. through. The ¼-in. groove engages a wooden key in the base, to prevent withdrawal when the belt is slackened.

To get the pitch of the thread, build a miter box, ¾ in. wide, 1 in. deep and 4 in. long. With a backsaw, inclining ¹⁄₁₆ in.

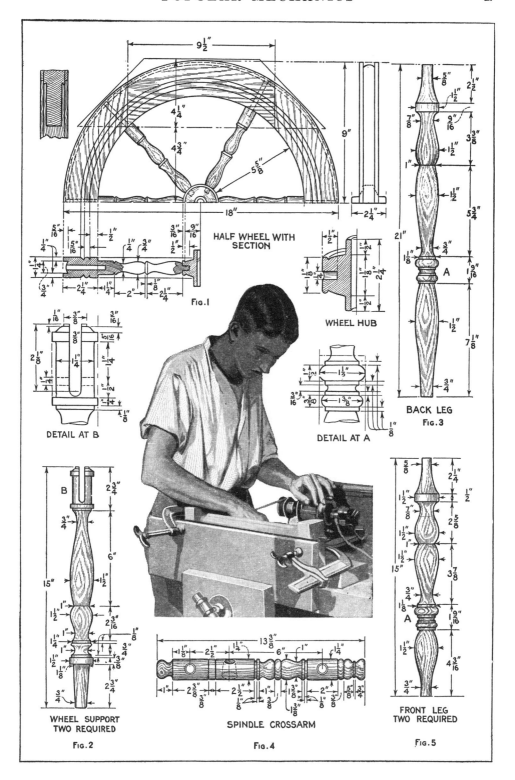

9½"

4¼"

4¾"

5⅝"

9"

18"

2¼"

HALF WHEEL WITH SECTION

Fig. 1

WHEEL HUB

21"

BACK LEG

Fig. 3

DETAIL AT B

DETAIL AT A

**WHEEL SUPPORT
TWO REQUIRED**

Fig. 2

SPINDLE CROSSARM

Fig. 4

13⅜"

**FRONT LEG
TWO REQUIRED**

Fig. 5

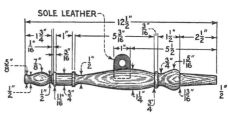

SPINDLE SUPPORT   FIG. 6

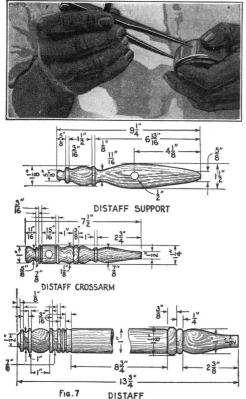

DISTAFF SUPPORT

DISTAFF CROSSARM

FIG. 7   DISTAFF

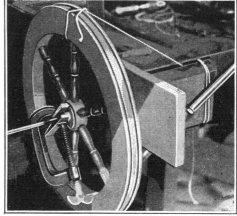

Upper Left, Spacing Spoke Holes in the Hub; Lower Right, Truing Up the Wheel

from the square in the ¾-in. width, make a cut, ⅜ in. deep, across the middle. Insert the end of the screw blank and cut a groove about 1/16 in. deep, turning slowly and moving the saw in two or three short strokes. Next, draw a pencil line midway between the grooves and whittle the thread roughly to shape. Smooth the groove with a saw file, and trim the threads evenly to final depth with the knife. Finish smoothing with the file. A surprisingly accurate thread can be made in this way.

The nut, Fig. 8, having a square portion, 2⅝ in. long, to slide in the base guide, is turned off on the corners to a diameter of 1¾ in. Bore a through hole 1⅛ in. in diameter, centering 1¼ in. from the taper shoulder. Cast the threaded nut in plastic wood, as indicated in one of the photos. Bore a 1¼-in. hole through a 2 by 4-in. piece, 1 in. from the end, and rip out the end. In the bottom, lay a thick bed of plastic wood. Press the oiled screw into it, mold the top and force the piece sawn out of the block against it. Cut the

wooden mold to liberate the bushing, leaving it on the screw until well hardened. Afterward trim the bushing to fit the tapered nut and glue it in place.

The turned spindle base, Fig. 9, is best made from 4 by 4-in. solid stock, but if this is not available, glue two pieces of 2-in. stock together with the grain running at right angles, bore the hole and taper it, and drive it over the nut taper for an arbor. Turn to dimensions. It is recessed in the bottom ½ in. deep. The bobbin, dimensioned in the same drawing, is pierced with a ¼-in. hole, so as to turn freely on the spindle.

The spindle can be made from a 3/16-in. curtain rod, obtainable at most 10 and 15-cent stores. Split the end for ¾ in., bending the halves outward and back parallel, to give an inside width of ⅜ in. Cut the rod to 8¾ in., and file a taper, 1⅝ in. long, on the solid end, reducing it to ⅛ in. Thread the rod for ¼ in. just above the taper where a nut sunk in the flier pulley engages. The eye bearing is a ferrule cut from the base of an oilcan spout and filled with plastic wood. When dry, fit the eye ends solidly and bore out the center. The flier and pulley are also detailed in Fig. 9.

The flier is sawed from ¾-in. stock. Through a ¾-in. button, ⅜ in. long, and the slightly less than ⁹⁄₁₆-in. hole in the flier, the spindle is forced until the eye sinks into the button enough to grip it strongly. Screw nine small iron hooks into each flier arm, and, lastly, screw on the flier pulley. (In use, the flax or wool is fed through the eye bearing and looped over the hooks, with the end tied to the bobbin. The flier, rotating, twists the yarn, while the bobbin, having a smaller pulley and revolving faster, winds it up.)

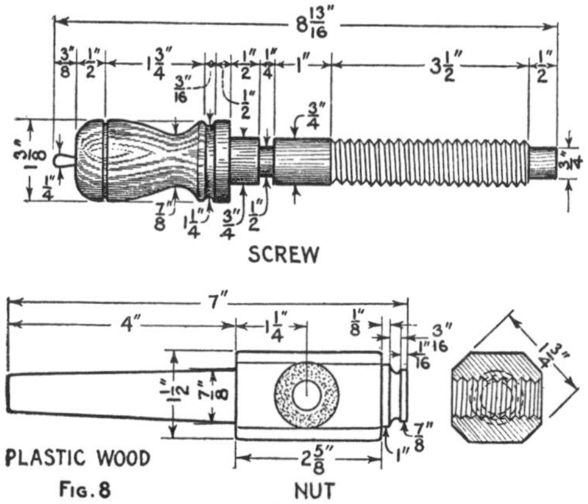

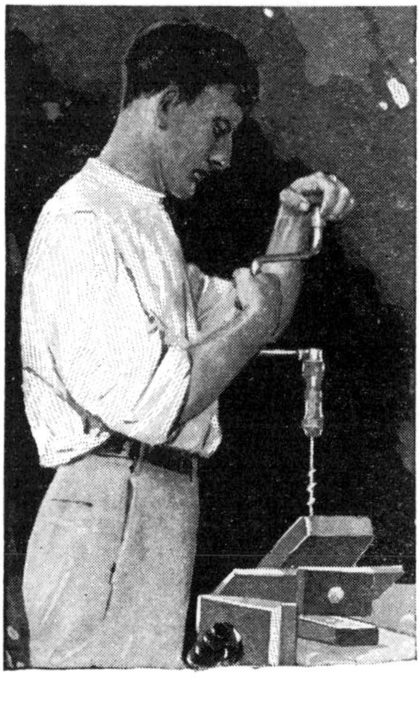

Two small pins, shown in Fig. 11, are turned to hold the wheel axle in the slots. The axle is a 5½-in. piece of ⅜-in. round iron. For the crank, bend a ⁵⁄₁₆-in. bolt to an arc of about 1⅛ in., hammering it to a thickness of ³⁄₁₆ in. Near one end, drill a ³⁄₁₆-in. hole, to be filed square. Centering 2 in. from this, drill the crank-pin hole. File a square end on the axle for riveting to the crank. Use a piece of hinge pin for the crank pin, supplying washers, as in Fig. 13.

Scribe the inner and outer diameters of the wheel with a pivoted stick, as in the photo, and cut the outside with a keyhole saw. Smooth with a spokeshave. Nail, across the two faces, pieces of 1 by 4-in. stock with the nails in the waste wood. Locate the wheel center by scribing intersecting arcs from various points on the inner rim line. (See photo.) Bore holes

Upper Right, Paring Molding on Base to Make Bead; Lower Left, Boring Distaff Hole

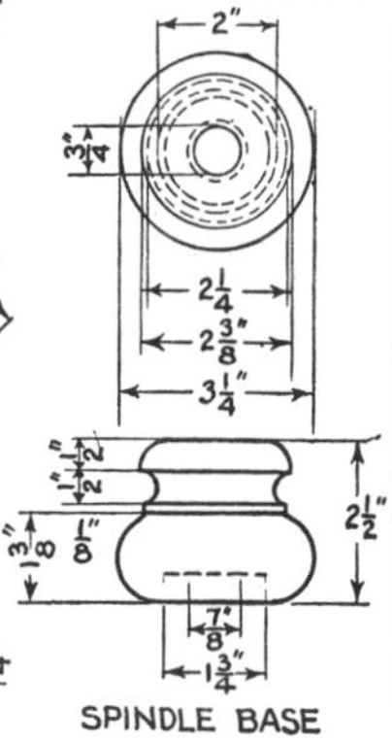

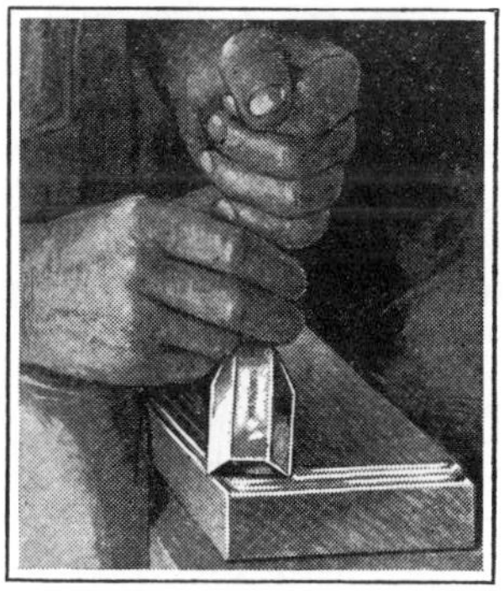

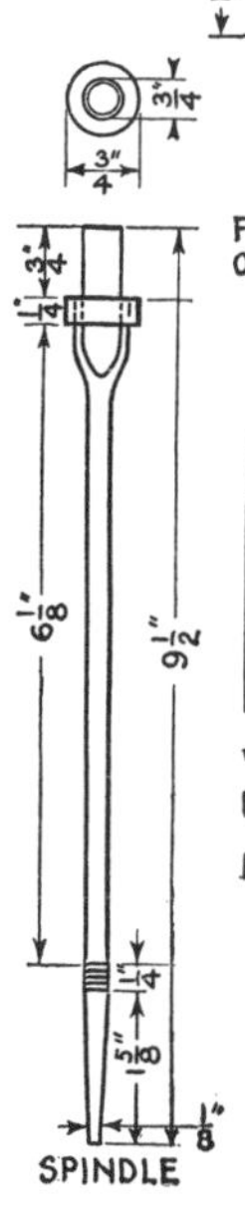

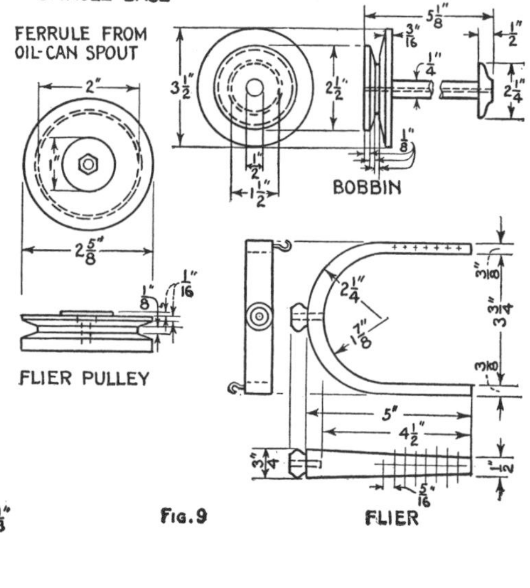

FIG.9

in these temporary "spokes" to fit a piece of broomstick snugly; the spokes are nailed to the broomstick and a stout wooden crank is attached, after mounting in 2 by 4-in. bearings held in the vise. Stand on the floor a board long enough to serve as a tool rest, bracing it to the bearings. On each side of the wheel, with the least possible clearance, nail a guide piece, preventing side wobble with relation to the tool rest. If another person turns the

---

MATERIAL LIST

1 piece, 1½ by 5 in. by 5 ft., maple.
1 piece, 1½ by 8 in. by 4½ ft., maple.
1 piece, 1 by 6 by 12 in., maple.
1 piece, 4 by 4 by 12 in., maple.
1 piece, 2 by 10 in. by 2 ft., oak.
1 hinge pin from loose-pin butt, 2½ by 2½ in.
1½ doz. small steel hooks.
1 leather shoelace.

---

crank, the belt groove detailed in Fig. 1 can easily be turned.

Turn the spokes and hub, bore ¼-in. holes, ½ in. deep, in the large ends of the turned spokes, and locate the holes in the hub by stepping around the circumference with a pair of dividers spanning the radius of the hub, as in the photo to the left of Fig. 6. When the inside of the rim is cut and smoothed, bore ¼-in. dowel holes through it at the proper points for the spokes. All being ready, glue up, inserting the spokes in the hub and inside the rim, driving the dowels from the outside.

The photo below Fig. 6 shows a method of holding the wheel true until dry. Insert a ⅜-in. rod into the hub and clamp it level in the vise. Tack a board across the bench end, shimming it square with the rod, and place the wheel. If the spokes are tightly fitted, the hub will bulge outward. Force it into position and hold with sticks clamped to the axle. Rotate it until the part of the rim inclined outward is at the top, where it can be tied with a string, its position being proved by a square held along the shaft.

Figure 12 dimensions the oak base. Cut the stock 18 in. long, and work from a center line. To make the molding, rabbet the top edge ⅛ by ⅜ in. Round the corners to a radius of ½ in. Plane off the bead corner and work it round. Bore 1½-in. holes for the ends of the guide, and saw out the material between. The

screw bearing is ¾ in. in diameter, 1 in. from the bottom and centered on the nut guide. A ¾-in. hole, ⅝ in. deep, receives the end of the screw. Make a ¼-in. square key hole ½ in. from the end and ¼ in. from the screw center. The nut is slipped into the slot in the base and the screw turned into the nut until the ¾-in. nose on its end is fully seated in the corresponding hole in the bottom of the slot. Then a ¼-in. key is inserted in the key hole above referred to, and driven in until it passes across the ¼-in. groove in the screw, locking the latter in place, and enabling the nut to be traversed back and forth by turning the screw. The spindle base fits on the taper portion of the nut, and the spindle crossarm on the upper part of the nut taper, above the spindle base. Next, the spindle supports are driven into the crossarm, and the spindle fitted into its leather bearings between them. Block the base in the vise at an angle of 3⅜ in. rise in 6 in., and, holding the bit vertical, bore the distaff-support hole, centering 1½ in. from the narrow end and 1 in. from the base center. This hole tapers from ¾ in. at the top to ⅝ in. at the bottom.

The ⅝-in. hole in the bottom for the long leg is 3 in. from the narrow end and 1¾ in. from the center, leaning toward the wide end 1¾ in. in 10 in., and toward the center 1 in. in 20 in. The angles of the front legs can be accurately bored by the use of a guide, as indicated in the photo showing this operation. They incline outward from the center 4½ in. in 12 in., and, parallel to the base center, 4¼ in. in 4½ in.

Assemble the legs with the base, stand on a floor, and scribe the leg ends ¼ in. up for cutting.

Dress the wheel to thickness. Scratch the bead V's with a nail point in a pivoted stick. Clamp the axle in a vise, push the wheel against the bench end, and, holding a ¼-in. chisel against the bench top with the right hand, turn the bead by rotating the wheel with the left hand, pressing the rim against a stop on the bench end to secure a uniform cut. Sand the wheel, assemble the spindles and put the wheel on its axle. Aline the grooves with the spindle and bobbin pulleys so as to mark the axle. Drill a ⅛-in. hole through hub and axle to receive a piece of nail as a key.

Forming the Nut in Mold by the Use of Plastic Wood

Assembly of Flier, Pulley and Spindle Eye

Slotting Upper Ends of Wheel Supports

Locating Center of Wheel on Temporary Spokes

Scribing the Rim of Wheel Preparatory to Sawing

Sawing Out Inside of Rim with Keyhole Saw

The pivoted member of the treadle (Fig. 13) is 1 in. square, with the ends turned to a taper. Use pieces of spikes as pivot pins, and hang 2 in. above the floor. The pitman, Fig. 10, has a ¼-in. slot at its

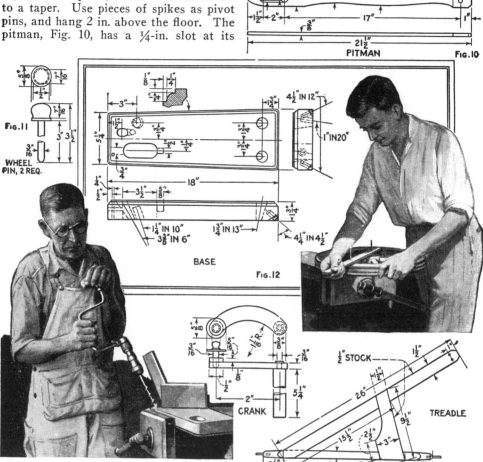

FIG.10 — PITMAN

FIG.11 — WHEEL PIN, 2 REQ.

BASE — FIG.12

CRANK

TREADLE — FIG.13

Upper Right, Cutting Beads in Wheel Rim; Lower Left, Boring Holes for Legs

upper end to accommodate the crank-pin body. In order that the head of the crank pin, and its washer, may be passed through the slot, the latter terminates, at its lower end, in a ⅝-in. hole. Centering 2 in. from this, at the other end of the slot, is another ⅝-in. hole; this is drilled only ¼ in. deep. From this hole to the first, another slot is cut, ⅝ in. wide and ¼ in. deep, as indicated by the double lines in Fig. 10. This makes a shouldered slot, ¼ in. wide, on one side of the pitman and ⅝ in. wide on the other. The head of the crank pin with its washer rides on the shoulder. Attach the pitman end to the treadle with a leather thong tied underneath.

Give the wheel a coat of oil, and when

dry and sanded off, give a second coat. Splice a single-string belt around the wheel and both pulleys.

Paper Used as Tire Flap

The tough paper tape used on new casings will protect the inner tube from rust on a clincher rim. The tape is wound around the rim, making several turns, and the tire applied as usual. The loose end of the tape should be held by patching cement so that the wrapping will lie flat while the tire is being applied. Such a tire flap will not stand water as well as one with rubber in it, but costs nothing and is easily obtained when needed.

Repairing Broken Laundry Tubs

By R. H. KASPER

WHEN the household laundry tubs, which are usually made of an imitation stone, begin to leak, the housewife may tolerate the inconvenience for some time, but eventually the tubs have to be discarded. The following method was successful in repairing a set of tubs which leaked in practically every joint; in addition to this, many pieces were broken out and some of the panels were cracked. The condition of the tubs may be seen from the first illustration.

One point which it is necessary to observe is that the repair must be made from the inside; for any repair made from the outside will allow the water to seep through the cracks and, in a short time, leakage will again take place. The tubs should first be carefully examined for cracks. These may be very fine lines, scarcely discernible, but nevertheless they let water through, especially if it is hot. As the cracks are found they should be marked with chalk or crayon, as it is otherwise easy to lose track of them.

After the cracks have been found and marked, the first thing to do is to bevel them; that is, to cut a V-groove along the cracks. The "V" may be cut with a cold chisel, or may be scraped with the

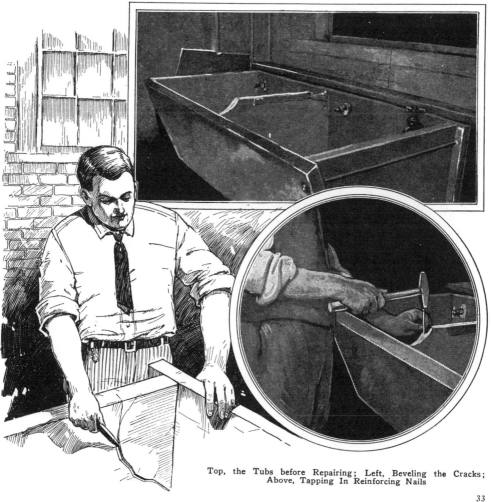

Top, the Tubs before Repairing; Left, Beveling the Cracks; Above, Tapping In Reinforcing Nails

corner of an old file. As the material of
the tubs is quite hard, the file edges will
be rapidly dulled; a new sharp surface
may be secured by breaking a piece off
the end of the file. Laundry tubs are usually made with the end panels fitting into
grooves in the front and back panels. This
is a common point of leakage, as the original cement deteriorates and breaks out.
These corners should be scraped thoroughly, so as to remove as much of the
old, loose cement as possible.

If any of the panels are broken, which
they usually are if a wringer or other ap-
pliance has been attached to them, the
broken sections must be built up with
cement. Some method of reinforcing
these parts is necessary. With a regular
machine drill, make a number of small

holes, about 1 in. apart and 1 in. deep,
into the broken sections. The drill
must be sharpened frequently, to keep it
cutting clean. A wire nail is then driven
into each hole so that the head will come
slightly below the finished surface. Care
must be used in selecting the drill size, as
the nail should be a light tapping fit in the
hole; if driven too tightly, it may crack
the composition.

After the nails have been placed, a mold
is built around the broken sections. This
is done by clamping a piece of wood on
each side of the panel, fitting it well into
the corners and flush with the finished
surfaces. A mortar is then prepared by
mixing two parts of fine white sand with
one part of Portland cement, adding
enough water to make a paste which pours
easily. After wetting the broken surfaces
with water, pour the mortar into the
mold, working it well down into the cor-

Lower Left, Mold in Place; Right, Drilling
Holes for Reinforcing Nails; Above, Finishing
Repaired Sections

ners with a thin stick. Any excess is scraped off flush with the top of the mold. For filling the beveled cracks, the mortar should be of a heavier consistency, and should be worked in very carefully and smoothed with a trowel

Twenty-four hours later, the mold may be removed and any irregularities filled in or smoothed off. The cement is then permitted to set until it becomes hard to the touch. Finally, a wash is made with Portland cement and water, the mixture being about like heavy cream. This is applied to the repaired parts and to the corners with a varnish brush. Drying will take place rapidly, usually within an hour, after which a second and third coat should be applied, also with a brush.

After the repaired parts have become stone-hard, scrub the inside of the tubs with a stiff bristle brush and clear, cold water. A soap mixture is then made, cutting a cake of yellow laundry soap into small pieces and dissolving it in ½ gal. of water; warm water will dissolve the soap more rapidly, but the mixture must be applied cold. A varnish brush is used, and the solution rubbed in well so as to fill all the pores. After drying overnight, a mixture of alum, 1 lb., and water, ½ gal., is applied with a brush. It must be brushed in well, as the soapy surface repels the alum water in much the same manner as an oily surface repels water. After drying, the tubs should be filled with clear, cold water and permitted to stand for a few days to thoroughly harden the cement, after which the tubs will be ready for use.

A set of laundry tubs repaired by this method held water for two weeks without any noticeable drop in the level, whereas, before the repair, they would leak empty in a few hours.

¶An ever-ready auto creeper can be made by putting casters on one of the car's floorboards.

When the Grease-Cup Cap Is Lost

Small grease-cup caps disappear and become lost with an aggravating frequency. You can still keep the cup lubricating very satisfactorily, however, if a light grease is used at the time. Take an old tire-cement tube or similar collapsible tube, and cut it in two. One of the halves

is cleaned out, filled with grease and tied securely to the post portion of the cup. Squeezing the tube from time to time forces plenty of the light grease down into the bearing.—Frank W. Bentley, Jr., Missouri Valley, Iowa.

Simple Yardage Checker Aids Engineers

A yardage checker of the kind shown in the drawing should be of interest and value to engineers and contractors for making preliminary estimates, and for a close check on final estimates. Its use is simple, reasonably accurate and avoids the possibility of error in division. The number of cubic feet is read on the inner circle and cubic yards directly opposite on the outer circle. For quantities from 1,000 to 10,000 cu. ft. the decimal point of both cubic feet and cubic yards is moved one place to the right; from 10,000 to 100,000 cu. ft., two places to the right, and so on. For example, 200 cu. ft. equals 7.4 cu. yd., 2,000 cu. ft. equals 74.0 cu. yd., 20,000 cu. ft., 740 cu. yd., and so on, for larger quantities.

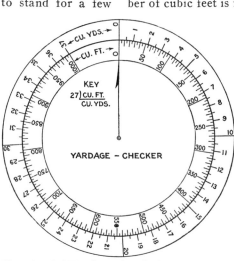

KEY
27) CU. FT.
CU. YDS.

YARDAGE – CHECKER

Chart for Quickly Converting Cubic Feet to Cubic Yards and Vice Versa

Restoring Contact of Third Generator Brush

When the third brush on a Ford generator is shifted to change the output, it sometimes fails to make a good contact with the commutator and there is no output at all. This is often caused by a little dirt or an uneven surface on the brush. The proper method is to sand the brush to fit, but if the brush is pressed down gently with a small stick while the motor is running slowly, it can often be made to "run itself in" and the generator will charge.

Fitting Lathe to Do Job That Requires Larger Swing

The photos show how a job of boring automobile wheels to fit the hubs was done by fitting a faceplate to the back end of the lathe spindle. The faceplate was mounted on a shaft extending through the hollow spindle and was fastened in place by means of a nut and washer. The wheels were centered by means of a tapered cone, which was mounted on a stub mandrel screwed into the opening in the center of the faceplate after the wheel was lightly fastened with bolts and clamping pieces, as indicated. The cone was then removed and the boring done by means of a tool consisting of a suitable guide piece screwed into the faceplate opening, the guide carrying a sliding member with an adjustable cutter and an operating handle.

Portable Bin Which Can Be Taken Down When Not Needed for Coal Storage

Easily Built Portable Coal Bin

Many home owners have only small basements and during the months when no coal is used, a bin is not needed, unless it is filled during the summer for the following winter. A portable coal bin of the kind shown in the drawing can readily be built by anyone. It can be taken down when not in use and put up again when coal is to be taken in. It is constructed of 1-in. boards which are slipped into grooves formed by nailing strips to 2 by 4-in. uprights. These extend from the floor to the joists above, to which they are bolted with ½-in. bolts. The boards are slipped into the grooves near the top and are forced down tightly. These boards should not be over 4 or 5 ft. long, unless an extra 2 by 4-in. upright is provided on the outside as a brace.

Etching on Aluminum

Etching on sheet aluminum is made better and more simple by using a solution of weak hydrochloric acid. It is important that this acid be diluted and not used in its full strength, for in a diluted state it will produce better work.

Boring Auto Wheels on Lathe Which Is Too Small to Handle Them in the Regular Way

An Automatic Boiler Man

Simple Attachment, Operated by Cheap Alarm Clock, Makes Boiler Warm House in Morning

MANY are the homemade devices that have been constructed to open the drafts of the hot-air furnace in the early morning, so that the house will be warm when the occupants get up, but similar devices, designed to do the same job on residence steam boilers fitted with pressure draft regulators, seem to be few and far between. There is no more difficulty in fitting such an attachment to a steam boiler than to a furnace; the one described in this article took approximately an hour to make and has functioned perfectly for two years. It is a great convenience, in

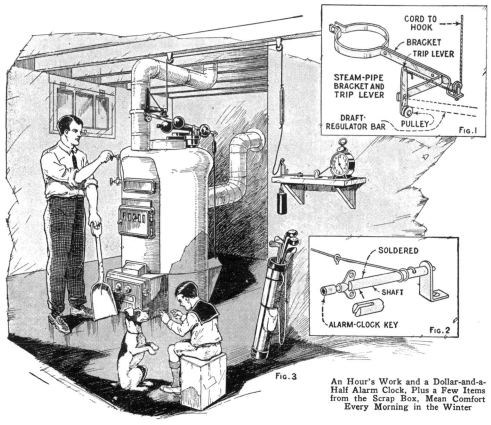

FIG. 1

CORD TO HOOK

BRACKET
TRIP LEVER

STEAM-PIPE BRACKET AND TRIP LEVER

DRAFT-REGULATOR BAR

PULLEY

FIG. 2

SOLDERED

SHAFT

ALARM-CLOCK KEY

FIG. 3

An Hour's Work and a Dollar-and-a-Half Alarm Clock, Plus a Few Items from the Scrap Box, Mean Comfort Every Morning in the Winter

cold weather, to come out of a chilly bed-room and find the rest of the house at 70°, without having to get up at some unearthly hour of the morning to fire up the boiler.

The basis of the attachment is an ordinary alarm clock. This should be a fairly good one; although the one in the original installation cost only $1.50, still the better the clock the longer service it will give, and it must be of the type in which the key revolves when the alarm rings.

Boilers of the type mentioned have a diaphragm in a casing on top, which expands and contracts under the rise and fall of pressure in the boiler. Operated by the diaphragm is a weighted lever, which opens and closes the ash-pit and check dampers as the pressure varies. The first thing to do is to make the steam-pipe bracket and trip lever shown in Fig. 1. The clamp part of this bracket is formed to fit the main steam riser from the boiler, and is held firmly to it by means of a couple of stove bolts. The arms of the bracket are extended to within about 1 in. of the regulator lever; here another bolt is inserted in a hole drilled through the bracket arms, and the front arm is then bent parallel to the regulator lever, and cut off an inch or two longer than the latter. On this end the trip lever is mounted. This consists of a strip of flat iron, about 3½ in. long, pivoted on a small bolt at the end of the arm. About 1 in. below the pivot, a small grooved pulley is mounted, and the whole bracket is then so adjusted that the end of the regulator lever will rest on the pulley when the trip is vertical, and will fall clear when the trip lever is pulled backward at the top. A small hole for a stout cord is drilled in the top of the trip lever, then the rear arm of the bracket is twisted and bent as shown in Fig. 1. On this a small pulley is fastened so that the end of the cord from the trip lever can be passed through it; be sure that the regulator lever can move freely past the bracket.

Now to fix up the operating end of the device. Slot the end of a piece of ¼ or 5⁄16-in. brass rod to fit over the wings of the alarm key, drill a small hole near the other end and solder to the key, Fig 2. Solder two sheet-metal brackets to the clock, as in Fig. 4, so that it can be fastened firmly to a shelf, and mount shelf and clock on the boiler-room wall so that their relation to the boiler is somewhat as shown in Fig. 3. Make and screw to the rear of the shelf a small bracket to act as a bearing for the end of the brass rod. Knot a length of strong fishing line through the hole in the rod, and lead it under a small screw-eye or pulley screwed to the shelf. On the extreme edge of the shelf, pivot the simple lever shown in Fig. 4, and fasten the end of the line to it as indicated. Leave enough line so that, when the alarm is about half wound, the end of the lever will project about ½ in. over the edge of the shelf. The cord is wound on the alarm-key extension so that, when the alarm goes off, the lever is pulled in toward the clock. Bend a stiff wire hook to the shape shown in Fig. 4, and fasten a weight to it. To the top loop hook a short length of chain and a spring. Directly above the end of the lever, on the ceiling, screw in a pulley, and mount a similar pulley directly over the small-pulley bracket on the boiler. Thread the cord (fishing line) from the end of the trip lever through the small pulley just behind it, then over the two pulleys on the ceiling and fasten the end to the spring at the clock mechanism (See Fig. 3). Set the hook on the shelf lever, adjust the weight on the regulator lever so that it will fall, then pull the trip lever to a vertical position and set the end of the regulator lever on the pulley. Wind the alarm about half, and spring it. The device looks, when in action, like one of Rube Goldberg's cartoons, but it works. The alarm winds up the cord, pulling in the lever on the edge of the shelf, and the

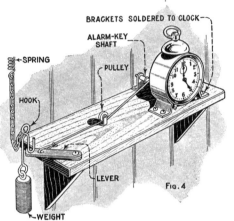

BRACKETS SOLDERED TO CLOCK

ALARM-KEY SHAFT

SPRING

PULLEY

HOOK

LEVER

WEIGHT

Fig. 4

shelf pushes the weight off. The weight pulls the trip lever down, thus allowing the regulator lever to drop and open the drafts. The weight need not be a heavy one, since all it has to do is to pull down the trip lever. Don't try to hook the alarm clock directly to the trip lever; it will work all right, but it imposes rather too much strain on the clock. It is better to use the clock merely to throw off the weight, and let the latter do the work.

Bronzing Cast Iron

The following process will be found effective for imitation bronzing of cast iron: Thoroughly cleanse the iron and rub it smooth. Apply evenly a coat of sweet or olive oil and heat, being careful that the temperature does not rise high enough to burn the oil. Just as the oil is about to decompose, the cast iron will absorb oxygen, and this forms upon the surface a brown-oxide skin, which holds securely, and is so hard that it will admit high polish.

An Improved Chuck Wrench

One end of a small chuck-wrench handle can be drawn out to a spoonlike end and makes a very handy and practical tool. It is an ever-ready implement for "flipping" out cuttings or loosening and lifting out stud shells after they have been drilled and broken down with a round-nose chisel. Shaped as a spoon, the end is much easier on the ball of the thumb when tightening the chuck screw.

Handle of Lathe Chuck Wrench Ground Down to Spoon Shape Adds to Its Usefulness

Old Truck Tire Rims Can Be Used to Make a Convenient Foundry Flask

Handy Foundry Flask Made from Tire Rims

By burning the rubber off two old truck tire rims a very handy foundry flask can be made. Use one of the rims for the top, or cope, and the other for the bottom, or drag. A bracket and pin hold the cope and drag together. Pieces of pipe are used for handles.—Carlton Groat, The Dalles, Oreg.

Reversing Coil Points Aids Spark

After considerable use, the platinum points on an electric vibrating coil often become pitted and the spark will suffer in intensity and regularity. A good method of overcoming this trouble, temporarily at least, is to take out the screws holding the points in position over the core of the coil and reverse them. Take care to get the points exactly in line again and the proper distance apart to give the best and fattest spark. This simply reverses the current through the points and as the action differs, one pitting and the other building up a cone, the points will change their surface shape accordingly and tend to become more normal. Of course, when it can be done, they should be removed and filed smooth for best results.—L. B. Robbins, Harwich, Mass.

Metal Cone Fitting over the End of Logs Prevents End Friction; Chains Are Provided to Hold the Log Securely and Fasten It to a Doubletree

Metal Cone Facilitates Hauling of Logs

Made of sheet iron or steel, the cone shown in the drawing has been found handy for hauling telephone poles. The cone reduces end friction when the pole is dragged over the ground. The insert clearly shows its construction. Three chains are attached to the flat-iron frame of the cone, dogs being provided on the ends of the chains by means of which these are securely fastened to the log. A ring and chain are attached to the apex of the cone to permit a doubletree to be attached. This simple device carries the front end of the log over all obstructions and saves much time.—G. P. Melrose, Victoria, B. C.

Moisture-Proof Coating on Cellar Walls

In many locations it is impossible to drain off moisture on the outside of cellar walls to insure a dry basement. The next best remedy is to apply a waterproof coating on the wall. Melt 4 oz. of grease with 4 qt. of tar in an old pail or other container. While the grease and tar are being melted, thoroughly mix 2 lb. of pounded glass and 4 lb. of slaked lime, and then add this mixture to the former only in quantities sufficient to cover a few square feet at a time. Apply the mixture with an old brush to a thickness of approximately ⅛ in. This coating will waterproof the walls effectively, no matter how much moisture accumulates outside.

Stretching the Point

Lawyers are not the only ones who must often stretch the point. Mechanics frequently have to do it, too. On some repair work, the other day, my dividers were too small. I sharpened a short piece of wire on both ends, bending one of them

at right angles. I then forced the straight end through a cork, and stuck it on one point of my dividers, as shown. The extra point was quite firm and rigid.—Frank W. Bentley, Jr., Missouri Valley, Iowa.

⊄A metal chip from a cutting tool should never be pulled off with the bare hand.

Cheap Glass Stirring Rods

Glass makes the best material for chemical stirring rods, but such rods cost money and are easily broken. Good glass rods that cost nothing can be obtained as follows: Go to a paint shop or hardware store and ask for some narrow strips of glass. These can usually be had and are left-overs from cutting odd sizes of glass. They vary in width from ½ to 2 or 3 in., and also in length. The sharp edges of the glass can be removed by means of a file so that there will not be any danger of cutting the hands.

Removing Roller Bearings on Fords

Quite often it is necessary to remove a roller bearing so that felt washers may be inserted behind them to prevent grease from leaking out on the wheel. A simple tool for pulling out the bearing and the method of using it are shown in the drawing. It consists of an iron rod flattened at one end and bent to the shape shown. The flat end is slipped under the bearing, a length of iron rod is put through the eye and a block of wood is used as a fulcrum under one end of the rod while the other end is pulled, which immediately

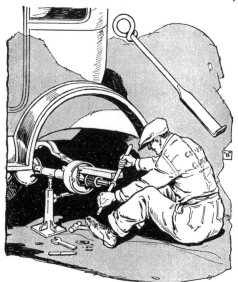

Roller Bearings on Ford Axles Can Readily Be Removed with This Simple Tool

removes the bearing.—C. C. Stuart, Bridgeport, Conn.

Using Two Vises and an Improvised Jig for Pressing Pulleys into Large Wheels

Double-Vise Press

If two vises are set close enough together, they can be used for much press work that could not ordinarily be done in a small shop. Most mechanics have found a vise a handy tool for pressing bushings into pulleys, but this can only be done when the pulley is small enough to allow the bushing to touch the vise jaw. For larger pulleys the two-vise method, shown in the drawing, can be used effectively. A length of angle iron is cut in two, clamped together and drilled in three places to take three rods. The end rods are to hold the angle irons in position when they are laid on the vise jaws and the central rod is to support the pulley while the bushing is being pressed into place. One man can operate this improvised press by opening the vise jaws first, then laying the angle irons on top and dropping the pulley, with the bushing started, between them, and inserting the pin to support it. The vise handles must be operated together.— Harry Moore, Montreal, Can.

¶Aluminum surfaces may be cleaned with a stiff-bristled brush and a solution of from 5 to 8 parts of water to 1 part of sulphuric acid; then a mixture of fine emery and turpentine should be applied vigorously with the same brush.

Black-and-White Striped Jackets for Street Workmen to Prevent Accidents

Striped Suits Insure Safety to Workmen

Shirts and jackets having broad black-and-white stripes have proved quite effective in preventing accidents to highway workmen. Clothes thus striped are more conspicuous than plain ones, and autoists, as a rule, immediately identify the wearer as a workman. This precaution is a good, cheap insurance and it is an easy matter to paint the stripes on the cloth. If this method is not desired, separate black and white stripes can be sewed on.—Harry E. Gifford, Medford, Mass.

Save the Drops

Little is known about the proper quantity of lubricating oil to be used in a steam engine. How many drops per minute are right? One drop may not be enough in your engine and ten may be too many. A good test to determine the correct amount of lubricant to use is a "flywheel test." While feeding, say, ten drops of oil per minute to the cylinders, just after a long run and while running at a normal speed, throw off the load from the engine. Then suddenly close the steam valve. The flywheels will cause the engine to continue to run for some time, and that is an important factor. How long does it take the flywheel to stop? By the use of your watch you can determine this to the second. Make a note of the time required to stop from the instant the steam valve is closed until the engine stops entirely. Do it accurately. The next time try nine drops of oil per minute, but do not allow any other condition to be changed. If the stopping time is the same, you may as well save sixty drops an hour, 600 drops a day, or 180,000 drops a year. Then try eight drops, seven drops, six drops, etc. Finally, use the least number which permits maximum stopping time. Of course, judgment must be used when making this test. Do not choke down the lubricant until the cylinder is likely to be ruined. But as long as the stopping time is at its highest you may feel certain that the cylinder is well lubricated.

Wheelbarrow Fender

A builder noticed that the men pushing the wheelbarrows indoors had trouble in dodging around small pieces of wood that littered the floor. It was almost impossible to keep the floor clean as operations were going on continually and sawed-off blocks of wood were thrown down wherever the workers happened to be. It was thought the best thing that could be done would be to equip the barrows with some simple device to push the obstructions out of the way, and the fender shown in the drawing was found effective for this purpose. It is simply a piece of flat metal, bent to the shape shown, and with both ends drilled to fit over the shaft at each side of the wheel. When the barrow is needed outside of the building the fender is not used, but is laid back against the body. When it is used indoors, where the floor is level, it is dropped and effectually pushes aside any obstruction of reasonable size, enabling the worker to go ahead in a straight path.

Tin-Can Mechanics

By L. R. ROBBINS

WHEN tin cans are emptied they are usually thrown away. However, a great many useful devices can be made from them, some of which are shown in the accompanying photos and illustrations. Persons living far from centers of trade, and from the cheap-price notion or variety stores, can turn tin cans into real value for the home. All that is necessary is a little patience and the knack of using a few simple tools. The photos show what has been done with tin cans to lighten kitchen labors, and these are only a few of the practical applications, as anyone can devise many more.

The tools necessary for the work are a good pair of small tin snips, a drill or a metal punch, a file, a pair of pliers and a small hammer. Use clean cans and provide a well-lighted bench to work on. It is a good idea to wear a pair of old kid gloves while working, to protect the hands from cuts and to keep them clean. To make the soap dish, shown in Fig. 1, get a can of medium size and one with a cover of the type used on baking-powder cans. Remove the cover and lay it aside. Then, with the snips, cut in a straight line up the side parallel to the seam, and continue the cut to the can bottom. Next cut across the bottom along a center line and start up the side at the other end of the cut so that the can will be split about in half along its length. Two tabs are formed in making the last cut up the side. Cut the cover in half and fit the halves to the open ends with a few drops of solder, or by drilling or punching a couple of holes through the can edge and cover to permit riveting. Turn over all uneven edges with the pair of pliers, and hammer down or file off all sharp edges and corners. By giving the completed soap dish a couple of coats of bathtub enamel, or similar waterproof finish, it will make a fine article for the sink and will not rust as long as it is covered with paint or enamel. If placed over the sink, punch two or three holes in the bottom to allow water to drain out. If desired, the holder can be fastened to the wall with screws through the holes in the tabs.

A reflector for a droplight, as shown in Fig. 2, can be made in a very short time. Use a can with a shiny inside. Cans with mottled or enameled linings are not so good for this purpose. Mark a vertical line up the side opposite the seam. Cut along this line with the snips, as straight and evenly as possible, to the end of the can. Cut a round hole through the end just large enough to take the electric-light socket. If the fit is inaccurate, wind the ferrule with a turn or two of tape until the fit is snug. Next cut the sides of the can close to the end until points are reached on each side of the vertical cut about opposite each other. Bend these portions of the side back until they project outward like wings and crease the lines down the side of the can. The result is a semicircular reflector fronted by two wings. The bulb can be screwed into the socket and the light turned on. Such a reflector directs the light down onto the work and in front.

Soap shakers are always necessary in dishwashing, and a good one, shown in Fig 3, can be made from a small baking-powder can and a length of galvanized-iron wire. Remove the cover and slip the can over a piece of round wood which will just fit inside. Using a spike, punch a number of holes through the can all around its circumference. Punch a single hole through the center of the bottom and the cover. Twist a handle from wire and arrange it so that the tines must be sprung out before they will engage in the holes in the ends of the can.

Cooky and doughnut cutters, as shown in Fig. 4, are also easy to make from can covers. For the former use a suitably sized cover with an even edge. No handle is needed. To make a doughnut cutter, it is only necessary to solder a small cover to the inside of a larger one, as indicated, in the center and so that the two cutting edges are even. If you have no soldering outfit, make a hole in the center of each cover and rivet or bolt the two together, using wood, paper or metal washers, if necessary, to hold the edges of the small cover even with those of the larger one.

When it comes to a double boiler for small quantities of material, two tin cans can be used to good advantage, as shown in Fig. 5. It is especially handy for heating glue, chemical mixtures, etc. To make one, get two water-tight cans, one about the size of an apple can and the other about half as large. Cut clear around the apple can with a can opener about halfway up from the bottom, leaving only a narrow section uncut. Then start from the two points where the opener left off and cut a narrow strip to the

edge of the can down toward the inside for the same reason. Fill this can half full of water and then place the smaller can, with the contents to be heated, inside of the larger one. Such an outfit can be made in fifteen minutes or less, and it will be worth making for emergency work.

To make a vegetable slicer, take a long, slender can, such as one in which some brands of round cookies are packed, and peel off the paper or burn off the enamel label. Place the can over a round stick that will fit snugly inside of it. Putting this on a bench, use an old knife blade and a hammer, as shown in Fig. 6, to cut a gash in the tin. Repeat this operation half a dozen times at various points, about 1 in. apart, on the same side of the can. Pry gently under one edge of each cut, to raise the adjacent tin up at a slight an-

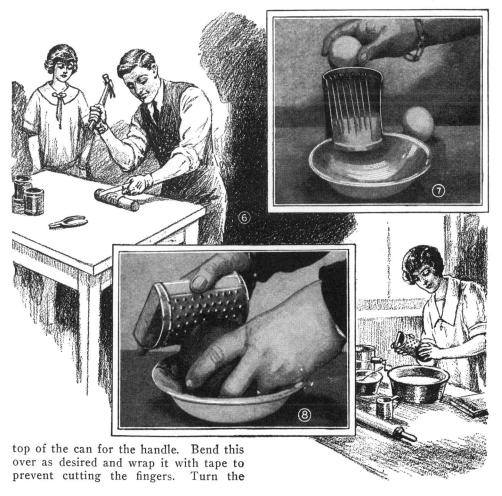

top of the can for the handle. Bend this over as desired and wrap it with tape to prevent cutting the fingers. Turn the

gle to form cutters. To test the implement, pull a raw potato across the cutters, adjusting these until they peel the potato in long thin slices.

Good cake making often calls for an egg separator which is not always handy. One that does the work effectively is shown in Fig. 7. It consists of an empty tin can and a 3-ft. length of wire. The side of the can is cut down for about 3 in. and half the depth of the can. This free piece is flattened slightly by thumb pressure and is then bent out and down at the angle shown. The remaining portion of the top is laid on a block of hardwood and eight holes are punched through the rim just opposite the opened part. Eight 4-in. lengths of the wire are cut and hooked on one end. These are pushed through the holes from the back and allowed to rest on the slanting apron in front. If properly made, the wires will rest parallel and about ⅜ in. apart. A dish is placed under the apron and an egg is broken and held over the wires. The white runs through to be caught in the bottom of the can, while the yolk runs down the wires into the dish.

A grater, shown in Fig. 8, can be quickly made by splitting a clean can in half lengthwise. Lay it, hollow side up, on a block of wood, and punch holes in it with a large, blunt-pointed spike. This forces a barb on the outside. Turn the edges in and nail it to a piece of wood fitted into the open side. By rubbing it briskly back and forth over the cheese, vegetable or food to be grated, the job is done just as nicely as can be desired.

Now for a suggestion for opening tight-fitting tin cans: If the cover is driven on so that it cannot be twisted off, make a loose loop of soft wire just under the cover edge around the can, and place a large nail in the loop to twist the wire up tightly. This squeezes the can together, enabling the cover to be pried off without any trouble. The method of doing this is shown in Fig. 9.

Tin Foil for Packing Glands

Packing glands often stick tightly when close to the edge of the stuffing box, and

can be removed only by driving them out against the collar. However, owing to hardened oil and presence of scale, forcing the gland from one side often makes it stick more firmly, Several small nicks or grooves cut in the collar, as shown, when a new gland is applied, make it possible to use a small

spanner to turn it a little
before trying to get it out.
Several half turns of a
gland will invariably
loosen it sufficiently to
enable starting it easily.
This also helps to keep
the nut face of the collar
true and even.

Keyhole-Saw Vise

Anyone can readily
make a keyhole-saw vise
for filing, in a short time,
as follows: Get a block
of wood, about 12 in. long
and 2 in. high, and nail it
to your bench, then saw
a slot, about ¾ in. deep,
in it. It will be found
that the narrow blade of
a keyhole saw can be in-
serted and held securely
for filing without diffi-

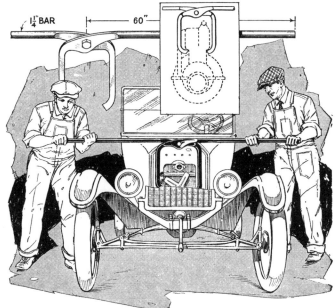

Long Tongs Enable Two Workmen to Lift Automobile Motor from or onto
the Chassis without Difficulty

culty. The blade of the ordinary keyhole
saw is just a trifle thicker than the blade
of a standard crosscut saw, so that the
groove will make a tight fit, preventing the
keyhole saw from slipping out when the
pressure of the file is on it.

Scribing Circles with a Rule

You can scribe large circles very nicely
with nothing but a 2-ft. rule. The wire
dowel pin near the middle hinge makes a
good pivot, so that it is only necessary to
pinch the pencil between the 6-in. sections
of the other half, as shown in the photo.
This method is much better than a string,

Large Circles Can Be Scribed Accurately by Means of
a Rule and a Pencil

for both the pencil and the point are rigid.
—F. W. Bentley, Jr., Missouri Valley, Ia.

Tongs for Removing Auto Motor

To remove auto motors quickly and
with little trouble, one garage uses a pair
of tongs with extension handles. The
latter are 5 ft. long, to provide considerable leverage and to enable two or four
workmen to take hold of them from opposite sides of the car, as shown in the illustration. The tongs are made of 1¼-in.
bar stock, bent as indicated and forged
flat at the point where they are pivoted
together with a loose bolt. With the aid
of these tongs the motor can be readily
lifted from or returned to the chassis.—
G. A. Luers, Washington, D. C.

Repair for Broken Spoke Tenon

It is not necessary to remove a spoke
from a wheel because of a broken tenon. A
repair can be made as follows: Wrap
the end of the spoke evenly, for about 3
in., with fine wire. Drill a small hole in
the end of the spoke and drive a 20-penny
wire nail through the broken tenon and
into the spoke. A coat of paint will make
the repair practically invisible. If the
spoke is to be repaired without removing
the tire, drill a hole through the tire for
the nail, countersinking it for the head.

How to Care for Balloon Tires

By G. A. LUERS

THE facility with which balloon tires ride over cobble stones, broken macadam or concrete, and their cushioning effect, which protects the car and gives comfort to the passengers, must necessarily be accounted for either by additional tire expense or by extra care in order to obtain maximum mileage from this type of tire with its relatively thin walls.

The inner tube of a balloon tire has more than double the wall area of the high-pressure type of tube. It is essential that every precaution be taken to protect the tube, as any hole in the wall will deflate it and may then ruin the casing in a short time. A spare balloon tube should be carried in a bag of heavy duck or waterproof canvas. This will prevent chafing from contact with tools. The procedure

of rolling the tube is to deflate it by removing the valve and flattening the tube, with the valve in the center and held up as shown in the upper left-hand detail of the illustration. It is folded into a rectangular bundle, which is held together securely by means of one or more rubber bands, after which it is slipped into the tube bag. Talcum powder or soapstone should be applied liberally before closing the bag.

In case of a flat tire it is essential that the tire be changed immediately, as the thin wall of the casing and the tube will soon be cut and bruised beyond repair. Therefore, do not drive on a flat balloon tire. The use of a cold patch on a balloon tube is not advisable, as the flexibility of the tire will allow it to work

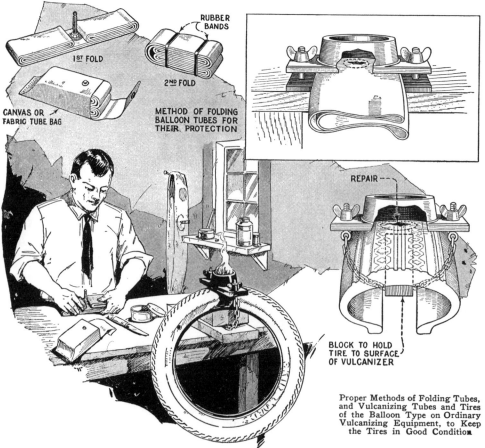

RUBBER BANDS

1ST FOLD

2ND FOLD

CANVAS OR FABRIC TUBE BAG

METHOD OF FOLDING BALLOON TUBES FOR THEIR PROTECTION

REPAIR

BLOCK TO HOLD TIRE TO SURFACE OF VULCANIZER

Proper Methods of Folding Tubes, and Vulcanizing Tubes and Tires of the Balloon Type on Ordinary Vulcanizing Equipment, to Keep the Tires in Good Condition

loose, causing the tube to leak slowly, and a soft tube may endanger the casing before the leak is discovered. For this reason leaky tubes should always be vulcanized. It will be found that a balloon tube is too wide to fit into the usual type of vulcanizer. To accommodate the tube to the vulcanizer it is possible to fold it once, making four layers of the wall, and the patch can then be vulcanized in the usual way, as shown in the upper right-hand detail.

Due to the relatively small number of layers of fabric in the casing of balloon tires, it is necessary to protect them against the entrance of water and grit through small cuts. A heavier tire wall, with the reinforcement of numerous layers of fabric, will withstand considerable usage before blowing when the rubber is cut, but a balloon tire has a weak side wall and fractures in the rubber must be repaired immediately to prevent the fabric from weakening. Also, in this case, the usual vulcanizer, possessed by many auto owners, does not readily lend itself for use on balloon tires. However, to use it for this purpose, the casing must be made to fit the curvature of the vulcanizer. This can be done by inserting a small convex block inside of the casing while clamping the vulcanizer over it on the outside. This method will push the patch into contact with the vulcanizer and permit it to be used effectively. Too much emphasis cannot be placed on the necessity of making vulcanized repairs to breaks in balloon tires and tubes.

The pressure for balloon tires varies from 25 to 40 lb., depending on the make of tire used. This information is given the buyer at the time of purchase, and is often printed on a sticker attached to the windshield of a new car. Although high-pressure tires will stand up when inflated 10 or 15 lb. below their required pressure, a drop of 5 lb. is the limit for most balloon tires. To safeguard against the deflation limit, weekly inspection and replenishment of air should be made. An air gauge specially made for balloon tires should be used in order to get accurate readings.

Many chains available for balloon tires are similar to those used on trucks. Obviously, such heavy chains are really unsuitable for passenger cars. When buy-

ing tire chains, the purchaser should assure himself that he is obtaining the chain made especially for balloon tires.

Electric Fan Helps Sell Goggles

In a Los Angeles motorcycle shop, an electric fan on the accessory counter has

Testing Goggles or Driving Glasses in Front of an Electric Fan

been found a valuable adjunct to the sale of goggles and driving glasses. The prospective purchaser when trying to determine whether or not the goggles or driving glasses offer him the protection desired, is asked to step in front of a fan, which is then turned on. With his face in front of the fan, the customer decides whether the goggles fit.

Leather Piston Packing

A service pump in a street-railroad power plant gave considerable trouble by water slipping past the plunger. The engineer could find no remedy until he tried six ordinary leather packing rings, which easily fitted in the water cylinder when dry. These were placed on the piston just as ordinary packing, and the follower plate and nut put in position. Since using this packing the pump will often run eighteen months without attention.

Burglar Alarm for Windows

Recently I installed a burglar-alarm system in a small shop, using radio jacks

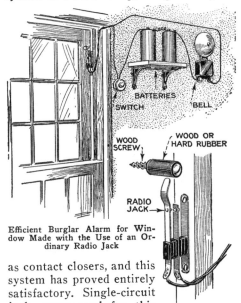

Efficient Burglar Alarm for Window Made with the Use of an Ordinary Radio Jack

as contact closers, and this system has proved entirely satisfactory. Single-circuit jacks were used for this purpose. No change was made in them except to flatten the bent blade slightly, as shown, and to cut off part of the frame, the remaining part being drilled for wood screws with which the jack was securely fastened to the upper sash. A 1-in. length of ½-in. dowel stock, hard-rubber or bakelite rod, with a hole drilled through the center, was used in conjunction with the jack, being so installed that when the window was opened, the round rod would press the outer blade of the jack against the inner contact, closing a circuit and causing a bell to ring. If the lower sash is not permanently fastened, a jack should also be installed on it as well as on the upper sash. The same type of circuit closer can be used on a door, the round rod projecting from the door and the jack being placed against the wall.—Herman R. Wallin, Brooklyn, N. Y.

Belting Horizontal to Vertical Pulleys

Quarter-turn belts connecting horizontal with vertical shafts often give trouble. The belt on the vertical pulley is attracted by gravity and does not stay up where it belongs. This difficulty can usually be overcome by employing a vertical pulley having more than ordinary crown. It is not always necessary to use an idler pulley on drives of this sort. If possible, it is best to avoid the use of idlers because they consume power and cause wear. Another thing to bear in mind is to use as light a belt as possible. Where the distance between pulleys is so great that the weight of the belt causes it to leave the vertical pulley regardless of the crown, it is best to use a guide pulley. Some belt men use two guide pulleys, but unless the distance between transmission pulleys is unusually great, only one guide pulley should be used. It should support the side of the belt going onto the pulley, on the vertical shaft. The side of the belt leaving that pulley does not need support. Where distances between pulleys are exceedingly great on quarter-turn drives of this kind, the problem is sometimes solved by shifting the pulley on the vertical shaft up or down, as the case may be, until a position is located which holds the belt centrally at all times.—W. F. Schaphorst, Newark, N. J.

Improvised Depth Gauge

When drilling a number of holes to a certain depth with a wood auger, a depth gauge is necessary. If one is not available, take a block of wood, 1 to 1½ in. square and as long as the distance from the tip of the auger to the chuck. Drill a hole lengthwise through the center of the block and cut off a section equal to the depth of the hole desired. Slip

the block over the auger and push it tightly against the chuck. The size of the hole in the block should be the same as the size of the auger so that it fits tightly.

¶Uneven heat in tempering causes irregular strain and cracks in tools.

Oversize Printers' Rollers

Rollers for presses are cast larger than the bearing rollers at the ends, and as a result the rollers jump when passing onto the type forms. This is especially troublesome with small forms as it not only fills the type with ink but is wearing on the rollers. The usual remedy is to lock up type-high roller bearers in each end of the chase. The bearers will take the ink and smear it on each end of the drawsheet where one is likely to get his fingers into it. A better method is to get one or more strips of felt and fasten them with glue to the roller guides at each end of the press. This raises the rollers so that they pass over even single-line card-job forms smoothly. The felt will wear for months in the ordinary small-town job shop before replacement is necessary.

Handy Wooden Chute Conveys Parcels from Second-Floor Shipping Room to a Loading Platform Below

Guard for Gas-Tank Filling Pipe

Gas-tank filling pipes that extend above the ground at auto-service stations usually come up through well-sodded ground. However, as gasoline is ruinous to grass, if spilled on it, which usually happens when the tank is being filled, one station owner placed an old auto rim around the pipe, and filled the space inside with gravel. The rim was painted to give it a neat appearance. If any gasoline spills, it falls on the gravel, where it evaporates without hurting the sod outside the rim.
—Dale R. Van Horn, Lincoln, Nebr.

Old Auto Rim and Gravel Filling around Pipe of Gas Tank Protect the Grass

Chute for Parcels

Shipping departments located on the second floor will find this method of handling wrapped parcels of great value to them, inasmuch as it saves labor and floor space. A window, facing the alley or street where loading takes place, is boarded up in the manner shown in the illustration, and an inclined chute, made of 1-in. lumber, is run from the window to the loading platform or bin into which the parcels slide. Ordinary large furnace piping can be used instead of 1-in. lumber, if care is taken when assembling it. The lower end of each section of pipe is slipped into the upper section of the length below it, so that there will be no edges for the parcels to catch on.

Two-Sided Dolly Which Is Handy for Moving Pianos and Similar Heavy Objects

Dolly Facilitates Piano Moving

Moving pianos and similar articles is hard work at the best, but here is an improved dolly which will make the task much easier. It is really two dollies combined, at right angles to each other. Both parts are equipped with casters, the two on one end being of the bed-post variety. The piano is strapped on the dolly and left there until the destination is reached, making it easy to handle at any time.—Jos. C. Coyle, Denver, Colo.

Repair for Galvanized Tanks

It became necessary for us to have additional tank space but we did not feel justified to purchase a new tank. We found an old tank on the junk pile. The seams had opened and rust had eaten through the bottom at a dozen places. We gave it a thorough washing out and then applied a coating of ordinary street asphalt. For the seams and holes along the sides, we applied the asphalt in the same manner as solder, melting it with a blowtorch just enough so that it would roll out into a strip, wedging this into place and then flowing it with the flame. We spread a thin layer all over the bottom of the tank, and a thicker layer around the seams at the edges. Then we poured in the water, which caused the asphalt to set almost instantly. We intended this simply for a temporary job, but the tank has not shown a leak after two years of service. The asphalt in the bottom, where it is always covered with water, never softens. In very hot weather, the patches along the sides soften until the asphalt gets pliable like rubber, but it has never run. Recently we cleaned out our good tank and also spread a thin layer of asphalt over the bottom to prevent it from rusting.—Ralph W. McPherson, Wahoo, Nebr.

Screwdriver Attachment Holds Screws Securely

Various methods have been adopted for holding screws securely to a screwdriver, and the one shown in the accompanying drawing has been found particularly useful for holding screws in deep recesses. It also enables one to remove a screw from such a place without any danger of the screw falling down into the machinery or other place where it is not wanted. The screw-holding device can be made by anyone and consists of a length of flat iron, bent to the shape shown, and a small coil spring. The only change made in the screwdriver is that the shoulders are ground on the blade, as indicated in the lower detail. The attachment is applicable to either large or small screwdrivers

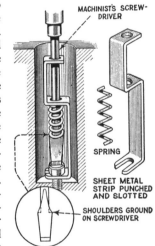

MACHINIST'S SCREWDRIVER

SPRING

SHEET METAL STRIP PUNCHED AND SLOTTED

SHOULDERS GROUND ON SCREWDRIVER

and can be used with wood or with machine screws. It is obvious that the width of the slot or recess in which the tool is used must be such that the screwdriver can be moved sidewise enough to disengage from the screw, after starting this.

Noiseless Wagon

By using both front and rear axles and wheels of a discarded auto, an easy-riding

Using Discarded Auto Wheels and Axles on a Wagon Makes It Easy-Riding and Noiseless

and noiseless wagon can be made. Such old auto parts can usually be purchased much cheaper than wagon wheels.—Carlton Groat, Portland, Oreg.

Automatic Chamfering Attachment on Parting Tool

Many lathe and screw-machine operators use a file or a hand tool to break the corners of the slot made by a parting tool. In the absence of a double toolpost, the parting tool can be fitted with a chamfering tool, which can be adjusted to suit the work and will thereafter automatically perform its task without further attention on any brass-rod work. First of all, cut off a piece of round steel for a toolholder. Drill this through the center to take the tool, tap it for a tightening screw and tap it again for the connecting piece, which is flattened at the other end to fit in

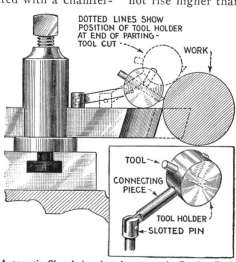

Automatic Chamfering Attachment on the Parting Tool, Useful in Absence of Double Toolpost

the slot of a pin driven in the tool. A small pin through both parts completes the assembly. In operation, the diamond-pointed tool enters the slot made by the parting tool and breaks the corners. As the parting tool is fed further in, the round tool holder strikes the work, causing the holder to ride up the work and permitting the parting tool to complete the cutting off. When the parting tool is withdrawn, the attachment drops down ready for the next cut.

Insuring Proper Chimney Draft

Down draft and "choking" in a chimney often occur when the chimney top does not rise higher than the peak of the roof. This is especially true when the chimney is an outside one and comes up alongside the house. The smoke is cut off and is held up in the chimney. To overcome this difficulty the chimney should be three feet above a horizontal line from the peak of the roof. Often a group of trees stand close to the house, the tops rising above the top of the chimney, and the same trouble may occur.

Old Crankcase Oil Burned in Garage Stove Gives Heat at Small Cost

VALVE

Burning Crankcase Oil in Stove

Most garages have a large quantity of old crankcase and other waste oil. This is usually thrown away, but it can be used as fuel in a common stove or furnace by means of the simple arrangement shown in the drawing. A tank of 5 or 10-gal. capacity should be suspended above the stove, but a safe distance from it. An old auto gasoline tank will serve the purpose well. A ½-in. pipe is tapped in the bottom of the tank and run to the stove, as indicated. The pipe should project inside of the stove at least 8 in. and a valve is provided in the pipe line to regulate the flow of oil. When all connections have been made, the line and tank must be thoroughly tested for leaks. After the apparatus has been completed, the tank is filled with oil and a fire is built in the stove. The firepot should be well filled with fuel so that the dripping oil will not get into the ash pan before it is burned. When the fire is burning well, open the oil valve gradually so that the oil will slowly drop into the fire. A small amount of oil will keep the stove burning all day. In order to safeguard the oil tank against fire while filling it, a heavy felt washer should be placed around the pipe just under the tank to absorb any overflow oil, which might follow the line to the stove. A stove burning oil in this way has saved one garage owner about 80 per cent of fuel otherwise required during the season.—S. A. Marshall, Jr., Rome, Ga.

Grease Nipples for Large Grease Cups

When grease nipples for pressure grease guns are being fitted to machines, it is not always desirable to discard the large grease cups, which may be turned frequently with the fingers. A practice in one shop is to fit the cap of the grease cup with a grease nipple, and to fill it with the grease gun. This involves only drilling and tapping for ⅛-in. pipe thread. Apart from provision for making half turns or more of the cover between the intervals of grease-gun lubrication, the large supply of grease will feed at any time when the bearing becomes heated enough to make the grease flow.—G. A. Luers, Washington, D. C.

Novel Seat for Filling Stations

Many filling stations have a guardrail along the drive, consisting of a gas pipe run through 4 by 4-in. posts, set in the ground at 6-ft. intervals. If desired, a seat can be made by simply cutting square holes in a 2 by 12-ft. plank, to fit snugly over the posts, and nailing cleats to the underside of the plank on each side of the posts. The seat thus made is rigid, permanent and just the right height for most people to sit on it comfortably.—Dale R. Van Horn, Lincoln, Nebr.

Simple Seat on Filling-Station Guardrail Can Be Made from a Plank

Army Cots Become Attractive Twin Beds

By ALPHEUS LINCOLN

COMFORTABLE and good-looking twin or single beds, as shown in the photo, can easily be made from ordinary metal army cots, which, in themselves, are not by any means attractive in appearance.

The cost of these cots is slight in comparison with that of regular beds, as a spring and mattress have to be purchased separately for the latter in addition to the frame itself. The credit for devising the wooden endpieces to improve such cots is Lieut. Col. James M. Hutchinson's, U.

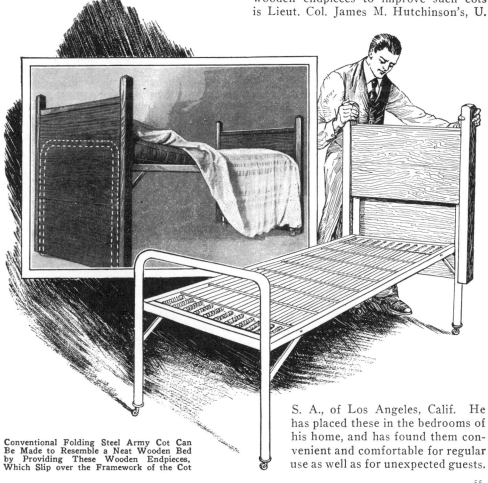

Conventional Folding Steel Army Cot Can Be Made to Resemble a Neat Wooden Bed by Providing These Wooden Endpieces, Which Slip over the Framework of the Cot

S. A., of Los Angeles, Calif. He has placed these in the bedrooms of his home, and has found them convenient and comfortable for regular use as well as for unexpected guests.

First, the bed is lowered by cutting a piece, 5½ in. in length, off each leg, the casters being replaced on the legs after the pieces have been removed. This procedure is not really necessary, but was de-

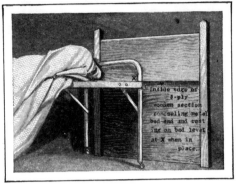

Inside View of Endpieces, Showing How They Rest on the Bed Frame

sired in this case, the bed being lowered from 21 in. in height to 15½ in. The wooden endpieces are then made. Lengths of 2 by 2-in. white pine are used for the posts, which do not bear the weight of the bed but are merely ornamental. Pieces of three-ply veneer are fitted and glued in grooves cut in the posts, as indicated, and a 1 by 2-in. rail of white pine is fitted on top of the veneer to give a more finished appearance. The rail is held in place between the posts by finishing nails, and, if desired, may also be grooved to fit on the veneer. The pieces of veneer are spaced far enough apart to permit them to be slipped over the framework of the bed as shown. On one side the veneer reaches down to the floor but on the other side it extends only to the spring. The side rails of the bed itself, which are level with the spring, bear the weight of the end-pieces, as shown in the small photo, the lower end of the latter being raised about 1 in. above the floor. This arrangement allows the bed to be moved about without any trouble. The wooden endpieces are carefully stained some suitable color and varnished when completed.

Cutting and Drilling Corks

There are many occasions when a stopper or other piece of cork has to be cut or drilled, and, unless one knows the method of doing the work correctly, the job is apt to be a ragged one. The best methods of handling cork are as follows: To cut it, provide a dish of water and a sharp knife. Then, dipping the knife almost continually in the water, rough-shape the cork. Then finish the job with a fairly coarse emery wheel, if available, or use a hand-sharpening stone and water, rotating the cork in the fingers while drawing it over the stone. For drilling cork, obtain a piece of thin-walled steel tubing the diameter of the hole desired and sharpen one end on a whetstone. Bevel the edge like a chisel. Drill a hole through the other end and drive a wire nail through for a handle. Hold the cork in the left hand and rotate the sharpened tube with the right, pressing it through the cork. Such a drill will cut a clean hole.

Useful Homemade Blowtorch

A simple, cheap and extremely useful blowtorch can be made from an ordinary atomizer, a piece of gas pipe or other gas-tight tubing, about 3 or 4 ft. long, and a piece of smaller tubing about 2 ft. in length. The latter is used to produce an especially hot flame, and is not necessary for general use. The nose piece or cap is removed from the atomizer, the glass un-

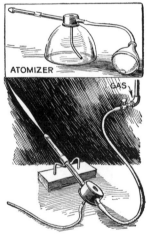

screwed and the large tubing is placed where the short tube to the bulb commonly is connected. This torch will serve well for general experimenting, as the tip is adjustable to various angles. If desired, the small tube may be slipped over the lower, bent tube, and blown through. Care should be taken to blow steadily in order to prevent extinguishing of the flame by a sudden blast.

¶A good rolling pin can easily be made from a 12-in. length of aluminum tubing.

Taking Long, Narrow Photos

When it is necessary to take a long, narrow photo like the one shown here, I set up my camera and take parts of the scene

Large, Narrow Photos like This Can Be Taken with Any Ordinary Camera, Two Halves Being Taken Separately and Joined Later

separately, joining them together. This can readily be done and the separate photos will fit together nicely, provided the camera is kept in the same position while being rotated on the tripod.—J. J. Brindos, International Falls, Minn.

Locating Air Leak in Condensing Turbine

Someone has said that a little leak will sink a big ship, and the same statement might easily apply to a condensing turbine, for if a turbine of about 500-kw. capacity were fully loaded and a hole, ¼ in. in diameter, should be drilled in the condenser above the water line, it is highly probable that, unless the load were reduced or the initial steam pressure increased immediately, the turbine would slow down until it stopped or until the load was light enough for it to pull it noncondensing. A leak of this size would no doubt be discovered, but small leaks that let in a small amount of air constantly cause a loss of efficiency. Trouble of this kind was experienced by the writer some time ago. All the joints in the machine and con-

denser had been gone over and painted with shellac, and every means tried to find this small leak but to no avail. Finally, someone suggested that the machine be shut down and the turbine casing and the condenser filled with water, for it was reasoned that if air could get in water would come out. The plan was given a trial and a tiny trickle of water flowed out over one of the clamping rings on the corrugated-copper expansion joint between the turbine and the condenser. The continued "breathing" action at this point, due to expansion and contraction, had finally opened a small crack, which, being behind the clamping ring, could not be seen. A new expansion joint corrected the trouble. —Earl Pagett, Coffeyville, Kans.

Cool Grip for Small Drain Cocks

When hot, the drain cocks on radiators or heating coils cannot be handled comfortably with the bare fingers or even light gloves. To remedy this, saw a wooden spool in two and cut a slot in it as shown in the photo. The slot should be formed so that the spool will grip the cock handle securely. The spool will always afford a cool grip, and a better one for turning the stem if the latter is a little tight.— Frank W. Bentley, Jr., Missouri Valley, Iowa.

Wooden-Spool Handle for Radiator Drain Cocks

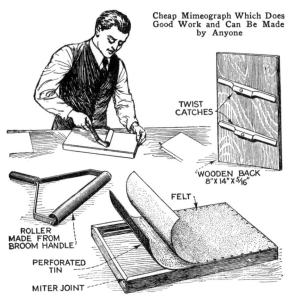

Cheap Mimeograph Which Does Good Work and Can Be Made by Anyone

TWIST CATCHES

WOODEN BACK 8"X 14" X 5/16"

FELT

ROLLER MADE FROM BROOM HANDLE

PERFORATED TIN

MITER JOINT

How to Make a Practical Mimeograph

A commercial mimeograph is usually rather costly, but one that will turn out good copies in any number can be made for almost nothing. Four lengths of ¾ by 1-in. wood are cut to form the frame, which measures 8 by 14 in., inside dimensions. The joints are mitered and nailed to make it rigid. A piece of wood, 5/16 in. thick, 8 in. wide and 14 in. long, is fitted loosely in the frame to form a removable back. The frame is laid on a level surface, the back is pushed down into it against the surface, then two pieces of ½ by ¾ by 8½-in. wood are made into twist catches and attached to the back with one screw in each, as shown, a groove being cut in each side of the frame to receive the catches. Turn the frame over and tack a piece of perforated tin over the entire top, nailing it to the frame only, so that the back can be removed by loosening the catches. Next tack a light piece of felt over the perforated tin surface; this is the ink pad. A light piece of bright tin is cut the same size as the back and put into the frame between the perforated tin and the wooden back in order to prevent the wood from soaking up the ink. This completes the mimeograph. A stencil sheet of the type used in mimeographs is obtained, and a negative stencil is made in a typewriter according to instructions on the stencil sheet. The back of the mimeograph is removed and mimeograph ink is applied to the perforated tin with a small paintbrush, until the felt pad is evenly soaked but not saturated. The tin plate and wood back are then replaced and the stencil sheet is spread out evenly on the ink surface and pressed lightly with the roller until it adheres to the inky surface. The mimeograph is now ready to print, and a sheet of paper to receive the copy is spread over the stencil sheet and rolled firmly but lightly with the roller. The copy is removed from the stencil sheet and the process repeated any number of times. If the copies become indistinct, remove the backing and apply a little more ink to the perforated tin surface; this is not necessary for less than 125 copies.—Steward A. Marshall, Jr., Rome, Ga.

Gauge for Measuring Latticework

In the construction of latticework, it is common practice to space the battens by their own width, and this distance is usually measured by means of a piece of batten. When doing some of this work, recently, I found that the method of spacing was greatly facilitated by tacking a short section of batten on the hammer handle, with its end slightly below the top of the hammer head, as shown in the illustration, so as not to interfere with nail pulling. The spacing block was thus

under the control of the hand holding the hammer handle, and this made the work easier.—Royle Snow, Westmount, Can.

¶A casting should be well pickled and free from sand before it is placed on a milling machine.

Truck Replaces Turntable Motor

The 25-cycle electric motor which operated the turntable in the motive-power yard of an eastern railroad failed. As the light for the work. A 5-ton truck was accordingly substituted and for two and a half weeks it pushed the turntable around until the motor had been repaired. To connect the truck to the table, a special

Five-Ton Truck Moved Heavy Locomotive Turntable While Electric Motor Was Out of Service, Doing the Work of Eighteen Men, Which Would Otherwise Have Been Required

turntable led to forty-six tracks, and it was necessary for the engines to utilize it in making return trips, all traffic would have been tied up had the table ceased functioning. This could not be permitted at any cost. At first, there seemed to be but two possibilities. A new motor might be purchased at a cost of from $1,500 to $1,800, but this plan was not feasible because 25-cycle motors of this type were not carried in stock, and it would have taken several weeks to manufacture one to order. The second possibility was the use of approximately eighteen men to keep the table in motion. But the trouble with this plan was that it would cripple operations in other quarters. The foreman of the auto-trucking department came to the rescue. He argued that a truck could be lowered into the turntable pit with a crane and that the truck could push the table around with the loss of but one man's time and one truck. A 2½-ton truck was first lowered into the pit, but it was soon seen that it was too

bar was made and clamped to the heavy front bumper of the truck and the lower portion of the turntable.

Good Packing for Small Valve Stems

Packing of small valve stems frequently gives out and this often occurs at a time

when there is nothing handy with which to repack them. The following emergency method will then be found helpful: Take the tinfoil from a cigaret package, roll it tightly to form a string, as shown, and slip it under the gland.

Stop Sign Made from Old Auto Casing

Stop Signs for Motorists

A number of unpaved side roads in a western town terminated in a busy boulevard and no regular electric stop signs were provided. To give proper warning, to the motorist coming onto the boulevard over these side streets, cheap and effective signs were arranged as shown in the illustration. They consist of old auto tires imbedded in the dirt so that only a section projects above the surface. The word "stop" is painted on the visible portion of the tire. Nearly every motorist is looking at the road while driving, and his attention is arrested by the sign, both during the daytime and at night. Such stop signs will not damage a car even if they are driven over accidentally.—A. Oscar Wiggenjost, Lincoln, Nebr.

How to Prevent Corrosion in Air Pipes

Corrosion in air pipes can readily be prevented by mixing about 2 gal. of water glass with 1 gal. of water. Open the air valve, allow all the air to escape from the tank and then pour in the mixture. Start the compressor and, when the tank gauge registers about 20 lb. pressure, the mixture can be blown through the pipes and out of the hose. All tools should, of course, be disconnected from the air line

before this is done. Open the valve only about one-fourth. The water glass will be deposited on the walls of the tank and pipes, preventing the formation of rust. Water glass should never be used without water.—August Jeffers, Philadelphia, Pennsylvania.

Gauge for Testing Try-Squares

The invariable dispute regarding the trueness of a try-square is not proved by reference to another square. Both may be out of true and consequently a check by this method is valueless. A cold-rolled steel gauge is used in the tool room of one shop for testing try-squares. It is about 5 in. long and 3 in. in diameter. The outside diameter is ground to a true cylinder and one end is ground at the same time or at the same set up, to provide an edge, circular in shape, on the test end of the gauge. The inner surface of the end is cupped or relieved. In use, the stock of the square is set against the end of the bar and the blade against the side. If the grinding machine is capable of grinding a true cylinder, this is one of the most accurate methods of forming a 90° angle.

Inside Calipers for Close Quarters

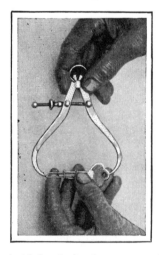

The writer had some small followers to turn for several cylinders, which, because of their location, could not be calipered with the usual small tool. A key and a short loop of wire were assembled as shown, the wire being held firmly in the grooves by twisting two shorter bits of wire around the key and the wire loop. It was easy to handle and adjust, the holes being satisfactorily calipered.—Frank W. Bentley, Jr., Missouri Valley, Iowa.

Making Chain Block Work Both Ways

On many jobs where hand lifting is necessary with a worm hoist, more commonly known as a screw or chain block, there is a time loss of 5 to 10 minutes on each hoist, depending upon the number of stories that the loads are being raised. In addition there is the extra labor of working the chain until the hook returns for its next lift. The loss and unnecessary work can be eliminated by making the chain block work both ways. Cut a link in the slack of the lifting chain and attach a hook as on the opposite chain.

Farm Sled from Old Auto Frame

The farm sled shown herewith was made from a discarded auto frame turned upside down. The engine hanger was left on the frame, but the cross members were removed, to allow sufficient clearance. The rod across the front of the sled was placed through the holes formerly occupied by the spring bolts. The rod forms the hitch and strengthens the sled at this point. Lengths of 2 by 6-in. wood were attached across the top of the runners and covered with 1-in. lumber, to form the top of the sled. The sled may be used both during summer and winter, being especially handy for hauling water, fodder, posts and for doing many odd jobs about the farm where a strong, low sled is required.— Stanley Russell, Winfield, Kans.

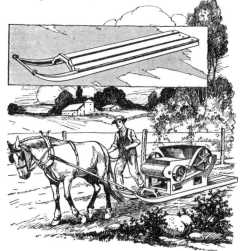

Old Auto Frame Makes a Strong and Useful Sled for Hauling about the Farm

Improvised Gauge for "Eight-Squaring" Large Tapered Pieces of Timber

Gauge Aids in "Eight-Squaring" Timbers for Spars

After squaring a timber and shaping it to the proper taper for making a spar, such as a mast, boom or flagstaff, the first move is to "eight-square" it. The accompanying drawing shows a simple and handy gauge for doing this. It consists of a length of 1-in. wood, cut as indicated in the detail and drilled at two points to hold pencils. A gauge of this type, having the dimensions indicated in the drawing, can be used on timbers 12 in. square or less. If a larger timber has to be marked, the gauge should be made correspondingly longer, say, 24 in. between points, the other dimensions also being doubled. The marking is done by holding the points firmly against opposite sides of the timber, and bearing down on the pencils, which are drawn over the surface of the timber as indicated.

¶Do not use wedges under shaper or planer work; use flat shims as these do not slip when the tool is taking a heavy cut and the work tends to vibrate.

Make These

CANDLE-

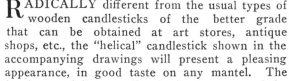

R ADICALLY different from the usual types of wooden candlesticks of the better grade that can be obtained at art stores, antique shops, etc., the "helical" candlestick shown in the accompanying drawings will present a pleasing appearance, in good taste on any mantel. The feature that is especially appealing is the symmetry of the spirals. Both are formed from a single piece of wood, a task which seems exceedingly difficult but is much easier than might be supposed. Only patience and care are required in doing the work, and any person who has a small wood-turning lathe, a coping saw, a metal hand drill and a few other common tools, can readily make the candlesticks.

It is absolutely necessary that a tough, close-grained wood be used. Mahogany, for example, was found entirely unsatisfactory, while a good grade of maple served the purpose very well. It is not advisable to turn the whole candlestick out of a single piece of wood, as the base and the drip flange will not be so strong nor show the beauty of the grain as is the case when it is made out of separate pieces as described in this article. The four parts are the base, the central section or body, the drip flange and the cup, these parts being finished separately, doweled and glued together securely and then gone over at the joints to insure smoothness and continuity of line. Accordingly, 2 by 6-in. maple will be satisfactory, and although the shortest stock available at lumber yards is usually about 10 ft. in length, it is well to have extra stock on hand in case some of the work is accidentally spoiled. A piece of 2 by 6-in. maple, 10 ft. long, costs about $2.50.

In making a pair of candlesticks of this kind, cut off two pieces 6 by 6 in. square; set up in the lathe and turn them down to form the bases, using a template in order to get both exactly alike in contour, height and width. Sand them down carefully until no tool or sandpaper marks can be seen on the surfaces. The dimensions and the curve of the base are given in Fig. 1. The center sections are turned according to the measurements in the same drawing. The pieces used for this purpose should be about 2 by 2 by 10 in. and are turned down to 9 in. in length, 1¾ in. in diameter at the bottom, and 1½ in. at the top. A neck is turned on the top end where the drip flange is attached. This end should be turned to ¾ in.

Attractive Sticks

By E·R·Haan

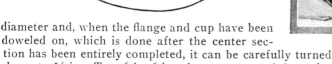

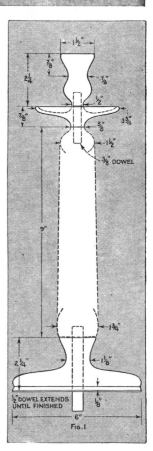

diameter and, when the flange and cup have been doweled on, which is done after the center section has been entirely completed, it can be carefully turned down to ⅝ in. Two 6 by 6-in. pieces are turned down for the drip flanges, a length of 2 by 2-in. stock is turned to 1½ in. in diameter, and the cups or candle holders are turned and finished, care being taken to make them exact duplicates.

The following method of turning the various parts has proved convenient. For the base, drill a hole in the center of the 6 by 6-in. blocks, cut off the corners at a 45° angle and attach the block to the screw faceplate of the lathe. The hole, which should be drilled just a trifle smaller than the screw on the faceplate, should extend entirely through the block so that the dead center of the lathe can be butted into the hole. Thus securely supported on both sides, the block will not chatter or get out of alinement. If the top and bottom sides are not perfectly parallel, face one side, then reverse the block and turn the other side. The neck part of the base should not be finish-turned until after the center section has been finished and doweled on. The center section is drilled lengthwise at both ends, at one end for the screw of the faceplate and at the other end for a ⅜-in. dowel, by means of which the drip flange and cup are attached later. The drip flanges are turned down in the same manner as the bases, a small hole for the faceplate screw being first drilled, the corners cut off and, after the base is completely finished, a ⅜-in. hole is accurately drilled all the way through it. In making a cup, the hole for the candle is bored first, to a depth of about 1 in. and not more than ¾ in. in diameter. Similarly the ⅜-in. dowel hole in the bottom, ½ in. deep, should be drilled before the cup is turned to shape. The wood may split if the cup is first turned and then drilled. A steady rest will be of use when boring the ¾-in. hole.

After the individual parts of each candlestick have been turned and finished, except at the ends where they join, the center section is taken and two strips of gummed tape, ½-in. wide, are wound around it as indicated in Fig. 2. The strips are wound around exactly 2½ turns and must be equidistant at all points; the starting points of the strips

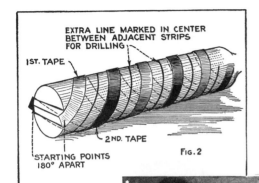

EXTRA LINE MARKED IN CENTER
BETWEEN ADJACENT STRIPS
FOR DRILLING

1ST. TAPE

2ND. TAPE

STARTING POINTS
180° APART

FIG. 2

the top of the sidepieces. The latter are screwed to the base, 7 in. apart, the screws being driven up from the underside of the base. Nails are not used as they might split the sidepieces. The top piece has a row of ½-in. holes drilled lengthwise in the center. After the work is laid in the vees, the top is screwed on as indicated, and will hold the work securely. It must be remembered that one sidepiece is ⅛ in. higher than the other to allow for the taper, and the end of the work having the 1½-in. diameter should rest on the highest piece. The row of holes in the top must be centered accurately over the work. Then, before clamping the top on the work, arrange the center guide line between adjacent strips to come directly under the center of a hole. Proceed to drill through the work slowly in order to avoid splintering the wood as the drill comes through. Turn the

are diametrically opposite each other at the lower end, that is, 180° apart. An extra line is marked in the center of the wood exposed between the strips to serve as a guide for drilling, which is done by means of an ordinary metal hand drill, using a ½-in. drill. It is necessary to drill holes through the center piece at various points and the holes must be drilled exactly at right angles to the axis, not to the surface. A good method of drilling the holes is shown in Fig. 3, a simple wooden jig being used to hold the work and to guide the drill. Although this method takes some time, it is accurate.

The exact construction of the jig is shown in Fig. 4. It consists of a base, two sidepieces with vees cut in them to hold the round piece securely, and a top piece. The sidepieces are made from ¾-in. wood and are cut the same dimensions, except that one piece is exactly ⅛ in. higher than the other. Clamp the two pieces, with the top edges flush, in a vise, and saw out the vees, which have previously been laid out. The vees should be just deep enough so that the work will be raised about ⅟₁₆ in. above

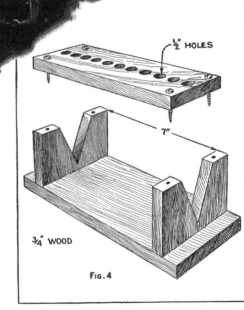

½" HOLES

7"

¾" WOOD

FIG. 4

work a trifle and drill another hole, adjacent to the first, and also centered on the guide line. In this way holes are drilled through the work to remove the bulk of wood between the helices. Do not drill closer than ½ in. from the bottom end and about 1 in. or so from the top end.

After the work has been drilled, it is set up in a lathe and the remaining wood is carefully cut away by means of a coping saw, as shown in Fig. 5. When doing this, guide the blade of the saw toward the waste wood. If you saw straight down a cut will be made in the wood forming the helices, and this should, of course, be avoided. Cut as much wood off in this way as possible and then take a round file and dress down the ragged sides of the helices evenly, which will give the work the appearance shown in Fig. 6. The rounding of the helices is the next

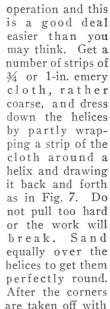

operation and this is a good deal easier than you may think. Get a number of strips of ¾ or 1-in. emery cloth, rather coarse, and dress down the helices by partly wrapping a strip of the cloth around a helix and drawing it back and forth as in Fig. 7. Do not pull too hard or the work will break. Sand equally over the helices to get them perfectly round. After the corners are taken off with coarse emery and the helices have assumed a round shape use a finer grade of emery or sandpaper and lastly fine steel wool to smooth off all scratches. The sections where the ends of the helices join must also be sanded down carefully. When completed, enlarge the hole in the base and in the lower end of the helical section, and dowel and glue the two pieces together. Then dowel and glue on the top parts. The ½-in. dowel in the base should be left extending, as shown in Fig. 1, so that it can be used to hold the work in the lathe chuck. After the candlestick is entirely completed, the projecting end of the dowel is cut off. The joints between adjacent pieces should be well finished. Sandpaper or steel wool can be used to remove all scratches.

Use a light-oak wood dye to get a colonial-maple effect. Do not use the shellac first as it will spoil the finish. Before the stain has dried, wipe off the high lights and then finish with a coat of white shellac. After this has dried thoroughly, rub it down with finely powdered pumicestone and oil, just enough to remove the luster and the brush marks, if there are any. Then apply polishing wax, which, after being rubbed down, will give the sticks a pleasing satin finish.

Simple Jack Facilitates Greasing and Repairing Wheels of Farm Wagons and Implements

Handy Homemade Jack

The drawing shows a type of lifting jack, which, although rather unusual in design, is nevertheless quite simple to make and use. It consists of a length of 2 by 4-in. wood as a lever, a half auto rim, a piece of 1-in. wood, hinged to the end of the lever, and a length of flat iron bent to a shallow "U" and bolted to the lever at the same end. The illustration shows how these parts are assembled, and the upper detail indicates the method of using the jack. It is especially useful on the farm to jack up wagons and farm implements when greasing the wheels or making repairs. In use, the U-shaped piece on the end of the lever is brought under the axle, while the rim is set on the ground. A little pressure on the lever will quickly raise the load and the hinged piece will drop to a vertical position, holding the load securely.

A Safe Match Container

Many shops object to keeping matches around to light up gas furnaces, blowtorches, and the like, because of the danger and the fact that some men are apt to help themselves rather generously for their own private use. Both these objections can be easily overcome by adopting the container illustrated, which holds matches safely and prevents more than one or two from being taken out at the same time. It is made of tin and is large enough to cover the inner half of a box holding about 500 matches. It has one slot cut out on top for the insertion of the thumb and forefinger and one at right angles to this for the removal of the matches. The container is held by means of a couple of screws and nuts in any convenient position. With the thumb and finger in the slot, the matches can be removed only through the narrow slot, which permits the passage of two matches at the most.

¶ Never brush chips into the running parts of a machine; use guards, if necessary, to keep the chips out.

Blocking Out Photo Backgrounds

By DICK HUTCHINSON

BLOCKING out the background of a negative is a tedious operation, and it is a hard matter to get a satisfactory job without allowing the brush to slip on statuary, etc. The following is the simplest and most satisfactory method of getting this effect: Develop, fix and wash the negative and let it dry thoroughly.

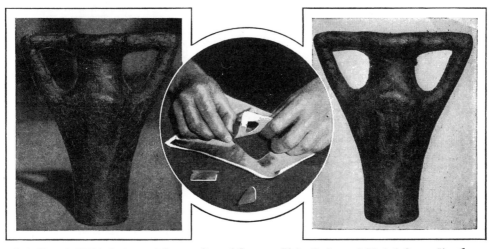

Left, Photo in Which Background Causes a Loss of Contrast; Right, Background Blocked Out to Give Contrast; Center, Cutting the Photo Out of the Background

some of the long lines, thus blocking out a margin of the picture itself and spoiling an otherwise good negative. For the commercial photographer, or anyone who has a lot of blocking-out to do, the following method will be found useful:

Place the negative to be blocked out in the printing frame and make a contact print on single-weight paper; develop, fix and wash in the usual way. While wet, place the print, face up, on a drawing board or some other smooth surface and cut out the picture along the outline with a safety-razor blade, care being taken that a good even outline is obtained. Put the cut-out part, face downward, on the original negative and press it down evenly all over, thereby covering all of the negative except the picture, or the portion that is to be printed. The moisture still in the paper will make it stick to the negative. Place in the printing frame and proceed to make prints. These will have a pure white background, which is seldom attained with the old method of blocking out.

A black background is often desired, and is especially suitable with photos of

Then take a safety-razor blade with a good sharp corner and cut through the emulsion all around the subject. Place in water again and let it soak for an hour or so, then remove, and with the razor blade scrape off all the emulsion outside of the lines, leaving only the subject itself. Let dry thoroughly and the negative is ready for printing. The prints should show a good sharp picture, with a clear black background.

Use for Vacuum Cleaner

Tool cabinets and their drawers collect considerable dust, mainly because many people consider it too much trouble to remove the small pieces in order to clean up. I keep my entire cabinet dustless by using a vacuum cleaner. From a piece of ordinary wire fly screen, I made a cover to fit snugly over the opening or mouth of the small nozzle used with the hose attachment. With this arrangement the nozzle gets into all corners and among small parts, sucking up every particle of dust.—Walter C. Michel, Jersey City, N. J.

Unloading Logs from Trailer

Three planks, nailed together and beveled on one end so that a trailer carrying

Timesaving Method of Unloading Large Logs from a Truck Trailer by Running It onto a Pair of Beveled Blocks to Tilt It Sideways

a load of logs can be pulled up on them, as indicated in the photo, have been found very useful to help unloading. The driver first loosens the chains holding the logs and then drives the trailer on the blocks so that it is tilted to one side. This causes the logs to roll off quickly.—Carlton Groat, The Dalles, Oreg.

Simple Rig Checks Accuracy of Level

All levels sold in hardware stores are supposed to be accurate, but unfortunately there are many grades of levels, and some of these do not come up to this requirement. In the drawing is shown a simple method of checking a level in a few moments. Drive a flat-head screw into any post or side wall and suspend a plumb line, as indicated. About 2 or 3 ft. below this screw, drive in

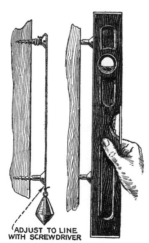

ADJUST TO LINE WITH SCREWDRIVER

another screw so that the head will be exactly in line with the plumb line. All that is necessary now is to place the level against the screws for checking, as shown in the right-hand detail.—L. H. Georger, Buffalo, N. Y.

Care of Pneumatic Tools

The life and efficiency of a pneumatic tool depend to a great extent on the care it gets. A clean air supply is necessary, and therefore it is a good idea to blow air through the hose pipe before connecting the tool, in order to remove moisture and dust. After use, a pneumatic tool should have a charge of suitable oil blown through it to remove any moisture, cover the metal parts and protect them from rust. All tools should be returned to the storeroom after the day's work. They should never be left in the open all night, as this will cause corrosion and consequent loss of efficiency. Tools should be placed in a kerosene bath once a week to clean them. Upon removal from the bath, they should be dried thoroughly and lubricated plentifully before use. Shanks of snaps, chisels, drills and reamers must be of exactly correct dimensions, as chisels and snaps with defective shanks are apt to ruin the hammer piston. Likewise, if drill shanks become bruised, bent or otherwise damaged, they will not fit the socket of the drill accurately. The result will be a damaged socket and perhaps a broken drill.

Only light oil should be used for the hammers and a good grade of heavy oil for drills.—August Jeffers, Philadelphia, Pa.

Atomizer Used for Oiling Firearms

Every sportsman knows that rust is highly injurious to firearms, fishing tackle and other sporting equipment, which must receive proper oiling and care to remain in good condition. In fact, more firearms go to the scrap heap every year from rust than are ever worn out by use in the field. The writer has quite a collection of firearms, and, in spite of the best care, they have suffered a slight depreciation from rust. Oil, of course, is the antidote for rust, but there are two problems to be met in keeping firearms properly oiled. One is to use the right kind of oil, and the other the method of applying it, for the oil must get into every crevice. Any special grade of good gun oil is suitable for rust prevention, but it cannot be applied satisfactorily with a cloth or with an oilcan. The application problem is solved in a satisfactory manner by the use of an old nasal atomizer, by means of which the oil can be sprayed into all the cracks and corners of the gun mechanism. The atomizer has a flexible nozzle which permits spraying the gun oil into the receivers of rifles and other parts of firearms that cannot be reached with any oilcan. It is also useful

Oiling Firearms with an Atomizer Insures Getting the Oil into All the Crevices

for spraying ferrules of fishing rods, metal parts of artificial fishing lures, and practically every other kind of sporting equipment which needs oiling.—John Edwin Hoag, Los Angeles, Calif.

Soap Has Been Used Successfully as a Medium for Architectural Models

Architectural Models Made from Soap

Standard cakes of white soap were used to make the architectural model shown in the photo. The surface of the cakes was cut smooth by means of a heated knife. The cakes were held together and grooves were cut on the sides where they joined. Soft soap, made by melting some of it, was poured into the groove and the cakes were pressed together firmly and allowed to stand for several hours. The result was a mass of soap of uniform consistency, which was easy to carve. This was done by means of a steel tool and an orange stick.—Henry Bern, Chicago, Ill.

Cutting Cast-Iron Soil Pipe

There is a trick in cutting soil pipe, especially when it is in the shape of a bend or elbow. First mark or score it where you wish to cut it. Then place a piece of 2 by 4-in. timber on edge. Have some one hold the bend by the end to which the collar is attached, and rest the part to be cut on the timber. Tap the pipe in several places on the scoring with a cold chisel and hammer, letting the helper rotate the pipe as you do this. With care and not too heavy blows, the material will break off clean along the mark.

❧In knurling a piece of work apply oil on the working face of the roll and also on the pin.

An Electrical Height Gauge

By JAMES McINTYRE

ACCURACY in using a height gauge usually depends on the sense of feeling. Some machinists, however, use Prussian blue on the measuring or transfer finger, noting the transference of this blue onto the point or object being measured, and in this case accuracy depends on sight. Both of the foregoing methods take considerable time, and the novel method illustrated in the accompanying drawing, will be found much more convenient, besides being just as accurate as the others. It consists in an arrangement using a flashlight battery and a buzzer, the latter being energized the moment a circuit is completed by the transfer finger making contact with the work.

Any height gauge can be equipped for this purpose by simply inserting a piece of electrical insulating material at the points indicated. In my case, I made a special finger, half the width of the one provided on the gauge, and then inserted a piece of fiber under it. The part that clamps the finger must also be well insulated to make a complete break in the circuit. The reason for this careful insulation is that the metal surface plate, or table on which both the gauge and the work are set for measuring, provides a path for the current and this would keep the circuit closed at all times. However, if a piece of plate glass is used as a surface plate, it is not necessary to insulate the gauge, and the wire can be attached to it at any convenient point by means of a spring battery clip. One length of insulated copper wire is connected to the transfer finger and to the flashlight battery; another is provided with a spring battery clip, which is clamped to the work, and this wire is connected to a terminal on the buzzer. The battery and the buzzer are connected as shown in the detail. If no buzzer is handy, a flashlight lamp will answer the purpose, or a radio headset can be used. As soon as the finger makes contact with the work, the buzzer will sound, the lamp will light or the headphone will "click."

Anyone can readily improvise an arrangement of this kind, which he will find to be of considerable help besides effecting a great saving of time. If any

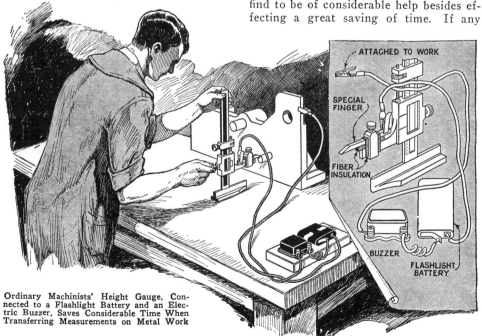

Ordinary Machinists' Height Gauge, Connected to a Flashlight Battery and an Electric Buzzer, Saves Considerable Time When Transferring Measurements on Metal Work

machinist or toolmaker desires to have his gauge arranged so that no addition is necessary when making measurements, all he has to do is to grind a shoulder on the back of the measuring finger, and to use a piece of insulating material the exact depth of this shoulder.

Salt as a Milk Producer

A Wisconsin dairyman has discovered that, although it is commonly acknowledged that salt is good for dairy cows, it does not receive the consideration it deserves in making up the regular diet. In comparative tests with two herds containing an equal number of cows, the farmer claims that the first herd, which was given access to salt at all times, consumed 25 per cent more water than the second herd, and the milk flow increased from 12 to 15 per cent, while that of the second herd remained practically the same. To give milk in any quantity, a cow must consume more water than her bodily health requires and salt must be provided at all times.

Melting Snow and Ice Quickly

Sometime ago, during the winter, we were building a concrete dam, having a gas-engine concrete mixer on the job instead of a steam-power mixer. We had no way of removing the ice and snow from surfaces where fresh concrete was to be poured, so we used an old range boiler in the manner indicated in the drawing. It was raised from the ground by setting the ends on stone or brick supports. A filler pipe was arranged at the end, as shown, the tank was filled about two-thirds with water and a length of hose was then connected to the tank by means of a short pipe nipple. A fire was then built under the tank and the steam produced was directed against the snow and ice.—A. C. Brundage, Rochester, Minn.

Snow and Ice Can Be Quickly Melted by Applying Steam from This Improvised Boiler

Draining Cellar with Siphon

There was quite a bit of water in my cellar. Being unable to drain it and not having a pump, I struck on the siphon

PUMP CYLINDER

BASIN   PISTON

¾" PIPE

RUBBER FLAP VALVE

Simple Siphon Made of ¾-in. Pipe Quickly Drains Water from Cellar

idea illustrated in the accompanying drawing. The house was situated on a slight rise of ground, which enabled me to extend the outside section of the siphon to a lower level than the cellar floor, for otherwise the siphon would not work. A number of lengths of ¾-in. pipe were coupled together, using lead in the joints to make them air-tight. A hand pump and a rubber flap valve were provided on the outside, as shown in the detail. The water flow was, of course, started with the pump. As soon as the water reaches the outlet, it will keep on flowing as long as the inside end of the pipe is immersed. It is a good idea to fit a short piece of rubber hose on the inside end of the siphon and extend this to the lowest point on the cellar floor in order that the water may be drained out completely.—Luther Strosnider, Onaga, Kansas.

Color Holders for Decorators

When doing stenciling and line work on walls and ceilings, it is necessary to have several colors at hand. To have these handy, it is best to arrange a sufficient number of tin cans on a stout cord or small rope, tying it as a belt around the waist. Holes are made in the tops of the cans to admit the cord or rope. This will save a great deal of stooping.

Non-Overflow Bucket

The type of bucket shown in the drawing was constructed to stop continual splashing on the floor of a manufacturing concern. The buckets are used to clean the chips out of drill jigs after each operation. They are filled with a soda solution, and, formerly, when an operator dropped a jig carelessly into the bucket, or dipped one when the bucket was almost full, the contents would overflow on the floor, making it slippery. To prevent this, a hollow handle was provided to take care of the overflow. It was made of 1-in. tubing bent to a semi-circular shape, as shown, and the ends fitted into elbows, which are threaded into short nipples passing through holes in the bucket. The nipples are tightened with locknuts on each side so that the

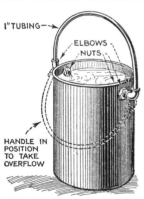

handle works on the threads of the nipples. Ordinarily the bucket is filled to within a couple of inches of the top. If the level of the liquid is raised, it runs into the hollow handle instead of overflow-ing. Lifting the handle causes the over-flow to run back into the pail.—Harry Moore, Montreal, Can.

Simple Lean-To Scaffold Is Easy to Erect and Takes Little Space in the Workman's Truck

Scaffold for Painting

For working at certain heights on the outside of buildings, as for instance when painting window sashes, the simple scaffold shown in the photo will be found to be of considerable utility. It consists of two supports, each of which has a 3-ft. horizontal member, a forked leg and suitable braces for holding the two members together securely. The end of each support is set against the wall of the building and a plank is laid across them. This scaffold takes little space in the truck and is therefore easy to transport, a feature which is especially appealing to the workman. It is, of course, necessary to set the legs squarely on the ground or the scaffold may collapse when the workman gets on it. The legs should not be set on smooth surfaces where they are likely to slip.—Edward A. Weatherston, Chicago.

Shop Notes

Exposure Meter for Reflex Cameras

By HERBERT J. SUMMERS

WITH small expense and a little time and ingenuity, a scientifically correct exposure meter, which is dependable, simple and almost instantaneous in operation, may be built into the ordinary reflex camera. It works on the photometer principle and depends on matching two fields of light to the same approximate intensity. One of these fields is the image on the ground-glass screen within the hood of the camera, and the other is the light from an ordinary pocket electric flashlight, the light being arranged to appear in a square in the upper right-hand corner of the ground glass.

The process of gauging the light, and hence the exposure, is this: Look in the hood at the image on the screen and press the button, illuminating a square in the upper right-hand corner of the screen. The image will be found to be either stronger or weaker than the illuminated square. Change the opening of the diaphragm until the two fields of light are approximately the same average intensity. Using, then, that particular diaphragm opening (or stop), the correct exposure will be a certain constant amount of time —say ½ second, which it is necessary to determine but once by experiment when your apparatus is first built.

Now, having the time (or speed) and the stop accurately known, say, for ½ of a second, it is a simple matter to com-

LIGHT-TIGHT BOX

A Simple Built-In Exposure Meter That Can Be Added to Any Reflex Camera

Above, Image on Screen, Showing Illuminated Square in Upper Right-Hand Corner; Below, Battery for Flashlight on Camera

chase from the hardware store a small, flat pocket flashlight, one of the type which has the lamp exposed and is without a lens or reflector. Then, from a photographers' supply dealer, obtain a monochromatic blue filter. These come in gelatin squares of various sizes. Get one slightly larger than is necessary to cover the lens of your camera, and mount it between two pieces of circular glass obtainable from the hardware store. This can be either fitted into the cell which holds your other filters, or some sort of holder can easily be improvised. The scraps from the corners of the blue square will suffice for the small illuminated field in the corner of the ground-glass screen. It will be noted from the photograph that the writer located the battery case on the side of his camera in such a way that the button was easily accessible to the right thumb. With some bits of fine insulated copper wire, make connections at the terminals of the flashlight where the lamp has been screwed out, and lead these wires through the case of the camera, through fine holes made with a pin, into the upper right-hand corner and on top of the ground-glass screen. There it is only necessary to construct some sort of box just large enough to house the lamp from the flashlight. A light-tight box can be built, of pasteboard and glue, around the lamp, just the same size as the black square in the corner of the finder used as an aid to framing the picture. Over the top of this box place one or two thicknesses of paper and the blue filter.

You are then ready to calibrate your meter, that is, to determine the time constant mentioned in an earlier paragraph. This can be done in two or three ways. Select a subject. Watch the blue fields of light as mentioned before and then with another (borrowed) meter, find out the time required for that particular stop. This is the quickest method. Another is to determine the stop again as above and then experiment on a few films exposing one at, say, $\frac{1}{10}$ second, one at $\frac{1}{25}$ second,

pute the speed for any other stop, or the stop for any other speed. Simply remember that an increase in the stop from one figure to the next, admitting more light, calls for one-half the speed. In short, every time the stop is changed from one figure to the next, the amount of light admitted to the film is either halved or doubled, according to whether the diaphragm is closed or opened. The speed must be halved or doubled accordingly.

In your apparatus, a correction must be made for the difference between the quality of the light as seen by the eye and the actinic light which is effective in making the picture. This is very nicely accomplished by means of monochromatic blue filters. The dark blue known as the "C4" passes a very high percentage of the actinic light of the ordinary film pack, roll film or orthochromatic plate or cut film. Viewing, then, the screen and the illuminated square through the blue filter, you are looking at the actinic light only, and the eye is prevented from being influenced by colors, and other light, such as red, which is not actinic. One of these filters may be permanently installed over the electrically illuminated square, and the other may be placed over the lens. The latter, however, must be removed from the lens before the exposure is actually being made.

For the construction of this meter, pur-

and one at ⅕₀ second. Then use the time constant which gives the best result. If it is found that, with an average picture, the stop comes out very small or very large, or perhaps the fields cannot be matched at all, take out some of the paper and filters (if more than one) in the illuminated square, or, if necessary, put in some more. It is best to have your time constant come out a relatively slow speed, say ⅒ to ⅟₂₀ second, so that in an average bright outdoor photograph, the stop will be small; then the meter will be fit for use in deep shadows, the limit being the dimmest picture you can take at that speed with your lens. Once this time constant is found, it will always be the same. Thus every time an exposure is calculated, you will use the stop found as told above, with this particular shutter speed. Then, if you wish to use another speed or stop opening, it may be computed as outlined.

The reason for the correct operation of this meter is fairly obvious. The square is always illuminated to the same intensity, and is constant within negligible limits. Hence, when the image on the ground-glass screen is matched with it in intensity, it, too, is always the same within the same negligible limits. With the same amount of light always admitted to the film, the shutter speed must necessarily be the same at all times. This shutter speed is the time constant determined at the outset.

It should be added here that the writer employed this meter for three months last summer making about 400 rather particular publicity photographs throughout Europe under all sorts of light conditions, and obtained excellent results. It might be thought that a battery would not be dependable, but it was found that, after the first day, it was so nearly constant that it was impossible to notice any change for nearly three months, until, by accident one day, a short circuit came somewhere

in the system and the battery died. It cost 25 cents to replace. Of course, care should be taken and the current used only a short time while testing the light.

Sliding Shelves in Store Save Space

Homemade sliding shelves solve the problem of storing and displaying large stocks of small merchandise, such as kitchen utensils, enamel and china dinnerware, in a western store. Around the sides of the walls, large cases holding a great number of these sliding shelves have been built. There are from five to ten shelves in each case, and the depth of each shelf or tray varies with the type of merchandise for which it is designed. The shelves slide on steel rollers, which were taken from roller skates, four rollers being attached to each cleat on which the edges of the shelves rest. In use, a shelf can be pulled out from the wall so that the customer can inspect every piece of merchandise displayed. Additional shelves of the usual rigid type may be built above the cases if desired.—Miss Mary Gleeson, San Francisco, Calif.

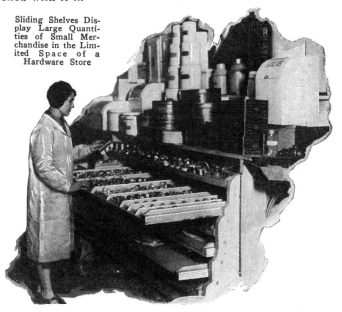

Sliding Shelves Display Large Quantities of Small Merchandise in the Limited Space of a Hardware Store

¶Tin can be removed from tinplate scrap by boiling in caustic soda, and the tin in the solution deposited on a sheet-iron plate by electroplating.

Wrecking Car Has Motor-Driven Hoist

Instead of having a hand crank on this wrecking car to pull autos out of the ditch,

Old Auto Engine on Wrecking Car Is Used to Operate the Hoist

a western garage man uses an old motor to do the work. The gear shift and clutch are retained so that the hoist can be driven at different speeds. A chain and sprocket are connected to the winch drum. This arrangement saves both time and labor. —Carlton Groat, The Dalles, Oreg.

Renewing Old Water Tanks

When a 15,000-gal. galvanized-iron cattle tank on a Texas ranch became old and leaky, it was repaired in a way that made it even better than a new one. The ranch was situated 80 miles from the nearest railroad station and about 3,000 ft. above sea level, so, when the tank began to rust, the manager of the ranch, if he had bought a new one, would have been faced with the problem of a long haul over a mountain road, 15 miles from the state highway, and the necessity of cutting down thousands of feet of mesquite, live-oak and cedar timber along the road to allow its passage. To avoid this and save time, the old tank was rejuvenated in this manner: It was first perforated until it looked like a huge piece of metal lath. Cement was then mixed and two layers applied to the tank, both inside and out. The result was a new and practically indestructible reinforced-cement tank, 4-in. thick. The work was repeated on other old tanks on the ranch, with the result that hundreds of

dollars were saved, besides the delay and risk incidental to the transportation of new tanks by railroad, state highway and the roughest kind of mountain road.— Solon K. Stewart, San Antonio, Texas.

Mixture for Cleaning Hands

I have a cleaner for the hands, which has been found just as effective as soaps and cleaning compounds commonly used for this purpose. It does not require any rubbing and need only be applied like soap. The ingredients are obtainable in almost any drug store or paint store. Get 1 pt. of Turkish red oil, which is also called soluble oil, and ½ pt. of xylene, which is more commonly known as solvent naphtha. Mix the two thoroughly and apply to the hands. The compound is readily soluble in water.—Walter J. Stefaniak, Buffalo, N. Y.

Chain Provides Positive Arbor Drive

When turning pulleys of small bore on arbors, the work will sometimes slip under a cut. To avoid this, I tried a new device in the form of a chain with a ring at one end and a hook at the other. I clamped the ring to the driver plate and passed the hook around one of the arms of the pulley. This eliminated the slipping and made it unnecessary to drive the work very tightly on the arbor. This chain drive will be found handy also in cases where the work is too far away from the plate to allow the use of a bolt. The chain can be put on and taken off readily and is adjustable to different lengths.—Harry Moore, Hamilton, Can.

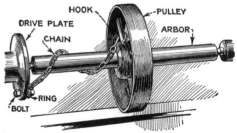

Positive Chain Drive Prevents Work, Mounted on an Arbor, from Slipping

Temperature in Developing Negatives

Many amateur photographers neglect the temperature factor when developing films or plates. This has much to do with success or failure. The best temperature is approximately 65° F. A difference of 15° usually spoils the negatives. At 50° the negatives invariably turn out weak and very flat; at 55° more strength will be evident but the image will still lack intensity, and at 60°, much longer development than normal will be required, and full intensity will still be lacking. At temperatures above 70° there is danger of the emulsion puckering away from the film base and also of too rapid development, causing "thick" negatives and chemical fog. So keep the temperature close to and slightly above 65°. Do not rely on the sensitivity of the fingers to tell the temperature of the solution, but use a thermometer, and take frequent readings, for this is the only reliable method.

Laying Out Keyways

The photo shows a tool that I have used for over ten years to lay out keyways and holes in long shafts. It consists of a V-block with a level and center punch, a small plunger, a small spring to bear against the plunger, and a headless set-screw, to increase or decrease the tension of the spring. The center punch is located in a hole drilled in the center of the block as shown. In use, the tool is set on the shaft, exactly level, and the punch is given a light blow. Without displacing the work, the tool is moved to another position to mark the shaft at a second point. After the tool has been set level, proceed as before, and you will be sure that the two punch marks are in line.
—John Snitil, Cleveland, Ohio.

Newsboys' Change Holder Made from Cigar Box Saves Considerable Time

Newsboys' Change Holder

While waiting for a street car on a busy corner, the writer noticed a newsboy using a novel device for holding change in readiness for his customers. During rush hours, when he was very busy, this holder enabled him to make change quickly. The holder consisted of a cigar box in which a block of wood was fitted. A series of notches or recesses were cut in the upper side of the block, deep enough to hold three cent pieces. The other part of the box was used for loose change. When not engaged with customers, the boy filled notches with pennies. Customers handing him a five-cent piece for a newspaper, would immediately receive their change.
—Leslie G. Roller, Cedar Rapids, Iowa.

How to Drive Nails to Avoid Splitting

When it is necessary to drive nails in places where there is danger of splitting, and a drill of the proper size is not at hand for starting a hole, simply file or grind the point of the nail to a chisel edge instead of the regular four-sided point, and drive the nail with the sharpened edge cutting across the grain of the wood. This practice will usually prevent splitting.

Conical Sheet-Metal Container for Tar, Which Facilitates Melting and Pouring It

Practical Container for Melting and Pouring Tar

For melting and pouring tar in small quantities, the scooplike container illustrated will be found convenient. It is made of heavy tin or sheet iron, bent cone-shaped, riveted at the overlapping edges, and closed at the large end with a sheet-iron disk, riveted on. A hole is cut at the large end through which the cone is filled with pieces of tar; the small end is left open to permit the tar to flow out when melted. A wooden handle is attached to the wide end. In use, a plumbers' blowtorch is held so that the flame plays against the container, melting the tar and causing it to run out as indicated. The outfit can be moved about at will and the flow of tar can be directed with precision. The tar hardens after the flame is extinguished.

Machining Cold-Rolled Steel

It will be found that, after machining, such as planing, milling or cutting a keyway in a bar of cold-rolled steel, the bar will spring to a considerable extent when released from the vise, owing to the relieving of the "rolling strains." This trouble can be largely overcome by first heating the bar to a dull red and then allow-

ing it to cool in the air on grates off the floor and out of a draft.—Frank N. Coakley, Buffalo, N. Y.

How to Repair a Door with Bolts

To repair a door when the stile has worked loose from the crossboards is a task within the reach of the ordinary house owner who possesses a brace with a large and a small bit, a file, a wide-bladed screwdriver, a hacksaw and a 6-in. carriage bolt. First file off the shoulder of the bolt so that the shank is smooth clear up to the head. Cut a slot in the head so that the screwdriver will fit it. Take the door down and drill a hole, large enough to let the bolt head slip in and just deep enough to let it come below the surface of the wood. Using the small bit, continue the hole through the stile and about 2 in. into the crosspiece. It is best to drill this hole about 1½ or 2 in. below the corner of the door. Drill a second hole into the end of the door. This hole must meet the first one, about 1½ in. beyond the point where the stile is joined to the crosspiece. Slip the bolt into the hole and insert the nut as shown in the drawing. A little manipulation will be necessary to get the threads started. When this is accomplished, screw up the bolt with the screwdriver, and the door will be as good as ever. The entire job can be done in about half an

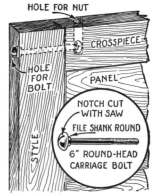

hour. If the hole into which the nut was inserted is at the top of the door, it should be filled with a wooden plug or cork, which is tapped in tightly and cut off flush. If this is not convenient, pour the hole full of melted paraffin or sealing wax.—F. J. Ward, Ismay, Mont.

❡Do not connect belt ends with a metal fastener and allow the hooks to be poorly clinched; the hands of a worker may be cut when shifting the belt.

MAKING A BIRD BATH IN CONCRETE

BY EDWIN M. LOVE

THE interesting bird bath described and illustrated in this article was turned from concrete, on a platform or wheel made of rough boards and rotated by hand, the concrete being built up on the wheel and the contour formed by turning the mass against a sheet-metal template, supported close to the side of the wheel. The same design would also serve for a fountain or a goldfish bowl, and the method of turning the column and base would work equally well for making a sundial or gazing-globe pedestal, or similar piece of concrete garden furniture.

Build the wheel or platform of rough 1-in. stock, in two layers, with the grain of one at right angles to that of the other. (See Fig. 1.) Nail the layers together well, scribe a circle, 28 in. in diameter, on the platform, and saw it to shape with a compass saw. Now bore a hole in the center, a driving fit for a 3-ft. length of ½-in. water pipe. Over the lower end of the pipe drive a length of 2 by 6-in.

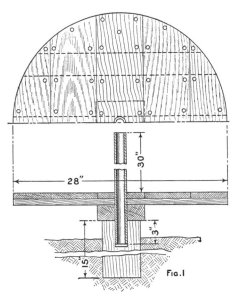

Fig. I

pine, which is to be tacked to the underside of the platform. Light hammer blows on this block will bring the pipe at right angles to the wheel, when the block can be nailed solidly in place, with the pipe projecting through the upper surface of the platform. The pipe should also project about 3 in. below the block.

Set in the ground a piece of 4 by 4-in. pine, with the end projecting 3 in. above the surface, and, centering on the end of the piece, bore a hole, ⅛ in. larger in diameter than the pipe, to serve as a socket for the projecting wheel pivot. Set the wheel in place on the 4 by 4-in. bearing, then drive a 1 by 3-in. stake into the ground close to its edge. The stake should be about 3½ ft. long and must be supported firmly. It can be braced to any convenient object near at hand, or, if this is not possible, to stakes driven into the ground behind it.

The upper end of the pipe is then secured so that the platform will be level in every direction, by means of two braces cleat at the side of the wheel at the proper distance from the center, allowing ¼ in. between the bottom of the template and the top of the wheel for clearance. The wheel is then ready for use.

Get some sand of the quality used for good concrete work and screen it through ⅛-in. mesh. A wheelbarrow makes a very convenient receptacle for the sand when screening, a hoe handle or similar tool being used under the screen as a roller, as in Fig. 4.

On top of the platform, build a pile of moist sand and shape it to the contour

bored to fit over it, and fastened to posts or stakes at the outer ends, or to the top of the long stake already in place. Rotate the platform. If the pipe does not turn with it, owing to loose fits in the wheel and block, make the necessary alterations so that the pipe will turn with the platform, for a stationary center will cause no end of trouble later, when the concrete is being shaped. At intervals of 60° around the circumference of the wheel drive short stakes as shown in Fig. 2, and nail guide cleats to them, projecting over the surface of the platform, to insure that the wheel will have a horizontal motion.

Make a paper pattern of the bird-bath profile given in Fig. 3. This is done by ruling the paper into 2-in. squares, locating a number of points on the profile in Fig. 3 with the dividers, and then marking similar points on the ruled paper, afterward drawing the profile through the points marked. Trace this on a sheet of tin or sheet iron, either with carbon paper or by cutting the paper pattern out first and then tracing along the edge. The template for the bottom may be cut separately, if desired. Cut the sheet-metal template out with tin snips and smooth with a file. Stiffen the iron with strips of wood nailed to both sides, as indicated in Fig. 2, then nail the template to the tall

Fig. 2, Setting Up Template on Wheel; Fig. 4, Screening Sand for Concrete and Bowl Mold

of the inside of the bowl, as shown in Fig. 5 and the dotted lines in Fig. 3. Pat over the sand core a small quantity of cement, and allow this to harden.

For turning the bowl, a fair quantity of concrete, mixed in the proportion of two parts sand to one of cement, may be stirred wet in the wheelbarrow, as indicated in Fig. 6, but for the column only a small quantity at a time should be wetted. The addition of a small quantity of slaked lime to the concrete makes it more plastic and easier to work. Now cover the sand with concrete, mixed wet enough to be handled easily but not sloppy, turning the platform slowly while doing so. The concrete, of course, settles outward, and consequently it must constantly be pressed upward with the hands until it has stiffened enough to hold together. A trowel, thrust between the template and the bowl, helps in this operation. If trouble is encountered, due to the material breaking away from the mold during this process, keep the main body of the material back from the template about ¼ in., then, when this has set, plaster with thin concrete and turn against the metal. The hands, rubbed over the surface as in Fig. 7, will smooth the work very well.

The photo, Fig. 7, shows a part of the column being turned with the base, but the writer found it advisable to cut the column away, down to the molding under the bowl. The bowl, allowed to harden, was then removed from the platform and pipe, and the base and the whole column were turned together.

In order to do this, the template, of course, was removed from the stake and reset upside down, taking care to get it in the same relative position as before.

For the column, use a mixture of one part sand to one part cement, a so-called "rich" mixture. If, as the column is built up, nails are stuck freely into its surface, much of the falling away of the material will be avoided. A small trowel, held between the surface of the work and the template, will be found useful in

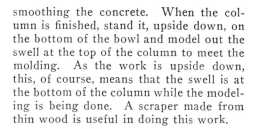

smoothing the concrete. When the column is finished, stand it, upside down, on the bottom of the bowl and model out the swell at the top of the column to meet the molding. As the work is upside down, this, of course, means that the swell is at the bottom of the column while the modeling is being done. A scraper made from thin wood is useful in doing this work.

When the concrete has thoroughly hardened, the bird bath is ready to be set up. Smooth off the inside of the bowl and build up a more or less symmetrical mass of concrete around the projecting pipe, to hide it; this forms a small "island" in the center of the bowl. Lastly, round off the rough edge of the bowl with a rasp. The finished bath is shown in the headpiece of the article.

Driving Finished Work without Dogs

Fig 5, Shaping Bowl Mold; Fig 6, Mixing Concrete; Fig. 7, Smoothing Bowl Surface

Some small pieces of finished work which it is not advisable to drive with a dog but on center of a lathe, can be driven to advantage by means of a length of belt lacing, passed around the work two or three times and tied securely. The free ends are passed through opposite slots in the faceplate and tied together. This will not mar the work or take up as much room as a dog driver.

Priming the Lighting-Plant Engine

The method of priming the farm-light engine shown in the drawing, while not

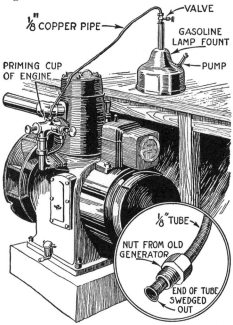

Gasoline-Lamp Fount Equipped with an Air Pump Can Be Used to Prime Gasoline Engine

automatic, keeps a large quantity of gasoline under pressure so that the engine can readily be primed by simply turning a valve, and thus avoids the trouble incident to the common method of priming.

The container consists of the fount and stem of a gasoline lamp, which is quite common in rural homes. The kind having an air pump built into the fount is the best for this purpose, but is not absolutely necessary. Remove the shade holder, air mixer and all the top parts until only the upright and valve are left. Locate the fount at any convenient point near the engine, either above or below it. Saw off the swedged end of a generator and remove the nut. Then arrange a suitable length of 1/8-in. copper pipe to reach from the lamp valve to a point just over the top of the engine priming cup. Place the generator nut on the tubing and swedge out the end of the latter with a blunt-nosed tool to resemble the generator end as much as possible. Insert the swedged end in the lamp and fasten it in place with the nut, just as though you were putting in a

generator. Fill the fount with gasoline, see that the valve is closed, and pump up a good head of air pressure. See that all plugs and connections are air-tight. If this is not the case, smear the threads with soap before threading home. To prime the engine it is only necessary to turn the lamp valve. The air pressure in the fount will force gasoline through the tube to the priming cup. A few seconds only will be necessary for this and the valve can then be shut off. If the engine slows down on the first priming, the valve can just be cracked open and the gasoline allowed to drip into the cup until the engine picks up from its own fuel supply. A fount of gasoline should last for more than a month for priming purposes, and, if all connections are made air-tight, the pressure will hold for a week or ten days without pumping.—L. B. Robbins, Harwich, Mass.

Holder for Cards Aids Typist

A holder for cards that are to be picked up quickly for use in a typewriter or for other purposes can be made in a few minutes from the top or bottom and one of the sides of a cigar box. The angle for cutting the boards used as stops at the back of the holder may readily be determined by placing fifty or more cards in a pile with the ends overlapping each other. A small quantity of glue and two or three small nails will hold the stops securely.— Herbert C. Crocker, Edwardsville, Ill.

Card Holder, Made from Cigar-Box Wood, Saves Time for the Typist

¶ When filing solder, a little machine oil will prevent the teeth of the file from clogging with the soft metal.

Wooden Structure, Made of Two-by-Four Framework and Ordinary Shiplap, Which Is Nailed on the Inside, Has Served as a Silo at a Fraction of the Building Expense

Cheap Homemade Silo

It was necessary to build a silo on our farm, but, as the cost was prohibitive to us, we decided to build a large bin or shed to hold the ensilage. It was made of 2 by 4-in. studs and rafters, while shiplap was used for the sides. Contrary to the usual procedure, however, we placed the studs on the outside. This method prevented the shiplap from loosening and perhaps coming off, owing to the weight and pressure of the contents, as would have been the case if it were nailed to the outside. Pegs were also driven into the ground and suitable bracing provided to prevent the bottom from spreading. In addition, a few braces were placed against the middle of the studs. In a silo of this kind it is necessary to pack the ensilage well, as the bin does not have the depth of a regular silo. The cost of this silo was only $47.50. If desired it can be dismantled and stored.
—W. E. Smith, Thief River Falls, Minn.

Handle Rest for Babbitt Ladle

It is often necessary to set a babbitt ladle down for a moment while resetting the work. The ordinary bowl-shaped ladle does not rest level unless it is packed up, but as babbitting always leaves little time to spare, I devised a rest to attach to the handle. I find this not only ideal for the purpose, but it also serves as an extra handle, allowing a firmer grip. The leveler consists of a piece of tubing, flattened to an oval shape and pivoted to the ladle handle with a rivet. When I am carrying the ladle or pouring the metal, the rest is in line with the handle, and if I want to set it down, I give the attachment a quarter turn to form a rest as shown in the drawing.—Harry Moore, Hamilton, Can.

PIVOT
HANDLE USED AS REST
BABBIT LADLE

Pumping Clean Water from a Cistern

Clean water may be drawn from a cistern in the following manner: Use a rubber hose instead of the lead pipe and attach a block of wood a little above the lower end to keep the end of the hose under water. The wood will float and keep the hose end just under the surface at any level of the water.

Auto Greenhouse Carries Flowers and Displays Them at the Same Time; the Outfit Did Much to Promote Sales

Flower Shop on Wheels

Considerable increase in the sale of flowers was experienced by an eastern florist, after he had made his delivery truck into a "flower shop" on wheels, as shown in the photograph. A large, sturdy truck was used for this purpose, and the framework of the shop was made of wood, especially braced to endure the jars of traveling. The top and sides were, of course, inclosed with glass. The truck facilitated moving the flowers from the greenhouse to the florist's shop.—H. L. Wheeler, Syracuse, N. Y.

Unwinding a Coil Spring

An old machinist saw one of the boys in the shop trying to straighten a coil spring with a screwdriver and a hammer on the bed of his lathe, so that he could rewind the wire to make a spring of smaller diameter than that of the original one. Telling the young fellow to "fetch the spring" over to his workbench, he took it and clamped one end in the vise, inserted an iron rod in the spring and then walked backward, unwinding the spring as he went, holding the rod at both ends. Although the wire was not made perfectly straight, it was in condition to be rewound. Besides the unhandiness of the method first employed, it was hard on the lathe. The bed of a lathe is not an anvil, and it should never be used for that purpose.

Emergency Router

On a repair job, a carpenter sometimes runs into work where he could use a router to advantage. Should he have none in his tool box, a router can easily be improvised by taking the plane bit out of a small wood plane and using a narrow chisel instead. Set the chisel edge to the right depth and tighten the wedge just as when adjusting a bit, and the router is ready. It takes only a few minutes to make the change, and this emergency tool will do better work than could be done by cutting the wood by the use of a chisel and mallet.

Cutting Wire Lath for Gables

Much labor is encountered when wire-lathing gables, owing to the fact that the lath must be cut at an angle on both sides. If the cutting is done on the scaffold and full-length pieces of the lath are used, it is slow work and rather hard to handle. To avoid this difficulty, cut the pieces short as shown in the drawing, being careful that they are cut to conform to the inspectors' requirements. The pieces left over can be saved for use on the gable at the other

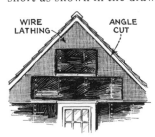

WIRE LATHING

ANGLE CUT

end of the house, so that there will be no waste. The lath can be cut on the ground and brought up, and full pieces can be lapped onto the square ends of the angle-cut parts. Any further cutting will be straight across the pieces which is much easier.—Robert Page Lincoln, Minneapolis, Minn.

Pneumatic Soldering Plant for the Shop

By L. B. ROBBINS

MANY workshops are located in the country where electrical house-lighting current is not available and, for this reason, an electric soldering iron cannot be used. However, by utilizing the water system to compress the air, a serviceable soldering torch can be cheaply made, burning either commercial gas or gasoline. The air pressure can be regulated to suit various conditions, and a small or large flame can be produced. The torch will be suitable for large and small work, except where a flame cannot be handled safely.

The pressure tank may be an expansion tank of the kind found in hot-water systems. It should test to 75 lb., and is conveniently mounted on suitable wooden brackets or a shelf, near the workbench. The air line, consisting of pipe and a suitable length of armored-rubber hose, is provided with a safety valve, pressure gauge, pressure-reducing valve, and a shut-off valve, arranged as indicated in the drawing. The gas line is run to the same point on the bench as the air line, a shut-off valve and a length of armored-rubber hose being also provided in this line. The lengths of hose are connected to the soldering torch, which is made from a piece of ⅛-in. brass pipe brazed into the end of a brass "Y." A straight length of pipe, provided with a shut-off valve at one end, a cock at the other, and a tee cut in between, is screwed into the bottom tank opening. The water main is connected to the tee and a supply valve is

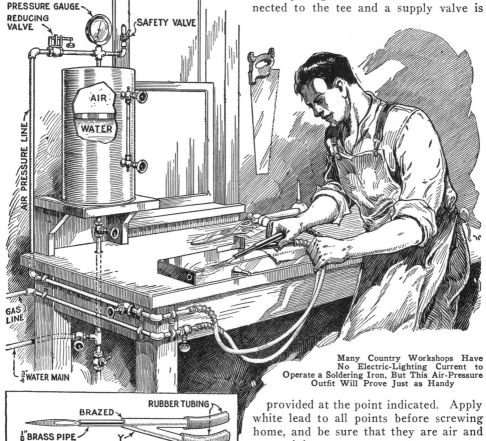

PRESSURE GAUGE
REDUCING VALVE
SAFETY VALVE
AIR
WATER
AIR PRESSURE LINE
GAS LINE
¾" WATER MAIN

RUBBER TUBING
BRAZED
⅛" BRASS PIPE
Y
DETAIL OF JET

Many Country Workshops Have No Electric-Lighting Current to Operate a Soldering Iron, But This Air-Pressure Outfit Will Prove Just as Handy

provided at the point indicated. Apply white lead to all points before screwing home, and be sure that they are air and water-tight.

When air pressure is desired, the tank

must first be drained by opening both valve and cock in the drain line and closing the supply valve. Then close the cock and open the water-supply valve. As the tank fills with water, the air above the water level is compressed. If the tank is capable of safely holding 75 lb., you will have a good reserve. Do not allow the water level to rise above the water glass, as it may then get into the air line. The required air pressure can be obtained by adjusting the reducing valve on the air line. With sufficient water and pressure in the tank, the air can be drawn out as desired, by opening the air valve. When the air pressure in the tank drops too low for use, the tank must again be drained and refilled as before. One filling, however, at 60 lb., will provide air at 15 or 20-lb. working pressure for a long time. Be sure that the safety valve is set to open before dangerous pressure is reached. Suitable small soldering jets can be made from $\frac{1}{8}$-in. brass pipe. A valve in each line will give positive pressure control at the jet and allow adjustment of the flame.

Where commercial gas cannot be obtained, gasoline will serve as fuel by utilizing an old gasoline lamp so common in thousands of homes. Simply connect the fuel opening of the jet to the lamp outlet pipe and inject the gasoline in the jet through the generator tip used in such lamps. By preheating the end of the jet and then turning on both the gasoline and a small quantity of air, a Bunsen flame will result when the jet is lighted, and the size of the flame and its intensity can be regulated by the valves.

Seat for the Harrow

A harrow having no seat can be provided with one as shown in the drawing. The seat support is made of 1 by 6-in. and 2 by 6-in. wood, securely nailed together as indicated in the lower right-hand detail. Two holes are drilled through the lower end of the 2 by 6-in. uprights to accommodate the axle of an old wheel,

Seat for Harrow Enables the Driver to Work in Ease and Comfort; It Is Easily Improvised from Materials to Be Found on Farm Scrap Heap

which can be taken from some discarded implement. Part of an old cultivator, with collars and a brace added as shown, is used as an axle for the wheel. It is securely fastened to a 2 by 6-in. "draw plank," which is attached to the front of the cultivator. Additional flat-iron braces are provided to hold the seat support rigidly to the draw plank, and a footrest, made of ½-in. iron rod and bent to the shape indicated, is also attached to the draw plank. An iron seat from a discarded implement is fastened to the support in the most convenient position for the driver. In use, the wheel rests on the ground, and when the horses are walking, the draw plank is raised from 2 to 4 in., while, at the standstill, it rests on the ground.—Willis Mehanna, Bussey, Iowa.

Pouring Two Liquids from a Single Spout

Two liquids of different strength are held in one can at the same time by a cleaning company that finds this method quickest and best to avoid mistakes. To outward appearances the can is much the same as an ordinary square 5-gal. oilcan with a spout in the center, and to anyone not in the secret it seems mysterious to see two different-colored liquids issuing from the same spout. The secret lies in a partition that divides the can in two halves. Anyone desiring to make a similar container can do so by taking a square can and providing a piece to fit in the center, leaving it projecting above the top a little. Next, two pieces are cut out for the top, each having half a hole in one side, and lastly a funnel spout is made and all the parts are soldered together. To pour either liquid, the can is held with the part containing that liquid on top. When filling the can a funnel is used to direct the liquid into the proper half and the can is never filled quite to the top. When the can is tipped to pour, the liquid in the lower half is below the spout and does not come out.

Rigid Vise Stand, Made of Pipe and Fittings, Is Bolted to Floor

Pipe Support for Heavy Vise

It is sometimes objectionable to support a heavy vise on the workbench as the vibration caused by its use may make it difficult for others to work at the bench. To overcome this trouble, a separate stand for the vise, made of pipe and fittings, was provided as shown. The stand has three legs, fitted with flanges, which are screwed or bolted to the floor. Additional strength is obtained by braces of ¼-in. iron rod. A number of elbows, couplings, nipples and a T-fitting are used to form the upper end of the stand, and the vise is bolted on top. When making the stand, start by fitting the top pieces together, then screw on the legs, brace them, and attach the flanges.

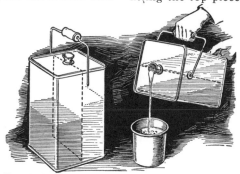

Two Fluids Contained in One Can May Be Poured Separately without Mixing

❡It is provoking to try opening a window at night for ventilation and find it frozen to the sill. This can be prevented by sprinkling a little salt on the sill every time the window is closed.

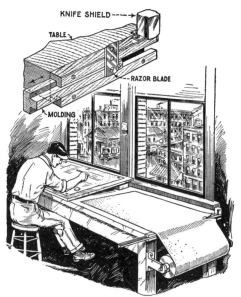

Razor Blade Attached to Simple Slide Cuts Drafting Paper Straight

Device for Cutting Drafting Paper Squarely and Quickly

It is difficult to cut a piece of drafting paper from a roll squarely with a penknife or scissors, and many rough edges have to be removed, the total being quite considerable in a large drafting office. The trouble can be overcome by providing the cutting device shown in the drawing. Two lengths of ½ to ⅜-in. rabbeted mold are tacked to the end of the drafting table to which the roll of paper is attached. Another length of molding, rabbeted on both sides and fitting in the rabbets of the two other pieces, forms a slide. A safety-razor blade is screwed to the back end of the slide in the position indicated in the detail, so that it projects just above the surface of the table. The slide should be a little wider than the other two pieces so that it can be moved back and forth and the razor blade will not bind or cut the upper rabbeted piece. A length of drafting paper is drawn from the roll and cut squarely and rapidly by pulling out the slide which carries the blade. When not in use, the blade is pushed into a small sheet-metal guard in the shape of a box. This avoids the danger of cutting one's hands when unaware of the sharp blade. Additional precautions should be taken by setting the table on which the cutter is mounted, against the wall, as shown.— S. A. Marshall, Jr., Rome, Ga.

How to Harden Chalky Plaster Walls

Plaster walls sometimes appear soft and chalky, which is not a good condition for the application of paint. In such cases it is, of course, necessary to harden the surface. A practical method of doing this is to dampen the wall with clean water, which is applied with a brush. When the wall has dried, the plaster will be hard. Although it may cause some delay in finishing the walls, the work is well worth while as the foundation of any painting job must be right if it is to be permanent.

Removing a Bushing

To remove a bushing in a hole that is not drilled through, is often a difficult task. A practical and novel method is to fill the hole with some plastic medium such as white lead or thin putty. A shaft, the diameter of which is just a fraction smaller than the inside diameter of the bushing, is held in a vertical position in the hole, as shown, and a sharp blow is directed on the top of the shaft. This will cause the plastic substance, under compression, to force the bushing out as illustrated in the insert. If the shaft is a good fit in the bushing, heavy oil may be used

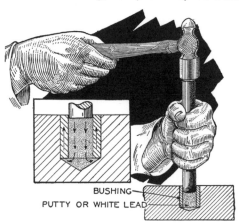

BUSHING
PUTTY OR WHITE LEAD

Easy Method of Forcing a Bushing Loose by Means of Putty or White Lead

instead of the white lead or putty.— Joseph W. Kelly, Brooklyn, N. Y.

Mantel Clock Made from Old Alarm

By R. W. MADDEN

MANY an alarm clock that has been discarded as worn out can readily be restored to useful life by a gasoline bath and a little oiling, and may be converted into an attractive mantel clock by making a wooden case for it, as shown in the illustrations. The better the grade of wood

FIG. 1

Those Who Like to Make Useful Things around the House Will Find Pleasure in Renewing an Old Alarm Clock and Mounting It in an Attractive Wooden Mantel Case

used for the case, and the greater the care taken in doing the work, the better will be the finished appearance of the clock. The writer made one of these clock cases of white pine and stained it with mahogany wood dye.

Using ¼-in. wood, first make a rectangular box, 5½ in. wide, 2¼ in. deep and 7⅜ in. high. The front and back should overlap the sides so that no joints will be visible from the front. The edges should be glued and nailed together with small brads. Carefully scribe the circles on the front and back, where the clock is to be located, and cut them out with a coping saw. These circles should be smaller than the face of the clock, so that they will hold it securely. The curved top is formed by steaming a piece of thin wood, 5¾ in. long and 1¾ in. wide. Boiling the wood in water will also make it pliable, but has a tendency to cause it to become spongy. The wood can be bent around a large tin can, tying or clamping it in position until thoroughly dry. Next, cut out the front section, which fits under the curved top. This piece should be ½ in. thick, 1¹⁄₁₆ in. wide and 6 in. long. A piece of ¼-in. wood, 1 in. wide and 2¼ in. long, is then laid on each side of the curved section, flat on the top of the case. Care should be taken to join all the edges well. The top molding is now applied. It is ⅜ in. by ½ in. wide. This can be either purchased or made. In the latter case, take a piece of white pine of the required dimensions and burn in the round or concave part with a heated rod or carve with a gouge of proper sweep. The charred surface is removed by rubbing with sandpaper wrapped around a rod. To bend the molding for the top curve in front, it is necessary to cut slots every ¼ in. on

FIG. 2

FIG. 3

the back side. The base, made of ½-in. wood, is then cut as indicated in Fig. 3. If a lathe is available, turn down the front pilasters or columns. A disk of thin wood is hinged on the back of the case to close the opening and a small turn latch can be provided to hold it closed.

All joints must be thoroughly sandpapered, as a small dent or depression will show up distinctly after the case has been finished, and a filler should be used before stain is applied. This is particularly necessary on end grain. Apply as many coats of filler as the wood will hold, or until a wax-like deposit covers the surface. Scrape off the surplus and stain the case with wood dye. Then give the case an application of white shellac. After letting this dry for 24 hours, three coats of varnish are applied, each coat being left to dry thoroughly and then rubbed down with powdered pumicestone and water before applying the next. Use a large brush with stiff bristles for this purpose, dipping it first in water and then in the pumicestone.

It may be necessary to provide a new face for the clock, if the old one is soiled. Remove the hands and then the face, which can be traced on a similar disk of good manila paper. With black India ink, make the numerals, using a fine lettering pen, such as a Gillot 303. Omit the small alarm dial on the face. The method of attaching the clock in the case depends on the construction of the clock used. After fitting the works in the case, the front ring around the face can be either gilded or gold-leafed. To apply gold leaf it is necessary first to brush on a coat of japan gold size. This is allowed to set for about five minutes until it becomes sticky, so that you can hear a slight snapping sound when pulling the finger away after touching it. The leaf, which comes backed on sheets of tissue paper, can then be put on, after cutting it into strips of the most suitable size for the purpose. After the leaf, with the tissue paper still attached to the back, is applied as evenly as possible, smooth it out with a camel's-hair brush, about 1 in. wide. Burnish the paper with the back of your finger nail, and then remove the paper. If there are any rough edges of leaf, press them down carefully with the brush. After the size has dried overnight, give the leaf a coating of transparent lacquer, which will prevent tarnishing.

Turntable Dispenses Poultry Netting

In a hardware store where floor space was rather limited, considerable inconvenience was experienced in the sale of poultry netting, as there was not enough space to lay the rolls down for measuring off to the desired length. To facilitate the work, the owner made the revolving rack shown in the drawing. The base was made of oak, two pieces being used as indicated. A hole was drilled at the point of their intersection to receive the stub of a buggy axle, with a small wheel mounted on it. The rack could then be revolved so that the netting could be unrolled, measured and cut off without any trouble.—G. E. Hendrickson, Argyle, Wis.

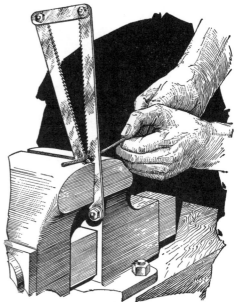

Device Made from Hacksaw Blades Is Useful for Stripping Insulation from Wire

Wire Stripper Made from Hacksaw Blade

Anyone doing electrical work will appreciate this wire stripper. It is made from two pieces of fine-toothed hacksaw blade, and will quickly remove the insulation from small or large-gauge wire. A blade is cut in half and a hole drilled in each at the cut. This may mean annealing the steel to do the job, after which it should be rehardened. Bolt the original ends together tightly and link the other two with a small rod of steel, using machine screws and nuts. This link should separate them at about the angle shown and the points of the teeth should point toward the crosspiece. In use, the stripper is clamped in a vise and the wire then pulled through the jaws. The saw teeth will remove the insulation quickly and neatly.

¶An ordinary wooden clothespin will serve as insulating pliers when automobile spark plugs are tested; a detached spark-plug wire is pushed into the slot in the pin, so that its end can be held close to the spark-plug binding post without danger of shock.

OAK FRAME
STUB OF BUGGY AXLE
SMALL BUGGY WHEEL

Turntable in Small Store Found Convenient for Storing and Dispensing Poultry Netting

Hastening Sand Sifting by Means of a Simple Sliding Device

Sliding Scraper Improves Sand Screen

Using the blade of a shovel to scrape damp sand through a sifter will soon ruin the screen. A much better method is shown in the drawing. A bar of ½-in. round steel is bent to a U-shape to fit inside of the sifter. Both ends are threaded so that a length of flat steel, drilled to fit on them, can be held by nuts. In use, the sliding device is moved back and forth, causing the sand to pass through quickly and with less wear on the screen.—G. E. Hendrickson, Argyle, Wis.

Guard for the Cellar Trapdoor

During summer it is often necessary to open cellar trapdoors in order to provide proper ventilation, but this involves a certain degree of danger to children. Accidents caused by falling down an unguarded cellar way can be prevented by the use of a guard rail, as shown in the drawing. It consists of two lengths of 1 by 5-in. wood, the edges of which are nailed together at right angles, and two 1 by 4-in. blocks at each end, with space between

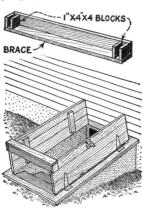

them to fit over the edges of the cellar doors. The way of using the rail is clearly shown.—Frank Harazim, New York City.

Eyelets for Paper Fasteners Protect Paper

Paper fasteners of the kind that are pushed through holes in the paper and then bent over, are rather sharp and the sheets are torn easily, especially when they are frequently handled. Paper eyelets are obtainable to overcome this trouble, one being placed under the head of the fastener before it is inserted, and the other slipped over the shank of the fastener before it is spread. A good substitute for these eyelets, in case they cannot be obtained, is those found on shipping tags. It is an easy matter to cut them out.

Homemade Facing Tool for Bibcock Seat

Small, flat composition washers used in hot-water bibcocks are very often dented by obstructions catching and lodging under them as the spindle is screwed down to the seat, and this causes them to leak. Trimming or facing them down with a pocketknife blade is not

satisfactory, as a perfectly smooth face cannot be obtained in this way. A simple homemade facing device is shown in the illustration. Whittle a stick down so that it can just be slipped through the screw hole of the washer. Force an old safety-razor blade on the end of the stick projecting through the hole as indicated, and then turn the washer against it. The face will be trued squarely and evenly.—F. W. Bentley, Jr., Missouri Valley, Iowa.

❡Machinists, mechanics, airmen, and others who wear goggles, are often bothered by grease collecting on the lenses; carbon tetrachloride removes it instantly.

Artistic Plaques ARE EASY TO MAKE

By R·O·Buck

THE vogue for gesso and plastic paints has brought back into popularity that most ancient of the arts, modeling. Done in low relief, it is surprisingly easy, and very pleasing results can be obtained with limited skill if a plastic compound is used. This material can be obtained at any art store for a small sum, or even from the 10-cent stores. Its advantage over clay is that it does not require experience in mixing to the proper consistency, nor does it dry hard, but remains in the same condition indefinitely, and may be used over and over again. Of course, the modeling compound is only a means to an end and you will want to preserve your work in a permanent form. This can be accomplished with plaster of paris or a marblelike cement used by dentists. For many purposes, such as plaques, a plaster cast is entirely satisfactory and less expensive than

cement. Plaster is used in either case for making the mold. The cast may be painted or enameled to obtain very beautiful effects. However, for articles that require greater strength and durability, the cement is recommended. This cement, which goes under such trade names as Weinstein artificial stone, Healy stone and clover rock, may be purchased from dental-supply houses or from your local dentist. It dries very hard and close-grained and looks much like marble. It is commonly used for casting so-called "marble" statuary.

Many beautiful articles can be made by the use of these materials at small cost of time and money. As the scope of this article is necessarily limited, I am describing only the modeling and casting of plaques of the type shown by the photographs. You need not confine yourself to these, however, for there are many other things you can make, such as desk sets, book ends, trays, lamp bases,

After you have selected a design of suitable size, or enlarged one to the size required, you are ready to begin. A piece of sheet iron or glass, somewhat larger than the size of the finished plaque, is used to do the modeling on, as any absorbent material, such as wood, soaks up the oil from the compound. Roll the material out smoothly and to an even thickness of about ¼ in. An olive bottle or glass rolling pin is convenient for this purpose. Fig. 1 shows this stage of the process.

The next step is the cutting of the background to size by the use of a cardboard pattern, as shown in Fig. 2. An ordinary vegetable knife is suitable for this. Modeling tools can be made

candlesticks, jars, vases and even copies of statuary and art pieces.

The first step in the making of a plaque is the selection of a design. If you have skill with a pencil, this will not be much of a problem. Assuming that you have not, I would suggest selecting some rather conventionalized drawing in a magazine illustration or advertisement, or perhaps you will prefer to use one of the drawings shown in this article. Modeling compound has certain limitations which must be recognized at the outset. Fine detail must be avoided and care must be taken that no backdraft or undercutting, which would prevent the separation of the cast and the mold, is present. Of course, if provision is made for dividing the mold into sections, as is done with statuary, you need not guard against undercutting, although it is best avoided at the start.

from slivers of wood that may be cut in a variety of shapes that will suggest themselves to you. They should be sanded so that they will leave the model smooth.

The actual building up of the design is largely a matter of patience and care. The drawing is placed on the surface of the compound and traced with a sharp pencil point to make an impression on the compound. Pieces of the material are then cut to the approximate size and shape of the raised portions of the design and put in their proper positions, and tools are used to work the material into place and to the exact size and shape desired. Parts that are to be raised are built up to height above the background. Some detail may be attained by cutting into the raised portions or even into the background. If greater contrast or an appearance of greater depth is desired, a roughening of the background will give this effect. Raised edges are formed by building on strips of the compound. The finished model must look as you wish the casting to be. Fig. 3 shows a model completed.

Now we come to the casting of the mold in plaster of paris. A band of cardboard or tin, about 1 in. high, is shaped to fit around the outside of the model and fastened with a wire or strong rubber band. (See Figs. 4 and 5.) A dam of the compound is forced against the band on all sides to keep the plaster confined. The latter is mixed as follows: Estimate the quantity of liquid plaster required, and fill a bowl with clean water to that amount. Take a handful of plaster and sift it into the water slowly. Keep adding plaster while stirring gently, until little deposits or islands of plaster appear above the surface. This is the saturation point, and only a small amount of plaster should be added after that has been reached. The mixture will then be about the consistency of rich cream. In stirring, the spoon or paddle must be kept below the

surface of the water, as raising it out of the water produces bubbles and results in a spongy mold.

The plaster should be poured into the mold slowly. It is best to cover the design only ⅛ in. deep at first, then rap the table sharply to break any bubbles which may have formed from pouring. Fill the mold even with the top of the band and allow the plaster to set. This re-

quires about 15 minutes. The dam and binding strip may then be removed, and the mold lifted from the pattern or model. It will probably be necessary to do a bit of trimming on the mold, especially at the edges. Smooth all irregular places and patch with plaster any portions that are rough or did not cast well. The mold may be used for casting with plaster while still damp; in fact, better results are usually obtained this way.

In order to remove the cast from the mold, it is necessary to employ some separating material. A soap paste is often used for this purpose, but you will have better results with "liquid glass" and oil, sandarac varnish and oil, or collodion. All of them are satisfactory and easily obtained. Cover the entire surface of the mold with the separating fluid, applied with a camel's-hair brush. After it has dried, which will be within a few minutes, a thin coating of oil is applied. Almost any kind of oil will do, but it must be a thin coating so that it does not make bubbles or discolor the cast.

A band and dam are placed around the mold just as they were around the model.

The height of the band should be such that the cast will be the desired thickness. If the cast is to be of plaster, the mixing should be done in the same manner as for the mold. Care must be taken to get the plaster into every corner and crevice, and to avoid forming bubbles. A small piece of wire, for a hanger, should be placed in the plaster when it is partly set. In case you overlook this, another method is to drill small holes diagonally from the top edge through the back, so that a light wire may be twisted in for a hanger.

The cast is ready to separate from the mold as soon as the plaster has set. You can tell when it is set by the fact that it will feel quite warm to the touch, because of the chemical action that has taken place. Scrape the edges of both the mold and the cast until the separation line is visible all the way around. Gently insert the edge of a case-knife blade along this line to a depth of about ⅟₁₆ in., as in Fig. 6, and all the way around again. Now, with the full length of the blade in this cut, gently pry the mold from the cast. If it does not yield readily, insert the knife on the opposite side and repeat. The cast should part from the mold cleanly if you have applied the separating material over the entire surface. After the cast is separated, it is ready to be smoothed and decorated. Do the touching up and smoothing while the cast is still damp, as it is more difficult after it is dry and hard.

If the casting is to be made with dental cement, estimate the amount you will need to fill your mold and mix the powder with water to the consistency of thin paste. This material is less liable to form bubbles, so does not require as great care in the mixing as plaster does, but it must be mixed thoroughly.

All dental plasters set slowly; about 24 hours are usually required before they set hard enough to be separated. This depends on the grade of cement used, however, as it can be obtained in quick-setting, medium and slow grades. A wire hanger should be inserted into the plaster when it is only partly solidified, as it is difficult to drill this material later. It may be necessary to tap the mold gently with a small wood block to start the separation. I found sandarac varnish better than the other materials for separating cement. This material can be obtained at the same place you get the cement.

The cement castings are pure white and resemble marble very closely, but may be painted or enameled as desired when thoroughly dry. A bit of dry color is sometimes added to the dry cement, to give an

ivory tint, which has a very pleasing effect.

Various shades of bronze, such as rose, fire, green, lilac, blue silver and old gold produce beautiful effects on plaques of either material. They may be bought in small quantities, at most paint stores, in dry form to be mixed with a bronzing liquid. It is important that the plaques or other castings to be decorated be thoroughly dry before bronze paints or enamels are applied, as the slightest bit of moisture will cause the paint to flake off in spots. Brushing lacquers are also suitable for this work and give very pleasing velvetlike results in combination with the above-mentioned bronzes.

Showcard or poster colors may be applied to casts of either material while still damp, and are particularly suitable where brilliant color effects are desired. Painting the entire plaque in a solid color, such as blue or red, and then high-lighting or touching up the raised portions with one of the bronzes, is one of the simplest, but not the least pleasing, treatments. Fig. 7 shows a conventional flower plaque completed, and, though it is impossible to do justice to the coloring with black and white, some idea of the possibilities is suggested.

The plaque in which the windmill is the central figure was painted in shades of blue and old gold with a border of black and stippled gold. The Venetian boatman is effective in brilliant orange with red-gold high lights, while the ship proved to be most attractive in a simple treatment of shades of sepia with the high lights rubbed somewhat lighter. The border was done in dull gold.

A mold can be used repeatedly, but it is then advisable to repeat the oiling for each casting and add a coat of separating fluid also, if many duplicates are to be made.

Wooden Guard Prevents Children from Climbing on Ladder

Guard for Stationary Ladder

Children often unthinkingly risk hurting themselves by climbing ladders that are permanently attached to tanks, barns and other buildings. To prevent this, a guard of the kind shown in the drawing may be provided. It is simply a wooden door of the same width as the ladder, hinged to one side and with a hasp on the other so that it can be secured with a padlock. The guard should extend over three or four rungs at least, so that a boy would not be able to climb over it, even if, in spite of its presence, he should attempt to do so.—F. G. Rempe, Oakland, Calif.

Precautions to Be Taken When Soldering Gasoline Tanks

Numerous serious accidents have occurred from attempts to stop leaks in gasoline tanks by soldering, brazing or similar processes. The use of an open-flame torch for work of this kind involves great danger, but under certain conditions even a soldering iron may cause an explosion. The danger is due to the inflammable fumes left in a tank after the gasoline has been drained out, and these fumes are really more dangerous than the gasoline itself. If one is not certain that all the explosive fumes can be removed from a repair job, it should not be undertaken, for the loss of the job is preferable to the loss of a hand, eye, or life itself. The best method of removing the fumes is as follows: First drain all the gasoline, providing a vent to allow the free entrance of air to replace the gasoline. Most tanks have a petcock or plug at the bottom, which can be opened for this purpose. After the tank has been thoroughly drained, it should be flushed by means of a water hose, making sure that the tank is filled with water all the time, the water entering the upper hole and escaping through the lower one. After the tank has been flushed for about 15 minutes, all the water is drained out, the inside dried by means of compressed air, and the tank is then placed on a hot-water or steam radiator, or other fireless heating device. When placed on the radiator, the tank should be set so that the largest hole is at the top to permit the free escape of fumes, and the smaller hole at the bottom to allow the entrance of air. These precautions may appear to be exaggerated, but the number of accidents that arise from attempts to solder gasoline tanks warrant them.

Non-Slip Holder for the Oilstone

When using an oilstone, inconvenience is often experienced due to the lack of steady support for it. Of course, it can be held in a vise, but when the latter is in use or is not available, a non-slip holder will be found handy. It can be made from a piece of sheet metal, cut and bent to the shape indicated. Such a holder provides pointed feet which grip the surface of the workbench tightly when pressure is applied to the stone.—Fred E. Hake, Cincinnati, Ohio.

Sal-Ammoniac Stops Casting Leaks

Small leaks or flaws in castings, that show seepage of liquid when filled, can be temporarily repaired with common sal-ammoniac. Dissolve ¼ lb. of this in warm water and let it cool. Pour the mixture into the casting and allow it to remain undisturbed for 24 hours. If it leaks through too fast, place a bucket underneath to catch it. Refill the casting whenever necessary. The leak will gradually become filled with a deposit of rust and it should be water-tight in 24 hours. Of course, this repair will stand no pressure, and a permanent one should be made as soon as possible.

Vise Helps Pipe Laying

Laying a long stretch of piping involves the difficulty of screwing new lengths onto those already laid. It is necessary to hold the end of the pipe that is placed with one wrench, and turn a coupling and a new length with another. The job is usually done by two men, but it can be made so simple that one man can do it without being handicapped in the least. All that is necessary is a pipe vise securely clamped to a plank, which is long enough to be laid across the ditch as shown. The end of the piping is securely clamped in the vise, and a new length can readily be screwed in. The worker can usually do most of this by hand, grasping one end of the pipe while the other end is supported by a second plank. The tightening is, of course, done with a pipe wrench.—James H. Brundage, Katonah, N. Y.

Pipe Vise Clamped on Plank Aids Worker to Lay Piping Single-Handed

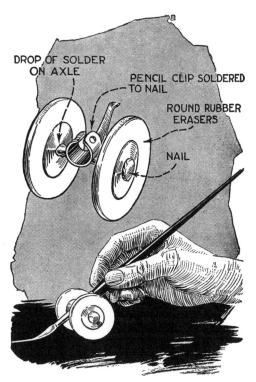

Simple and Easily Made Device Which Helps Amateur Stripers Do a Good Job

Device for Painting Stripes

Most people who paint their cars have considerable difficulty with the striping, which under ordinary conditions is an expert's job. With the aid of the simple device shown in the drawing, anyone who is careful can do the work satisfactorily. It is merely a rest for the brush and consists of a nail, pencil clip and two typewriter erasers of the disk type, assembled as indicated. The nail must be a sliding fit in the holes of the erasers, which are kept in place by means of a few drops of solder applied to the nail. In use, the brush is held by the pencil clip which is also soldered to the nail. It will be found, with this device, that a straight line of the same width throughout can be drawn even on curved and irregular surfaces.— S. A. Marshall, Jr., Rome, Ga.

¶An easy way to clean a pipe is to hold the end of the stem against the valve of a compressed-air tube, such as is to be found in nearly every garage.

Rope Dispenser for Hardware Store

A Wisconsin hardware dealer who had been in the habit of storing his supply

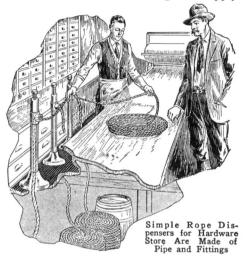

Simple Rope Dispensers for Hardware Store Are Made of Pipe and Fittings

of rope in the basement, where it would be out of the way, arranged to dispense it by threading the strands through holes drilled in the floor, so that any desired length might be drawn up and measured out. This, however, necessitated tying a knot in the end of each rope to prevent it from dropping down through the hole. The simple pipe arrangement shown in the drawing prevented this trouble. Lengths of 1¾-in. pipe and fittings were used as standards. They were attached to the floor over the holes and the rope was threaded through as indicated. Into the upper end of each, a short piece of 1-in. pipe, equipped with a cap, was inserted to drop down past the opening of the tee. In use, the rope is pulled out to any desired length and is prevented from dropping back into the basement by the 1-in. pipe, which rests on it.—G. E. Hendrickson, Argyle, Wis.

Extension Die Holder

We often had some small job where an extension die holder was needed, as, for example, in the threading of auto-spring clips. To facilitate this kind of work, we improvised a holder which cost us nothing to make and saved considerable time. It consisted of an old auto-wheel hub, obtained from the junk pile. The flange was

cut off, and a setscrew was threaded into the side to hold the die securely in the end. A handle was, of course, also provided.—H. W. Swope, Danville, Pa.

Calculating Number of Studs Required in a Wall

Studs, rafters and joists in frame buildings are usually spaced 16 in. from center to center. To calculate exactly how many of these are required in a wall of known length, divide the total length of the wall by 4, multiply by 3 and then deduct 1. For example, if the length is 20 ft., it will be found that 14 studs are required. In cases where one-fourth of the total distance is not even, the last space will be less than 16 in., and then you do not deduct 1. For example, if the wall length is 21 ft., which gives 15¾ studs, 15 studs are used. The fraction represents exactly 12 in. in this case. Where you have fractions of an inch, forget them. With rafters you do not deduct one, as you start and finish with a rafter. The same is true of joists.—T. E. Jeffries, Charleston, W. Va.

Phone Directory Saves Time

Busy executives who use their telephones considerably every day, will find

the phone directory shown in the photo a real time-saver. In one factory a number of these directories were made by photographing a typewritten original and printing as many copies as were necessary. Each print was glued to a piece of fiber board, in which a hole was cut at one end to fit the threaded section of the telephone mouthpiece. This was screwed up tight to hold the card. If desired, the card can be made to extend both above and below the mouthpiece so that a list of approximately 100 names will be in view.—E. H. Flaharty, Paroo, Wyo.

Covering Ignition Wires

High-tension cables and other insulated wiring on automobiles may be short-circuited after they have been in use for some time, causing the current to jump through the insulation instead of jumping across the gaps in the spark plugs. This is very annoying, as spark plugs will work well when they are out of the cylinders, but will not spark under compression. The trouble can be remedied by covering the cables with old rubber hose, which is much cheaper than buying new cables.

Reversible Box Lid

A reversible box lid, which can be locked as securely as one of the hinged type, is convenient for boxes which are used to carry material to distant points and then returned to the sender. Instead of a full hinged lid, only one board of it is hinged, as shown in the drawing. The remaining part, which is loose, is provided with extending cleats that straddle the hinged section. A staple is, of course, driven into the edge of the lid and another on the box to permit locking. When locked, the lid is securely fastened, side movement being prevented by the snug fit of the under cleats against the sides of the box. To render the use of the box simpler, the address of the receiver is painted on one side of the

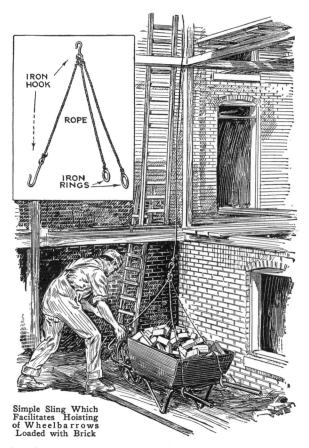

Simple Sling Which Facilitates Hoisting of Wheelbarrows Loaded with Brick

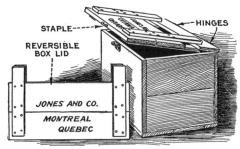

Reversible Box Lid Bearing Addresses Facilitates Return Shipments

lid and that of the sender on the other.—Harry Moore, Montreal, Can.

Hoisting Sling for Wheelbarrows

During the construction of a brick building, the task of hoisting the bricks to the third floor was greatly facilitated by the use of the sling shown in the drawing. It is fastened to the wheelbarrow at three points, so that the load can be hoisted safely, and when the barrow reaches the upper floor it can be wheeled to the particular place where the bricks are needed. The sling consists of three equal lengths of strong rope, one—for the front end of the barrow—being provided with an iron hook, while the other two are tied to iron rings, which slip over the handles of the barrow. This method has been found satisfactory for the average-size barrow, which will not be top-heavy in this way. —Chas. Latour, Jr., Plattsburg, N. Y.

⟨ Do not try to ream out more than $\frac{1}{64}$ in. with a hand reamer.

Convenient Mask for the Bee Keeper, Made from a Hat, Screen and Cloth

Face Protector for Bee Keepers

A simple face protector or mask for bee keepers can be made from an old broad-brimmed hat, a piece of fine-mesh screen, a light metal hoop and a piece of netting or cloth. The screen must be long enough to reach around the rim of the hat to which it is sewed. The other edge is attached to the hoop and the overlapping edges of the screen are sewed together. It will be found most convenient to have the screened section about 6 in. wide. The piece of netting or cloth is sewed onto the hoop and the overlapping edges stitched together. The cloth part must be sufficiently large to cover the user's shoulders and chest. It extends down to the waist. If the bees are not docile, cotton gloves should be worn, especially by persons unfamiliar with bees. When handling bees one should move about slowly and quietly, and refrain from noises or sudden, jerky movements, for the bees are easily excited and are then more likely to sting.
—Milton A. Ayers, San Francisco, Cal.

Finishing Wood Patterns

The finish on a pattern has a distinct effect on the finish of the casting produced. A rough pattern cannot leave a smooth mold in the sand. The dampness of the molding sand and the cleaning of a pattern by washing with water from a hose bring out all the "hair" from the surface of the wood, leaving it covered with small raised particles. Cleaning patterns by the use of water is, therefore, poor practice, as is also drying them near steam pipes. Places where the end wood appears on the surface of the patterns are most difficult to get smooth and keep smooth. After once smoothing the pattern, the least dampness brings out the roughness again to a greater degree than on portions with the grain. To prevent this, prepare some glue water and with a brush apply two coats to the end grain of the wood. This fills up the pores and effectively prevents "pulling out." Over this apply finishing paint as usual. This kink is also often applied to hardwood furniture.

One Lock for Six Doors

Most shops are equipped with metal clothes lockers for the convenience of employes, each of whom holds a key for his locker. One shop did not find this individual-key system satisfactory, mainly because of the frequent loss of keys which gradually resulted in most of the lockers being left open. To overcome this, a multiple-locking system was devised whereby six lockers are secured with one lock. Hinges were attached to both ends of a wooden bar, and fastened to the first and last doors of the set of lockers as shown in the illustration. In the shop where this idea has been adopted, it is the duty of one man to lock and unlock the last door in each set at certain times. This gives satisfaction to everyone, and it is impossible to tamper with any of the lockers during working hours.

Automatically Closing All Doors of a Six-Compartment Locker by Locking Only One

Safety Guard for Friction Drill

By ALBERT A. BAILLEY

HAVING a friction-driven drill fitted with a sliding head, we found it advisable to guard the spindle to eliminate danger of accident to the operator.

The problem involved was the design of a type of guard that would automatically rise and descend with the spindle. Attaching a metal shield to the sliding head in the usual way was impossible in this particular case, as it would have to project out too far, in order to provide sufficient clearance for the large cone. The guard we finally devised, which proved to be entirely satisfactory, is shown in the photos. It was made from an old inner tube, an old clock spring and tin can. A bracket, supporting a short shaft to which the clock spring was attached, was provided on the frame of the drill, just in front of the revolving cone. The inner tube was cut open to make a flat length of rubber, one end being attached to the short shaft and the other to the spindle bracket, as indicated in the side views.

The inner tube is always kept under tension by the clock spring, which is anchored to the inside of the tin can. The latter, which, of course, has to be covered to keep the spring safely confined, is rigidly attached to the bracket. With this arrangement, the spindle can be raised or lowered at will and the inner tube always remains taut in front of the spindle. The inner tube will effectively prevent the operator from accidentally coming in contact with the revolving spindle.

This device, of course, is adaptable to many other types of drill press where the same danger exists, and is especially suited to the school shop.

Effective Safety Guard for a Friction Drill Press Prevents the Operator from Coming in Contact with the Revolving Spindle; the Center Photo Shows the Danger Involved and the Side Views the Constructional Details of the Guard

Bending a Strip of Thin Wood over a Polished Axle or Pipe Heated with an Alcohol Lamp

Simple Way of Bending Thin Wood

It is often necessary to bend a thin piece of seasoned wood to conform to some shape or pattern, as in violin making or repairing. This can be done easily in the following manner: Take a polished shaft, such as the axle of an automobile, and drill a hole in the end, about 4 in. deep, so that the wall will be about ⅛ or ¼ in. thick. Drill a counterhole, ½ in. in diameter, through the shell, about 2 in. from the end. Clamp the shaft in a vise or fasten it securely to the workbench in any manner you choose, and put an alcohol lamp under the counterhole so that the flame goes inside of the hole. When the shaft is heated, dip the strip of wood in water for a moment and then slowly draw it over the polished surface of the hot shaft, as shown in the drawing, until the desired curvature is obtained. Wood bent in this way will hold the curve permanently,

although it can be taken out again by the same process.—Emmett Marshall, Seattle, Washington.

Painting Boat Bottoms

Most boats are kept in water where either weeds, barnacles or worms will attack the wood. For this reason copper paint is used below the waterline and has the tendency to prevent destruction by either or all of these parasites. Two or three good coats should be applied. Copper paint does not dry quite hard, so you need not hesitate to launch your boat even if the bottom surface does feel slightly tacky after 24 hours. Use a cheap brush in applying the paint but never use it for any other purpose. Small racing boats are often especially prepared by painting the bottoms with melted tallow or a mixture of graphite and oil. This gives a slick surface which repels water and reduces the friction, thus adding speed. Even vaseline may be used in emergency cases. These lubricants are applied over the regularly painted bottom and should, of course, be cleaned off after the race to prevent soiling other boats coming in contact with them.

Self-Tightening Chain Sling

It is often necessary to erect a chain block in various positions in a shop for temporary work. Sometimes a bar is thrown across two beams and the block is suspended from this, or the chain is simply wrapped around one beam. In the first case the bar may slide out of position with disastrous results, and in the second, the chain may slide on a diagonal pull, unless care is taken to wrap it well. To avoid both of these hazards, a support can be made that tightens itself under load and is consequently rigid and safe. Use 1½ by ⅝-in. bar stock. Three

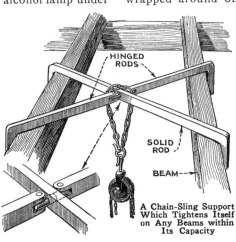

A Chain-Sling Support Which Tightens Itself on Any Beams within Its Capacity

lengths are needed, one solid piece, bent over at each end, and two pieces, half as long as the solid one. These are bent over at the outer ends only, and the inner ends are slotted and drilled for a pin, then hinged to the first piece by means of a cross pin. The pull of the chain tightens the device.—Harry Moore, Hamilton, Can.

Determining If Armature Shaft Is Bent

The armature shaft of the Ford starting motor often becomes bent from a severe backfire when starting. This causes the spring or setscrew to strike inside of the Bendix cover, and the motor turns so rapidly with the Bendix removed that the eye cannot be trusted to determine whether or not the shaft is straight. A good method of determining this is to hold a nail or a sharp-pointed punch in the center mark at the end of the armature shaft. The motor is then started and stopped several times by pressing and releasing the switch. As the motor starts and stops, a severe vibration can be felt in the nail or punch if the armature shaft is not straight.—E. T. Gunderson, Jr., Humboldt, Iowa.

How to Nail Roofing Paper

Roofing paper is usually applied as shown in the upper detail. This method is not entirely satisfactory, as the paper

contracts and expands, which in course of time will pull the nails loose or enlarge the nail holes, permitting leakage. To prevent this, drive the nails in a zigzag manner, as indicated in the lower detail. The edge of the paper may then buckle to some extent but will not leak.

Removable Feed Box

"Stationary feed boxes, generally used in horse barns, are decidedly unsanitary and cause many diseases," says a veteran horseman. Removal of the trash from the box is not sufficient, but a thorough clean-

Removable Feed Box on Manger Facilitates Cleaning and Airing

ing and airing in the sunlight is essential. Accordingly, the feed boxes must be made so that they can readily be removed, yet securely held in place while in use. A good arrangement is shown in the drawing. In this case, two 1 by 6-in. boards, 12 in. long, were nailed to two opposite sides of the box to project underneath. Two 12-in. lengths of flat iron were bent to the shape shown and fastened to the sides of the manger, providing slots into which the extending boards on the box could be inserted. Thus the box was held securely, yet was easily removable.

Safeguard for Railroad Crossings

Many serious accidents have occurred to people getting their feet caught between the planking and the rail at railroad crossings. A method of reducing this danger is shown in the drawing. It is very simply contrived, the edge of the plank adjacent to the rail being merely beveled. This affords plenty of clearance for the flanges of the car wheels and at the same time makes

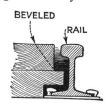

it easy for a person to pull his foot out, in case it is accidentally caught.—F. N. Hollingsworth, Boston, Mass.

Practical Method of Mooring a Small Motorboat to a Dock in a Harbor Which Is Affected by Tide; a Walk Is Provided on the Boom, the Latter Being Securely Attached to the Dock and Braced by Guys

Mooring Motorboat to Dock

When a small boat is tied to a dock in a harbor affected by tide, the rope is tight when the tide is out, and loose when the tide is in. In the latter case the boat is free to drift around and bump against the dock, which is, of course, not desirable. This difficulty was overcome, in one instance, by using a large boom, extended horizontally from the dock as shown in the accompanying photo. Pulleys are attached, as indicated, to hold a rope, one end of which is tied to the bow of the boat and the other to a counterweight. In this way the boat is held securely and the rope is constantly under tension, no matter whether the tide is in or out. Being kept away from the dock, the boat will not be damaged by battering against it. A walk was provided on the boom by nailing crosspieces at right angles to its length and laying boards over them. The boom must, of course, be properly supported by guys.—Carlton Groat, Portland, Oreg.

Doubling Length of Emery-Cloth Strips

When using strips of emery cloth torn from the usual 9 by 11-in. stock sheets, greater convenience can be obtained if the strips are joined together. This is particularly the case when circular pieces are being polished and the diameter of these

leave but little of the cloth free for the fingers to grip. Two small cotter keys can be used, as shown in the photo, to hold two strips of emery cloth together firmly, without touching the surface over which the cloth is being passed. The legs of one key are bent back to an acute angle with the head. Between the legs of this key the two strips are forced, abrasive faces together. The short ends are then bent out, and the key ends locked with another but shorter cotter key. The latter fits in the troughlike groove formed by the faces of the short ends. The two strips of cloth can be gripped by the ends and vigorously pulled back and forth, the keys holding them securely together. The cotters can be removed from old strips of cloth and applied to new ones.—Frank W. Bentley, Jr., Missouri Valley, Iowa.

¶To refinish tops of automobiles, use brushing lacquer instead of auto-top dressing; the lacquer makes a much better dressing and will not crack or peel.

Shop Notes

Handy and Compact Home Workshop

By F. L. COAKLEY

ORDINARILY the basement is the best place, if not the only one, to locate the home workshop, but space is often rather limited and it cannot be entirely devoted to this use. Other household duties are also performed there, and it is quite necessary to arrange the shop as compactly and orderly as possible.

meal, beginning with a few hand tools. Not being satisfied with these, I installed a small lathe, then a grinder and a drill press. By this time the equipment was pretty well scattered all over the basement, as my workbench was not large enough to accommodate everything. There were shavings here, chips there, dirt and oil spots everywhere. A storm of protest came, as this condition interfered with the washing.

Now, however, there are no more com-

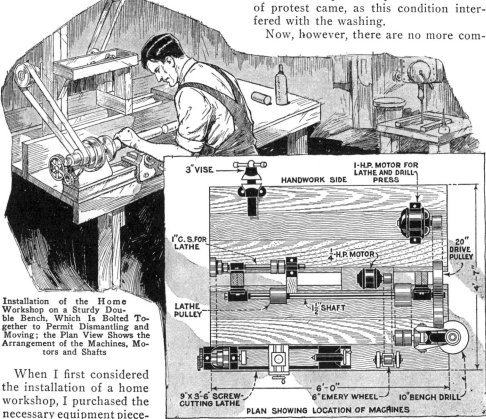

Installation of the Home Workshop on a Sturdy Double Bench, Which Is Bolted Together to Permit Dismantling and Moving; the Plan View Shows the Arrangement of the Machines, Motors and Shafts

When I first considered the installation of a home workshop, I purchased the necessary equipment piece-

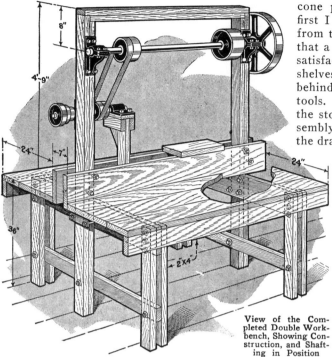

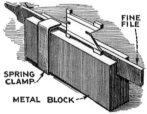

View of the Completed Double Workbench, Showing Construction, and Shafting in Position

cone pulley for the lathe. At first I drove the grinder directly from the countershaft, but found that a separate motor gave more satisfactory results. Two small shelves are conveniently located behind the lathe to hold the lathe tools. All the dimensions, size of the stock, and the method of assembly are clearly indicated in the drawings. Bolts were used to hold the parts together, so that tightening could be done when necessary, and so that the bench could be dismantled and moved, if desired.

Several friends predicted that the bench would prove weak, and would soon loosen up, but after three years of use, it is still perfectly solid, and the machines operate with a minimum of vibration, although the bench is neither fastened to the floor nor to the wall, and stands away from all other support.

plaints, for the basement is clean and tidy, and my workshop is confined to the double bench shown in the drawings. This is located in one corner, and if necessary, I can build a partition around it and provide a padlocked door.

The frames of the bench are of 2 by 4-in. stock, the upper rails being 1½ by 8 in. The top and back ledges are also made of 1½ by 8-in. boards, and the framework is bolted throughout. The center frame that supports the line and countershafts is made up from doubled two-by-fours, and in the manner shown clearly in the illustration. No further dimensions are necessary, as the length, width and height of the bench may have to be varied to suit individual conditions. A 9-in. screw-cutting lathe, grinder and a 10-in. drill press are mounted on one side, while all the hand tools, including a 3-in. vise, are kept on the other side. A 1-hp. electric motor is used to run the lathe and drill press, while one of ¼ hp. drives the grinder. The former is located on the left-hand side of the bench, and is belted to a 1½-in. shaft, which is held by suitable hangers. This is in turn belted to the countershaft, which carries the

Burr Remover for Matrices

An operation occasionally necessary in linotype maintenance is the removal of burrs on the ears of matrices, caused by their repeated striking on the front plate, or on the entrance of the matrix into the assembly stick. This is a detail that requires exceptional care on the part of the operator, as inexperience in the use of a file may damage the type face. The drawing shows a simple and effective way of doing this work without risk of injury to the working faces of the matrix. Along one edge of a piece of furniture, a metal block being preferable, a narrow slot is cut to receive a thin fine file, having a safety edge. The slot should be just deep enough to allow the file to project a distance equal to about one point less than the width of the ear or lug on the matrix. A small spring clamp, made of brass, is used to hold the file in the slot. This accessory has proved both speedy and accurate.

Getting Telegraph Line over Flooded River

A telegraph engineer, engaged in restoring telegraph service over a large flooded river, which had washed out the only bridge in the vicinity, found that the main river had changed its course. The torrent could not be crossed by boat nor by the most daring rider on horse and the use of harpoon guns and rockets was impossible. The difficulty was overcome by means of the device shown in the drawing. It consists of three boards, about 8 in. wide and 3 ft. long, nailed together as indicated and provided with a metal strip to serve as a weight, which holds the device upright when it floats. A short crosspiece of 1-in. wood is securely fastened about 10 in. from one end, and a light but strong line is attached as indicated. The current propelled this device across the river, the light rope was tied to a heavier rope and this to the telegraph wire.—O. Johnson, Pahaitua, New Zealand.

Tape Holder on a Belt Rack in Stock Room Facilitates the Measurement of Belting

SET SCREW

STRIP ON BELT RACK

WOOD DISK

DETAIL

Tape-Line Holder for the Stock Room Saves Time and Material

The holder shown in the drawing will save many broken tape lines in the stock or supply room when used to measure belting, etc. It consists of a square wood base, with two strips nailed at right angles and a space left between them at one corner for the line to run through, and a wood disk, such as a barrel bung, fastened to the base with a wood screw. The screw is placed off center so that, when the disk is turned, it will clamp the tape securely. The holder can be moved along the top of the rack to the belt to be measured, a wood strip being nailed on the top edge of the rack to prevent the holder from pulling off when the measuring is being done.—D. S. Jenkins, Xenia, Ohio.

Cutting and Bending Sheet Iron

We had considerable cutting and bending to do on a piece of sheet iron. Instead of marking the iron, we made an ink drawing on paper, which was much easier to do than marking off the design on the iron. The drawing was glued to the iron, and drilling, cutting and bending were then accomplished without any trouble.—W. L. Miles, Providence, R. I.

3 BOARDS 8 X 3/4" 3' LONG

10"

WEIGHT

Device Which Proved of Great Help to Get a Telegraph Line across a Flooded River

Trucks for Unloading Autos

By L. M. JORDAN

THE task of unloading automobile bodies and chassis from railway cars with ordinary trucks is quite hard. To make it easier, a Ford dealer built the two special trucks shown in the accompanying drawing and photos. They were constructed of iron pipe and fittings, securely joined by welding.

The right-hand photo shows a truck which is used for unloading bodies. The wheels and axle of an ordinary loading truck are used. Two lengths of 1½-in. pipe, bent to a V-shape, are bolted to the axle and serve as braces for the frame, to which they are welded. The latter, of 1½-in. pipe, consists of two sidepieces, which extend to serve as handles and are welded to the braces, three crosspieces and two short pipe nipples welded to the top of the sidepieces near the handgrip end. In use, the car body is lifted at one end until the truck can be run under it and the front of the body passes

over the two nipples on the handles. These prevent the body from slipping on the truck when the handles are pulled down.

The other photo shows the truck made for unloading chassis. Another set of loading-truck wheels with axle is used. A V-shaped or triangular frame is attached to the axle and the ends are welded to a single 2½-in. pipe, serving as a tongue. A 20-in. length of the same stock is welded to the underside of the tongue near the handle end, to serve as a rest when the truck is set down. A smaller V-shaped frame, of the same-size pipe, is welded, vertically to the axle, to the rear end of the main frame. A piece of 3-in. pipe, 8 in. long, is welded on top of the smaller frame and to the tongue. A 3½-in. sleeve union, drilled to receive two short pieces of ½-in. iron rod, which are welded in the holes and extend horizontally on opposite sides, is slipped over the 3-in. piece and left loose. The outer ends

Inconvenience Caused by the Use of Ordinary Trucks for Unloading Auto Bodies and Chassis from Railway Cars Can Be Overcome by Providing Two Specially Made Trucks of the Kind Shown in the Photos

PIPE NIPPLES WELDED TO HANDLES

of the rods are bent upward, as shown. When loading, the rear end of a chassis is raised until the truck can be run under it to a point where the oil-drain plug in the underside of the flywheel or clutch housing can be let down into the sleeve, while the housing rests on the bent rods. This holds the chassis securely. The handle or tongue is then brought down, balancing the chassis on the truck so that it can be readily wheeled about. The drive-shaft housing rests between a fork of bolts near the handgrip.

Torch Illuminates Writing Pad

Night clerks in railroad yards or manufacturing plants, or anyone who has to do writing at night out of doors, will appreciate a light on the writing-pad holder, as shown in the drawing. It is made up of a 3-cell flashlight battery, an auto dash lamp with switch incorporated, two small angle brackets, a spring clip and a few lengths of wire. Attach the battery to the top of the writing-pad holder. In order to make room for it, the writing-pad clip may have to be moved down. Screw the angle brackets to the board so that they make contact with the positive and negative ends of the battery. Also attach the spring clip so that the battery will not easily be dislodged. The dash lamp is fastened on next, the method of doing this depending on the particular construction of the lamp used. Connect the wires to the lamp and to the brackets. A good electrical connection to the latter can be made by inserting a soldering lug over the end of one of the screws holding the bracket and then driving the nut down tightly.—William C. Thomas, Chicago, Ill.

❡White woodwork can be kept fresh by rubbing it with a moistened cloth dipped in whiting; the surface should then be washed with clear water and dried.

High Folding Ladder for the Tree Trimmer Is Attached to an Auto Trailer

Help for the Tree Trimmer

For years Mr. Corliss, of Alhambra, Calif., has worked at trimming trees, and has experienced difficulty in finding a secure platform of adjustable height, which was at the same time portable. He devised an auto trailer fitted with an extension ladder, as shown, and this was found satisfactory. It folds to a height of 10 ft., can be extended to about 25 ft., and is secure so that the worker can mount it with perfect safety. It is also provided with wheels and fitted with a connecting tongue by which it can be towed. The ladder support is lifted off the ground when the trailer is being towed.—John Edwin Hoag, Los Angeles, Calif.

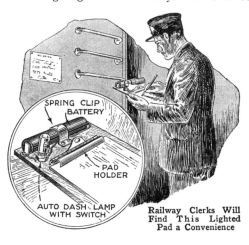

Railway Clerks Will Find This Lighted Pad a Convenience

This Motion Sign Is Actuated by the Printing Press and Attracts Considerable Attention

Motion Sign Advertises Printer

Motion usually increases the effectiveness of advertisements. The sign shown in the drawing was arranged by a printer in the following manner: One of the Gordon presses was located near the front window. A pulley was driven into the top of the window frame near the glass and a length of stout cord run over it, one end of the cord being attached to the roller frame of the press, and the other to the sign. When the press is in operation, the sign moves up and down. If the press is not situated near the window, a longer cord can be run over two or more pulleys to reach the press.

Draining Oil from Wooden Barrels

In some places where heavy fuel and lubricating oil is delivered in the ordinary 40 to 50-gal. wooden barrels, the bung is taken out and the oil removed by allowing it to run out. Then the bung is replaced and the barrel placed in a tank of hot water for about an hour. This treatment heats and thins the oil so that it drains out completely when the bunghole is again opened. Unless wooden barrels containing heavy oil are subjected to such treatment, from 3 qt. to 2 gal. of oil will

be left in each. This is no exaggeration, as I have taken barrels which had been set out as completely empty, placed them in a hot-water bath, as described above and then drained more than a gallon of oil from some of them. The treatment is particularly useful during winter when the oil is congealed. Storing the barrels in a hot and dry place will help to make the oil more fluid but will soon destroy empty barrels. The hot-water treatment will not injure them in the least.—James E. Noble, Hollyburn, Can.

Closing Small Leaks in Pipe Fittings

To close a pinhole in a cast or malleable-iron pipe fitting, take ordinary tin or lead foil, fold it to form several thicknesses and place it over the hole. With a small hammer drive the foil into the hole. This will usually stop the leak permanently, whether the pipe carries air, gas, hot or cold water or other liquids. But the method is not effective for leaks in steam pipes. Sometimes a pinhole in a malleable-iron fitting on a steam line can be closed by hammering the metal over the hole, but this cannot be done, of course, in the case of cast-iron fittings.

Tool for Driving Fence Posts Single-Handed

Usually it takes two men to set steel fence posts, one man to hold the post

while the other is driving it into the ground with a sledge. The work can, however, be done single-handed by using the homemade tool shown in the drawing. It consists of a length of pipe, large enough to be slipped over the fence post, and a weight securely attached to the top end. The weight can be made by setting one end of the pipe in a pail and pouring concrete around it.—John B. Smoller, Atlantic, Iowa.

Build Your Own Garage

by R·O·BUCK and
H·W·MICHELSON

PART I

A GREAT many men who are handy with tools and build little conveniences into their homes hesitate about tackling so large a project as a garage, because they fear it will be beyond their ability. With this in mind, it should be stated at the outset that one of the writers constructed the garage illustrated herewith during a two weeks' vacation, altogether unaided, and derived considerable pleasure from it, not to mention the profit.

There were two considerations which led me to build my own garage; first, because I wanted the pleasure of building it, but principally because I had more time than money. My experience was so altogether satisfactory that I think it is worth passing on to you.

My garage is a well-built and

roomy structure, large enough to house any make of car and with sufficient space on the sides for a workbench, shelves, etc. The floor is of concrete, pitched so that water will run off through a drain at the center. The garage faces the front, making it necessary to build tracks of cement to the street. This part of the work I did not attempt, but had a contractor put them in after the garage was completed, at a cost of $140. For an additional $60 he would have put in my cement pad also and I would have been saved some rather hard labor. However, I did this work myself at a fraction of the cost. If you have a good alley that stays dry and is passable the year around, you can save the expense of the tracks; mine is low and inclined to be bottomless at some

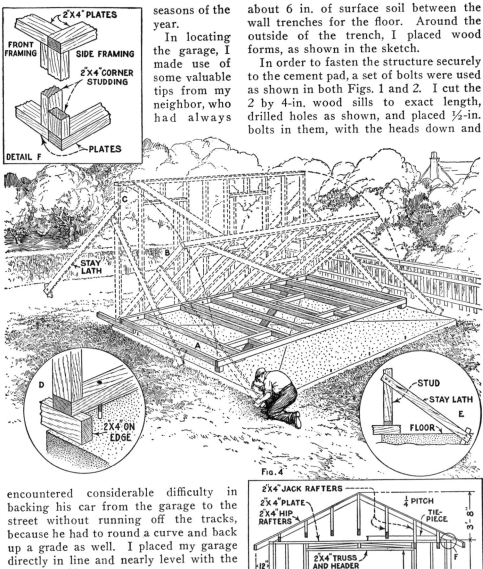

Front Framing — Side Framing — 2″X4″ PLATES — 2″X4″ CORNER STUDDING — PLATES — DETAIL F

STAY LATH — 2X4″ ON EDGE — STUD — STAY LATH — FLOOR — Fig. 4

2″X4″ JACK RAFTERS — 2″X4″ PLATE — 2″X4″ HIP RAFTERS — ¼ PITCH — TIE-PIECE — 2″X4″ TRUSS AND HEADER — 2″X4″ STUDS — 2″X4″ PLATE — FLOOR LINE — FRONT FRAMING ELEVATION — Fig. 5

seasons of the year.

In locating the garage, I made use of some valuable tips from my neighbor, who had always

about 6 in. of surface soil between the wall trenches for the floor. Around the outside of the trench, I placed wood forms, as shown in the sketch.

In order to fasten the structure securely to the cement pad, a set of bolts were used as shown in both Figs. 1 and 2. I cut the 2 by 4-in. wood sills to exact length, drilled holes as shown, and placed ½-in. bolts in them, with the heads down and

encountered considerable difficulty in backing his car from the garage to the street without running off the tracks, because he had to round a curve and back up a grade as well. I placed my garage directly in line and nearly level with the street for this reason.

It took me two days to lay the cement pad which served as both wall and floor. Incidentally, this proved to be the hardest part of the whole job from the standpoint of physical labor.

The floor of the garage was laid 2 in. above grade so that surface water would not come in under the door in the spring or during rainy weather. A section through the floor and wall is shown in Fig. 1. I dug a trench, 18 in. deep, all around the outer edge of the plot I had staked off for the pad and also removed

the nuts turned on. The sills were then put in position across the forms and fastened with light strips of wood for bracing. The purpose of all this, of course, was to space the bolts in the concrete to coincide with the holes in the sills. Do not fail to mark these pieces both as to side and end so that you can replace them later.

To square up the sides and ends, I took

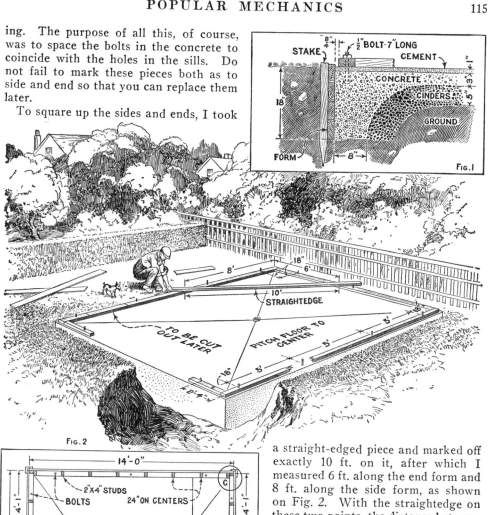

STAKE — ½"BOLT-7"LONG — CEMENT
⁸⁄₄"
CONCRETE
18"
CINDERS
GROUND
FORM ← 8" →
Fig. 1

8' 18" 6'
10'
STRAIGHTEDGE
TO BE CUT OUT LATER
PITCH FLOOR TO CENTER
5'
5'
18" 5'
2'-4"

Fig. 2

14'-0"
2"X4" STUDS
BOLTS 24"ON CENTERS
C
4-1
TROUBLE LAMP
DROP LIGHTS
2-11"
WORKBENCH
WINDOWS
2"X4" SILL
FLOOR DRAIN
4" TILE TO CATCH BASIN
6-LIGHT 9"X12" WINDOW
18'-0" 6'-1"
SHELF
4'-0"
SWITCH
2-8"X6-8" DOOR
2-11"
2-10"
CASE
A
4'-1"
D
2 DOORS-4'X8'
8'-1½"
B
2-1
2-11¼"
2-11¼"
FLOOR PLAN
Fig. 3

a straight-edged piece and marked off exactly 10 ft. on it, after which I measured 6 ft. along the end form and 8 ft. along the side form, as shown on Fig. 2. With the straightedge on these two points, the distance between them diagonally should be 10 ft. when the corner is square. Check the adjacent corner also.

The cement pad was made up of a layer of cinders, well tamped and about 5 in. thick, 3 in. of concrete, and 1 in. of cement. Cinders are often omitted on work of this type, but are specified in all first-class jobs and the result, I believe, is better. The wall, of course, was concrete all the way with the exception of the 1 in. of cement at the top. The concrete was mixed in the proportion of 1 part cement, 3 parts sharp sand and 5 parts gravel. For the finishing coat I used 1 part cement to 2 of sand.

It is important that the cement be well mixed with the sand and gravel before adding the water and again after this is done. I mixed the cement in a steel wheelbarrow, which made it much easier on my back and saved an extra handling, as I could wheel the mixture to the part of the floor I was making and simply dump the load. The mixing, of course, I did alongside the pile of sand and gravel.

The drainage of the floor, as mentioned previously, was planned toward the center. I ran a 4-in. tile line from the center of the floor to the catch basin, with a fall of 1 ft. in 25, as the distance was not very great. If the soil is very sandy where you are building your garage, you may be able to use a seepage tank for drainage purposes. This consists of an old oil barrel, well drilled with large holes and buried 1 or 2 ft. under the center of the floor. The concrete over the top of the barrel should be reinforced with some old iron rod or pipe to strengthen the concrete after the barrel rots. The seepage tank will take a reasonable amount of water at a time and is much easier to build and less expensive than the tile. Another way, of course, is to slope the floor toward the large doors so that the water will run out under them.

The concrete was allowed to set several hours before the finishing coat was applied. A plank was laid from one sill to the other to kneel on while finishing the center of the floor with a cement trowel, after it had been scraped to proper slope with a long straight-edged board in the usual way.

After allowing the floor to dry three days, I took out the forms, planned my framing procedure and started this part of the job. One of the greatest problems I had was how I was going to handle the job of framing alone, as none of my neighbors were home during the day. I found, however, that I could cut most of the material in advance and began with the plates, corner studs, etc. The sills were all cut and ready, as they were used to space the bolts in the concrete.

I had the framing material all laid out on the ground when it occurred to me that, by framing the corners as shown in detail F, Fig. 4, I could assemble each wall complete on the floor, then raise it into place and nail all together when done. Starting with a side wall, I securely spiked

the members of the wall together. The spacing of the studs, headers, etc., is shown on the floor plan and also on the side and end elevations, Figs. 3, 5 and 6, respectively.

It is advisable to check all measurements very carefully before cutting any of the material, as I found to my sorrow when I cut the material for both sides the same, neglecting to take into consideration that, while one side has a window and a door, the other side has two windows. The framing should also be squared carefully by using the 6, 8 and 10-ft. rule described previously.

After the side walls are all framed they should be held square with temporary diagonal braces, as shown in Fig. 4. These braces should be nailed on the inside of the frames so that they will not interfere with siding, and may be left on until the garage is finished. Fig. 4 shows one side assembled and ready to be raised. There were two problems to be solved in connection with this operation. First, the sill had to be raised above the level of the anchor bolts, yet in line with them so that the holes would coincide with the bolts and the frame could be dropped into position. It was also necessary to swing the frame to a vertical position. Of course, if you have some one to help you, this does not present such a problem, but I had to do it alone and I found it rather heavier and more unwieldy than I could manage conveniently.

The first part I accomplished by placing short pieces of 2 by 4-in. stuff, on edge, under the sill to raise it above the bolts, as shown at D, Fig. 4. To raise the assembled framing sections, I nailed stay lath on each end, as shown at E, Fig. 3, so that I could raise one end a few inches, brace it, then walk to the other end and treat it similarly. By repeating this operation, raising each end a few inches at a time, I was able to get the whole thing in position without much effort. As soon as it was vertical, I nailed stay lath from the other side as well, which held it into position until the blocks could be removed and the sill dropped over the bolts. After testing the wall with a level to be sure it was plumb, I secured the stay lath with additional nails, placed the washers and nuts on the bolts and tightened them.

The assembly and raising of the other side was accomplished in the same manner. The back framing being very simple and light, was swung into place easily.

The front framing elevation, Fig. 5, gives full dimensions for making a truss over the doorway so that it will not be necessary to put heavy timbers across the door span, as is the usual practice. Good tight joints are very important in the truss, however, as its strength depends on the bracing of the various members.

Care must be taken before nailing the corner studs into place that the structure is square and plumb. Detail F shows the method of

roof of the same size, is about the same, the difference being in the labor involved.

A roof-framing plan, together with a side and front-framing elevation, show

TIE-PIECE

HIP RAFTERS

2"X4" RAFTERS SPACED 24" ON CENTERS ← 2"X6" RIDGE

← 2"X4" PLATE

2"X4" JACK RAFTERS

2"X4" TIE-PIECES

ROOF FRAMING PLAN   Fig. 7

fastening the corners together. The three tie-pieces may be nailed into place at this stage, as shown on the roof-framing plan, Fig. 7. Their purpose, of course, is to keep the side walls from spreading when the roof, and the snow load the roof will carry, are placed on them. They will also be found convenient to support planks for staging, while you are nailing the rafters in place. It is convenient, though not absolutely necessary, to have a scaffold on the outside of the structure also. This should be built at this stage if it is to be of greatest use.

The type of roof I selected, the hip roof, is not the easiest type to frame, but is so much more attractive than the gable roof, that I felt it was worth the extra work. The material required for a hip or gable

the exact size and position of the various members. A skeleton view of the entire building will be given in the second article, so that there will be no doubt about the arrangement of the various rafters.

My first step in framing the roof was to space off, and mark on the plates, the center lines of all of the rafters along the four sides of the structure. All of the rafters were spaced 24 in. from the center of one rafter to the center of the next. I started the spacing from the center of the plates, working each way toward the ends so that any irregularity in the spacing would come at the corners where it would be less noticeable.

The various members of the roof are numbered, in Fig. 7, in the order in which I found it expedient to set them up. I started with the two end center rafters and ridge which I put together temporarily with cleats, then raised and fastened with stay lath. They must be perfectly plumb, of course, as they are to be used as a guide to measure others.

It is rather difficult for an amateur to cut all of the roof members in advance; however, if all of the rafters are cut "on the ground" and put into place, they will serve as a framework to which the hip and jack rafters can be fitted readily in the order suggested. Rafters 1, 3 and 4 are all the same length. Also the slope of the sides and ends of the roof are the same.

The method of determining the length of the rafters is as follows: A roof 14 ft. wide has a run of 7 ft. and a rise of 3 ft. 6 in., if the roof is quarter pitch, as in this case. This is equivalent to saying that it has a rise of 6 in. to every foot of run. If you place a square on your rafter so that the 6 and 12-in. marks are on an edge as shown in Fig. 9 (Part II), and repeat seven times, the length and cuts of the rafter will be determined. To this, however, must be added the width of the plate and the length of the overhang.

Of course you could figure the length of the rafters arithmetically also by getting the length of the hypotenuse of a triangle whose legs are 7 ft. and 3 ft. 6 in. That is, get

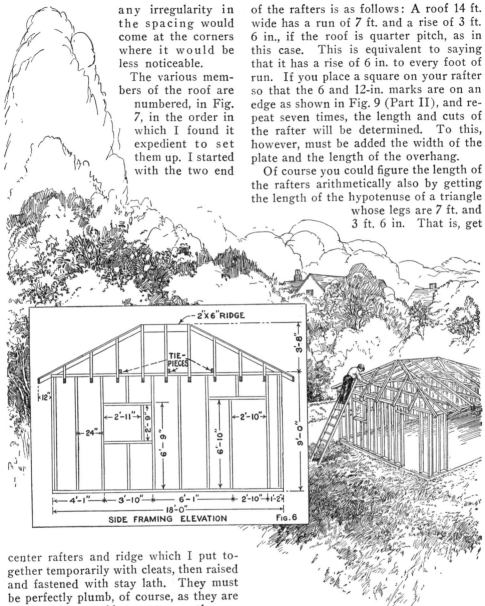

SIDE FRAMING ELEVATION　　Fig. 6

the square root of the sum of the squares of these two sides. (Get out the old school book and dig up the method for extracting the square root!) The slant of the cut can be obtained with the square as in the first method.

After all the rafters have been spiked into place, the roof framing is complete. It took me all of one day to do this part of the job, but I encountered no special difficulties and do not believe that you will have any trouble with this part of the job.

Preventing Tractor from Rising

To prevent his tractor from rising unexpectedly at the front end while disking, a Mississippi farmer fastened one end of a strong chain to the front axle and the other end to the disk harrow. This helped greatly in holding the front end down, as it could not rise until the chain was slackened. When arranged in this way, the tractor is held down by the weight of the implement it is pulling as long as the chain remains taut.—Bunyan Kennedy, McCool, Mississippi.

Permanent Stop Sign on Railroad Tracks

Sometimes the blue flag on railroad sidings, rip tracks or yards is forgotten, or is not placed at the proper location. This can be corrected by using a permanent sign, as shown in the drawing. It is made of sheet steel, a hinged joint being provided so that the sign can be dropped on the ground between the tracks when desired. It should be flat enough so that workmen will not trip on it accidentally. As such a sign is in view at all times and therefore is a constant reminder, it will not be forgotten easily.

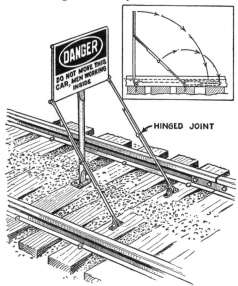

Collapsible Stop Sign on Railroad Sidings Is Always Ready for Use

The Manipulation of a Heavy Electric Rock Drill May Be Made Easy by Means of a Simply Arranged Counterweight as Indicated or in Some Other Convenient Manner

Counterweight for Electric Rock Drill

When preparing a site for a power house, considerable rock drilling was necessary. To make the work easier, the heavy electric drills were counterbalanced, as shown in the drawing, with the result that much labor and time were saved. A ladder was set in the position indicated and a length of sash rope, one end of which was tied to the drill and the other end to a pail, was slipped over a few rungs of the ladder. Enough sand was put into the pail to balance the drill. The same method can, of course, be applied equally well to other heavy tools and machines, which must be lifted by the operator while using them.—I. R. Hicks, Centralia, Mo.

How to Clean White Tile

Tile walls in bathrooms are usually washed with soap and water when they become dirty, but it has been found that, so treated, they soon show a series of tiny cracks which in time become larger. The water causes the trouble, not the soap. To prevent cracking, rub the wall with a soft cloth soaked in turpentine. Kerosene may also be used for this purpose.—L. H. Georger, Buffalo, N. Y.

Making Brake Bands Round

An important but often neglected part of relining auto brake bands is to true

Cast-Iron Rings Used as Forms on Which Auto Brake Bands Can Be Hammered True

the bands so that they are perfectly round before putting them back on the drums. We had considerable trouble in this respect, so we had a number of cast-iron rings made at a local foundry, to accommodate all the regular sizes of brakes. The rings were chucked in a lathe and those intended for rounding internal expanding bands were bored out, while those intended to be used for the contracting type of band were turned to the same diameter as the drums. The method of using the rings is plainly shown in the photos. The contracting band, after being relined, is placed around a ring of the right size, drawn tight and gone over lightly with a hammer until it is properly shaped. For the expanding type, the relined band is slipped down inside the right-size ring, expanded and then hammered to shape.—Avery E. Granville, LaGrange, Ill.

Cleaning Nozzle of Blowtorch

The nozzle of a gasoline blowtorch often becomes clogged with dirt. As the opening is too small to permit the insertion of a wire to clean it, and the nozzle is at the back end of the burner opening, it cannot be reached for blowing the dirt out. A good method of cleaning is to remove the needle valve and the pack nut, and pour out enough gasoline to eliminate the pressure. Then get a short piece of copper

tubing that will enter the burner end and fit squarely against the end of the nozzle. The dirt in the opening can then be removed by compressed air or by blowing through the tube. As the needle has been taken out, the dirt will be forced back through the opening and out of the torch.—E. T. Gunderson, Jr., Humboldt, Iowa.

Valve-Grinding Kink

When grinding valves, the compound used works away from the grinding surfaces and more has to be supplied, especially if the valve is badly pitted. This is necessary, because the compound will not flow back when the pressure forcing it from between the grinding surfaces is removed. A good mixture to use for this purpose consists of ordinary grease and abrasive compound. First heat the head of the valve with a torch, until you can barely stand to touch it with the hand. When the mixture is applied, it will melt and run together when the valve is lifted. This keeps the abrasive on the grinding surface.

Cable Stand for Linemen

Cable reels are heavy and hard to raise without special equipment. The task can be made much easier by the use of an

Wooden Frame Serves as an Emergency Cable Stand for the Lineman

emergency stand as shown in the photo. It consists of a 2 by 12-in. frame, set in the position indicated. After putting a length of heavy pipe through the core, the reel can be rolled high enough on the frame to clear the ground. A block of wood should be nailed on to hold the pipe in place.—Carlton Groat, Portland, Oreg.

Build Your Own Garage

by R·O·BUCK and
H·W·MICHELSON

PART II

THE building is now ready for siding. This should be done before putting on the roof boards so that the top pieces of siding can be notched to fit around the rafters, with the top edge flush with the bottom surface of the roof boards. Do not fail to do this, as it is much more difficult to block the openings between the plate and the roof boards after the roof is on.

There are several types of siding on the market, the most popular of which are shown by Fig. 8. It is advisable to choose the type that will match your house best. Before putting the siding on, I covered the studs with a heavy build-ing paper, placing one length of paper on at a time, starting from the bottom, and boarding over this until I reached the top of the paper, after which another was applied in the same manner. The paper makes the garage wind-proof and much warmer. The siding was sawed flush with the two-by-fours that formed the door and window openings. By following this method, only a few hours were required to inclose the entire garage.

Putting on the roof boards was now in order, and I found that this was going to be more of a problem than an ordinary gable roof would be, as all of the

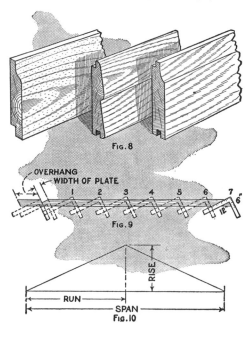

FIG. 8

OVERHANG
WIDTH OF PLATE

1 2 3 4 5 6 7 6"
12"

FIG. 9

RISE
RUN
SPAN
FIG. 10

corners over the hip rafters had to be mitered. This cut can be handled very well, however, if you follow the method I used. Starting from one side of the roof and at the bottom, lay the boards in the position shown by A, Fig. 12. After two or three boards have been nailed in place, saw the ends along the hip rafters even with the edge marked as indicated at B. This cut, of course, is at right angles to the face of the board, but follows the slant of the hip rafter. Continue the roofing all the way to the top in this manner and repeat the procedure on the opposite side. After both sides are covered and the ends sawed, a similar arrangement may be used for the ends by butting the boards D against the sawed edges of the boards C. The ends of these boards are then sawed off flush with the face of the boards that form the side covering.

Matched material of a fair grade is best for roofing, although builders use just ordinary No. 2 boards, with the edges butted. Joints between the ends of roofing boards should come over a rafter, as otherwise there is danger of the board warping, tearing off the tongue, and making a hole in the roofing. The roofing boards should be started about 1½ in. beyond the ends of the rafters so that water will be carried beyond the facing strips which are to cover the rafter ends.

On my garage I used individual asphalt shingles of the same color as those on the house. I laid them 4 in. to the weather for the same reason, although I believe the general practice is to lay them with

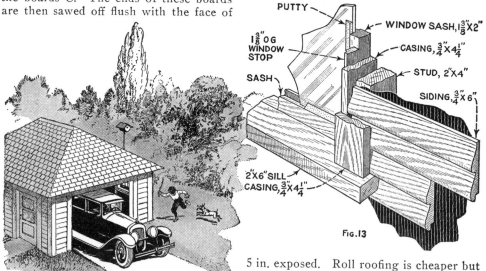

Fig.13

Fig.14

5 in. exposed. Roll roofing is cheaper but not so good looking or serviceable, yet very satisfactory. Roofing of either kind is always laid from the bottom up, so that the lap is on top. The roof on the garage is flat enough for you to stand on while working, but unnecessary walking on asphalt roofing should be avoided, as much of the gravel or slate is loosened or rubbed off, resulting in unsightly black spots on the roof.

Putting on the trim, hanging the doors and windows, etc., is the pleasantest part of the job, or so it seemed to me at least. You are beginning to see the results, the structure looks like a garage and you can visualize it with a tidy workbench, shelves and cases in position, as well as a snug

FIG.11

FIG.12

berth for the "little old boat." Perhaps I felt a bit glad, too, that the rough part was finished for I would rather work with the white pine in the doors and windows.

The series of detail drawings, Figs. 13 to 17, show you just how to put on the trim for the corners, cornice, windows and doors. They detail the garage exactly as I built it, with the exception that no window is shown in the back wall. I put a window in the end toward the alley, but found it of so little use that I have omitted it in the drawings. You will use your own judgment about this.

Fig. 13 is a section through a window, showing the sash, frame, casing and sill. The sizes and spacing of all these pieces are given in the sketch. The frames I made myself, buying only the sash ready-made and glazed. A 2 by 6-in. plank, planed as shown, makes a good sill, and as no machining was necessary, I used ordinary dimensioned lumber to make the rest of the frame. Ogee (OG) stops can be obtained at any millyard for a small sum.

The large doors were purchased from a mill company as I did not think that I could build doors that would be nice-looking enough for the front of the garage. However, if your garage faces the alley, it would be entirely possible for you to build the large doors with ¾-in. matched and beaded ceiling material, which would be satisfactory. Fig. 14 shows how to case the doorway, place the stops, etc.

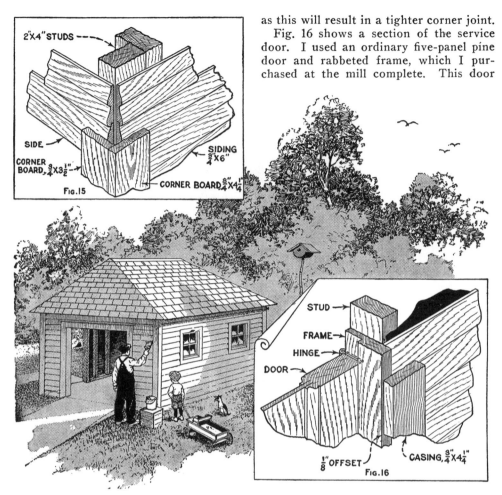

as this will result in a tighter corner joint.

Fig. 16 shows a section of the service door. I used an ordinary five-panel pine door and rabbeted frame, which I purchased at the mill complete. This door

The doors may be hinged or run on one of the various types of tracks on the market. I used a three-section door on a track for my garage and find it very satisfactory. This type has one of the doors hinged to one side of the opening and the other two hinged to the opposite side, and folding against each other. The purpose of the track, which is on the outside, is to carry the weight of the center door. The "roll-around" type of door is also very convenient, as the three doors roll against the inside of one of the side walls. In some cases, however, this is an objection, as it makes that part of the wall space useless for any other purpose.

Fig. 15 shows the method of placing the corner boards and is self-explanatory. It is customary to nail the boards together in a trough-shape before putting them up,

swings in. A lock is advisable. Around the rafter ends, I placed a facing strip, 4½ in. wide, as shown in Fig. 17. The lower side of the rafters I also cased in with ⅝-in. matched and beaded material.

My purpose in using so wide a facing strip was to give the effect of lowness, as my house is a bungalow. However, in the case of a two-story house, it may be advisable to secure the opposite effect, that is, one of height, by making the facing strip narrower. If the overhanging ends of the rafters are ripped along a line level with the top of the plate notch, you can use a narrow strip in the same manner. Many garage builders omit the cornice and facing strip entirely and leave the rafter ends exposed. I do not believe this makes as nice-looking a garage.

Not content with a facing strip, I placed

a box-type gutter completely around the garage, with downspouts at the ends toward the alley. This finishing touch completed the garage with the exception of painting, but it nearly finished me as well. I had so much trouble hanging and soldering the eaves trough that I am sure I would not attempt to put one up again, and unless you are experienced in that kind of work and have a tinner's equipment, I advise you against it. For this reason I have omitted it from the drawings, though it is shown in the photo.

Three coats of good-quality paint are required. The color scheme, of course, should be in harmony with your house so I will say nothing further about this.

Electric lights are a great convenience in a garage and may be installed at very small cost. The supply line can either be brought in from the house by means of overhead wires or, preferably, by laying a two-wire lead-covered cable, which is inexpensive and can be purchased from most electrical dealers. The inside wiring I did with armored cable (BX) and the usual iron outlet boxes. The circuit (see Fig. 3, page 115, of the first part) provides for a trouble lamp, a light at the front of the car and also one over the workbench. All are controlled by a single switch close to the service door. I find this very convenient and I believe it conforms with most city regulations.

If you submit the accompanying drawings to your dealer, you can obtain an estimate of the cost of material to construct this garage. Add to this an equal amount for your labor, and you will have the approximate cost of having this garage built by a contractor. My total cost for material, exclusive of the cement drive and approach, was $185, but this amount will vary greatly in different localities and according to the material used.

I have endeavored to make the directions and drawings of the garage so simple and complete that you should have no difficulty in successfully constructing a well-built and serviceable garage; and if you find the pride and pleasure in it that I did, you will feel well repaid.

Copperplating Small Tools

Copperplating small hand tools is frequently desirable, as it provides an easy method of marking the tools for identification of ownership. Besides, in many shops where soldering is done and where soldering acids are kept on hand, steel tools tarnish and rust very badly. A light deposit of copper will prevent this. The apparatus and material required for this work are: a storage battery, fully charged, a handful of copper sulphate (blue vitriol); a vessel of suitable shape and dimensions for containing the article to be plated and a small piece of copper or some scrap copper wire Dissolve the copper sulphate in water. The strength of the solution is not important for this kind of plating and a small handful of the crystals will be enough for about 1 qt. of water. To the wire connected to the positive terminal of the battery fasten the piece of copper or a short length of scrap copper wire twisted into a compact wad. The article to be plated is connected to the negative terminal of the battery. Both the copper piece and the article are supported over the container so that they are completely immersed in the solution, keeping them separated from each other. The length of time required for the plating operation varies according to the thickness of the plating desired. A few moments is sufficient for a thin protective coating. To obtain uniform thickness, the article must be clean and bright.

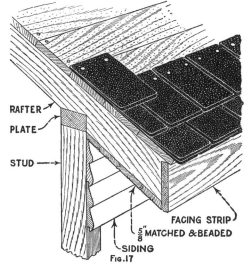

RAFTER
PLATE
STUD
FACING STRIP
$\frac{5}{8}$" MATCHED & BEADED
SIDING
Fig. 17

Locking Clamp for Pump Pipe

IRON STRIP

Anyone who has attempted to raise a water pump with a length of pipe attached to it knows that it is a hard task. When the pipe is raised half-way, the whole is top-heavy and almost unmanageable. Hence it frequently happens that it is dropped back into the well. The drawing shows a simple brace that catches the pipe at each lift, steadying it and preventing it from dropping back. It is simply a strip of flat iron, about 1½ ft. long. It is bent, and screwed to the well cover as indicated, the free end being rounded off to fit the pipe. After a lift has been taken, the clamp will automatically bind against the pipe and hold it until you have moved your hands for another lift.—C. M. Wilcox, Torrington, Conn.

Convenient Location for Auto Tool Box

Having other use for the running boards of its business cars, one concern disposed of the tool boxes in a novel place, namely, between the frame members where they extend in front. The customary running-board tool box, as a rule, will fit this space. It is located behind the bumper where it will not be easily damaged, and is, at the same time, readily accessible. The box is attached, at each end, by means of two bolts and wingnuts, the latter being inside of the box. The use of wingnuts is preferable to regular nuts as it may be necessary sometimes to remove the tool box in order to crank the car. As the box must be unlocked to remove the wingnuts, safety against theft is insured. This location for the box is especially convenient for tourists, as the running boards are loaded with other things, and the tool box forms a shelf in front on which a roll of baggage, the tent, or the like, may be packed.

Forming Small Brass Tubes

On one of the new radio devices several ¼-in. brass tubes, 1¾ in. long and bent to a quarter circle, are used. As these must be produced quickly and at as low a cost as possible, the method shown in the illustration was employed with satisfactory results. The forming device consists of a punch, or forcing tool, for driving the tubes through the forming-die hole. The upper part of the die is fitted to the lower part by tongues and grooves and the necessary dowel pins. The lower part is made in two pieces, each grooved to receive one-half of the tube. It is easy to mount the two blocks on a lathe faceplate, and cut the grooves with a round-end tool. The two parts are then fitted together. By this method the tubes are bent without the slightest kinking and as fast as an operator can feed the cut pieces to the 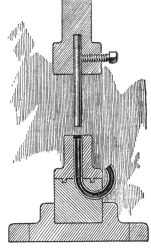 punch press. While a power press is used for this job, a hand-operated arbor press will do if the output needed is not large. The same method can be used for heavy-walled brass tubing up to ½ in. in diameter, and larger, if the bend is not too sharp, but thin-walled tubing, larger than ⅜ in., is likely to buckle.—A. E. Granville, Cleveland, Ohio.

❡Several turns of tape around the middle of a pulley face will prevent a belt from working away from the center.

Casting Box for Printers

Printers often receive paper matrices for making stereotypes. Those not possessing a regular casting box have to send the work to some other printer. A practical box can be improvised without any trouble. Take a chase, lay the matrix, face up, in the center, and place four brass rules around the matrix, and lock it up in the usual manner. See that the corners of the rules butt against each other so that the melted metal will not leak through when poured. Melt some linotype metal and pour it over the matrix to the top of the brass rules. Then let it cool until hard, which can be determined by touching it with a screwdriver. When cool, the stereotype is unlocked and trimmed to the required size. To make the stereo type-high, place a 36-pt. slug against the trimmer knife on the saw and bring the gauge against it, which will give an accurate measurement for height. If no saw trimmer is available, use a piece of coarse emery cloth or sandpaper on a flat block of wood.—Samuel Rubin, Holyoke, Mass.

Belt and Pulley Shifters Installed Directly on the Lineshaft without Extra Support

Old Boiler Flues Used as Fence Posts

In a western irrigation district old worn boiler flues were used as posts when building several miles of hog fence. The flues were cut to equal lengths and were set about 8 ft. apart. The top and bottom wires were stapled to 2 by 6-in. boards, which were fastened to the flues by means of threaded U-bolts and nuts, as shown.—Ivan E. Houk, Denver, Colo.

Belt Shifter Installed on Lineshaft

Some time ago I installed a hundred automatic machines. This was not such a difficult task but each row had to be driven individually with a clutch arrangement. Just how to arrange the shifters was a problem, as there was no ceiling, wall or any solid support near the lineshaft. However, the novel type of shifter illustrated, installed directly on and supported entirely by the lineshaft, was found a satisfactory solution. While the exact dimensions depend, of course, on the size of the shaft, etc., the drawing shows the construction of the shifter. In this case three standard $1\frac{15}{16}$-in. collars were used. One was flattened for the handle or pivot bracket and was made a running fit between the two others, which were securely set on the shaft.—F. W. Schrader, Woodstock, Can.

¶A large spring cotter may be converted into a serviceable pair of tweezers by grinding the open end to a point; before grinding, wrap the cotter with a string, near the eye, to close the open end.

Paint-Removing Fitting for Blowtorch

The attachment for a painter's blowtorch shown in the drawing enables him to apply

Pipe Attachment on the Painter's Blowtorch Applies the Flame Uniformly

the flame more uniformly over the painted surface, previous to scraping, and this feature is of special advantage on windy days. It is made of 1-in. pipe and fittings, drilled with ¼-in. holes, to permit the escape of the flame, and provided with a setscrew so that it can be securely attached to the nozzle of the torch.—G. E. Hendrickson, Argyle, Wis.

A Simple Magnetic Chuck

A machinist friend of mine recently had occasion to put into shape some of the plates of a meat grinder. General machine shops are often called upon to resurface these, so that the little device used by him for holding them on a lathe faceplate will be of interest. It consists of an old U-shaped magnet, the kind that is used in magnetos, and is fitted with a block of soft wood between its sides, the wood being fastened with a couple of screws. Through the center of the block a hole is drilled, large enough to take the tip of the plate. A small screw was driven into the block to engage the plate

and afford a positive drive, and the device was ready for use. In order to prevent the magnet from losing its strength, an iron bar is kept across the two ends.— E. P. Shockey, Bowling Green, Ohio.

Keep Your Watch Clean

Some years ago, I met a man who said that he could wear his watch several years without having it cleaned. He turned his watch pocket inside out, and showed his trick. He had provided a buttonhole in the bottom of the pocket, which allowed the dirt to sift through, and the watch was always in a clean pocket. Many workmen cannot help getting dirt and sand in their pockets, and if they let it remain there, the watch will get dirty and cease running very soon.—A. L. Neuenschwander, Miami, Fla.

Focusing Cloth for Windy Days

Photographers who engage in outdoor photography are frequently inconvenienced by the difficulty of keeping the focusing cloth in place, especially on a windy day. The cloth is also likely to be blown away when left on the camera. To avoid such annoyances, one photographer sewed a length of small chain to the hem of the cloth. This weighted the cloth sufficiently to hold it in place.

Small Chain Sewed to the Edge of a Focusing Cloth Makes It Easier to Handle

Shop Notes

Artistic Doorplates Beautify Home

By MAURICE M. CLEMENT

THE other day my wife had an idea. Not that this is anything to rush into print about; she gets them often, and her ideas have made our home the talk of the neighborhood for sheer beauty and comfort. But this idea was so simple and the results so splendid that it is very much worth while passing on.

Her idea was that the glass plate on the

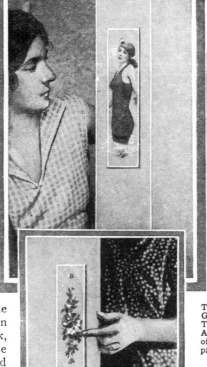

swinging door between the dining room and kitchen had rather a blank look, and that it would be the easiest thing in the world to change this condition, and make it an attractive ornament, simply by putting some kind of a picture under the glass. I

objected immediately that, while the idea was a good one, I didn't want to go downtown to hunt for a picture that would fit behind the narrow glass panel.

That objection was killed at once, however, when she produced a last year's calendar that she had been sav-

The Ordinary Blank, Unattractive Glass Doorplate at the Left Is Transformed into a Thing to Be Admired with the Aid of a Pair of Scissors, Some Scrap Wallpaper, Pictures or Thin Linoleum

ing, womanlike, because the picture on it was "too pretty to throw away." She trimmed it to the size of the glass while I got the screwdriver, and a few minutes later we stood back to survey our work. "Isn't it beautiful?" cried my wife, her face aglow. I was compelled to admit that it was. "What about the plate on the other side of the door?" I demanded. "It's inside the kitchen, and hardly anybody ever sees it. Why not stick an old piece of linoleum or wallpaper under the glass?" This I said in jest.

She opened the door and looked thoughtfully at the inside plate. "An excellent suggestion," said she. "We have two fine pieces of figured linoleum and a dozen small pieces of wallpaper in the garage.

Get them, and we'll see how they look." It was useless to protest that I was only joking, so I got them, and, before the evening was over, we had learned many things about "picturizing" doorplates. For instance, the linoleum and wallpaper suggestions which I had offered in a facetious mood proved to be an absolute knockout. Three other calendars furnished subjects for as many plates. Popular magazines of the larger size yielded innumerable pictures, drawings and reproductions of oil paintings fit to put under glass. Several decalcomania designs mounted on parchment proved particularly attractive.

Non-Reversible Reamer Holder

When hand reaming is done with a reamer held in a vise and the work in the

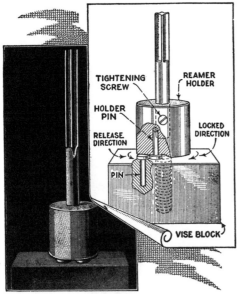

TIGHTENING SCREW
REAMER HOLDER
HOLDER PIN
LOCKED DIRECTION
RELEASE DIRECTION
PIN
VISE BLOCK

Holder Which Prevents Turning the Reamer in Left-Hand Direction

hands, it often occurs that the work is revolved toward the left when it is removed from the reamer. This soon dulls the edge and spoils the tool for finishing work to size. A good method of avoiding this trouble is to use a vise holder like that shown in the photo and drawing. It locks when the reamer is used in the ordinary way and releases when the opposite movement is attempted. To make the device, take a piece of square or rec-

tangular steel, drill and tap it in the center. Next make the reamer holder of round steel, threading it on one end to fit the tapped hole in the block and drilling it out at the other end to take the reamer. Drive one pin into the block and another into the holder, their heads being slightly less in thickness than the pitch of the thread in the block. The pins will prevent the holder from turning when it is used in a right-hand direction, but when used in the opposite direction the holder itself turns. One revolution clears the heads of the pins so that further turning the work in the wrong direction only results in unscrewing the holder.—Harry Moore, Rosemount, Can.

Using Erasers

To erase fine lines use a sharp or narrow-edged eraser. When erasing broad or thick lines hold an eraser at an angle of about 15° to the surface of the paper, alternating the sides of the eraser. This procedure will prepare the eraser for the finer lines. It will be found that better work can be done by erasing a small section of the drawing and redrawing than by using an erasing shield. The eraser should always be used carefully. If the surface of the drawing paper or tracing has been roughened by careless erasing, the drawing will gather dirt. Never use an ink eraser on tracing cloth. It takes longer to erase with a soft eraser, but the surface is left smooth and the ink will flow better when applied. When an eraser becomes hard and smudges the drawing, it can be restored to good working condition by rubbing vigorously on a clean piece of drawing paper. If you have roughened tracing cloth by erasing, the ink will have a tendency to spread. This can be prevented by dusting the surface with soapstone or ordinary talcum powder, and wiping off the surplus before applying the ink.—Frank N. Coakley, Buffalo, N. Y.

Milk-Cooler Spout Shifts Automatically

The accompanying photo shows a milk cooler on the farm of L. C. Young, of Montgomery, Ala. The delivery nozzle of the cooler is equipped with a double, tilting spout, of such a length that it can discharge into either one of two cans placed as shown. The spout is fitted with a float, which is dropped into one of the cans, so that this can will be the first to be filled. As the milk rises in this can the float also rises, until, when the can has been filled to the proper level, the float tilts the spout so that it discharges into the empty can. Each can is filled uniformly, and all the operator has to do is to have an empty can ready to replace the filled one.—J. C. Allen, Lafayette, Ind.

Iron Hook Pivoted to the Center Bar of a Truck Facilitates Handling Tote Boxes

Adjustable Tote-Box Truck Handles Boxes of Varying Height

In a shop where small or medium-sized tote boxes are used, it is an easy matter to arrange a truck to carry them about from place to place. An iron hook is pivoted to the center bar of the truck frame, as shown, so that it can be slipped over the edge of a box, while the rear part is used as a foot lever to raise the hook. The latter should be heavier than the pedal part so that it will not slip off the side of the box. A number of holes are drilled at regular intervals in the center bar so that the hook can be attached at various heights to suit boxes of different sizes. The device is held in place by a bolt and nut.—Avery E. Granville, Cleveland, Ohio.

Homemade Floor Oil

A mixture of equal parts of turpentine and linseed oil is recommended for pine floors. Most floors will readily absorb two applications of this mixture, and it will leave no objectionable coating. For varnished floors, use one part of linseed oil to three of turpentine. Barely moisten the mop with the preparation. An occasional slight oiling prolongs the life of varnish considerably.

Spout of Milk Cooler Which Shifts Flow of Milk from Full to Empty Can

Non-Slip Base for the Camera Tripod Can Be Made of
Furniture Webbing

Cure for Slipping Tripod

The accompanying drawing shows a simple device which will prevent a camera tripod from skidding when it is set on steep or slippery inclines, or on polished wooden or marble floors. It consists of three strips of heavy webbing, each 22 in. in length and arranged to form a triangle, as indicated. At each corner a piece of rubber, ¼ in. thick, which may be cut from a discarded auto tire, is placed underneath the webbing, the straps overlapping above it. A sheet-metal socket for the tripod leg is placed on the webbing at each corner and the assembly riveted together.—Leslie H. Phinney, Springfield, Mass.

Oil-Seated Valves for Hydrogen Sulphide

In order to prevent valves of the ordinary type from clogging up when used for hydrogen sulphide, and to forestall the loss of gas with its attendant discomfort, often caused by careless students, special valves have been installed by the University of Oregon in the chemistry laboratory. In the construction of these valves use was made of an oil-sealed trap. Each valve consists of two cylinders, approximately 13 in. in height, and connected at their bases by a small tube. The larger cylinder, which is made of 2-in. galvanized-iron pipe, contains a plunger of 1¼-in. pipe, 8 in. long and plugged at both ends. The plunger, of course, makes a sliding fit in the cylinder, and can be raised or lowered by means of the rod screwed into one of the plugged ends and extending through the top. The smaller cylinder, made of 1-in. pipe, is tapped and fitted for two ¼-in. gas connections. The intake is located about 4 in. from the top, while the discharge pipe goes through the closed top of the cylinder and extends downward 8 in. Both cylinders contain oil. The desired level of oil can be maintained by means of a small drain hole fitted with a removable plug about halfway up on the smaller cylinder. When the plunger is down, the surface of the oil is at its highest, that is, even with the plug. It is also about 3 in. above the end of the discharge pipe which dips into the oil and consequently is effectively trapped, or closed. When the plunger is lifted, the oil level falls below the open end of the discharge pipe, and the gas that was confined in the chamber above flows out. When the plunger is released, it settles back and the oil level rises again, automatically sealing the discharge. Pressure in the gas mains is regulated so that it never exceeds the pressure of the 3-in. column of oil. To prevent oil from being blown out of the discharge pipe, a small compartment has been provided in the top of the smaller cylinder to stop the oil

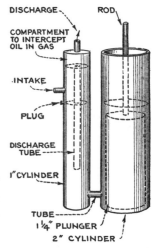

while gas is flowing. Mica gaskets with a tiny perforation are put in the unions on the intake line, close to the valves, in order to cut down the flow of gas to the valve, as a great quantity is never desired. A wooden box, 14 in. high, 6 in. wide and 3 in. deep, houses the assembly.

How to Remove a Broken Spindle Bolt

I had to remove a broken spindle bolt from the axle fork of a Chevrolet. I had intended to saw a slot in the bottom of the bolt and turn it out with a screwdriver, but the bolt was casehardened and this made sawing impossible. I first took off the nut and washer, after which the threads at the bottom were well doped with rust-removing fluid. The bolt was then turned as far as possible by means of a punch stuck into the cotter hole. A piece of 20-gauge soft-iron wire, about 3 ft. long, was wrapped once around the bolt where the washer had been, and, while both ends of the wire were held firmly in the hands, a steady pull was exerted toward the left. The friction of the wire loosened the bolt, although it had been in place several years.—Neil Nelson, Kansas City, Mo.

Moving the Kitchen Range

One of the most awkward and heavy articles to move about is a kitchen range, and as nearly all the individual parts are castings, care must be taken to avoid breakage. To facilitate the task, two 5-ft. lengths of 1½-in. iron pipe, with hooks attached, as shown in the detail, can be used. The handles extend beyond the ends of the stove, and two men can readily carry it. Hardware dealers will appreciate a pair of these handles.

Carrying a Range with the Aid of Two Handles Fitted with Hooks

Adjustable and Comfortable Seat for the Garage Worker Greasing an Automobile

Seat for Auto Greasing Attendant

After going to the trouble of providing the garage with two of the usual inclines, so convenient for greasing and repair, it was found that their use caused more or less discomfort for the attendant working underneath. After some consideration, the problem was solved by providing a seat as shown, which can be adjusted to suit the worker. Two boards make up the seat and backrest, four lengths of 2 by 4-in. studding form the frame, and two small bolts hold the separate parts together, while holes in the backrest sidepieces permit adjustment.

Steel Wool for Oilcan Strainer

The man who wants to keep his oil as free from dirt as possible, will find it advisable to put some sort of filter at the base of the spout. A piece of fine copper or brass gauze is commonly used for this purpose, but if it cannot be obtained, a small wad of steel wool may be substituted. This makes an excellent filter and is even better than gauze, but it should be changed often.

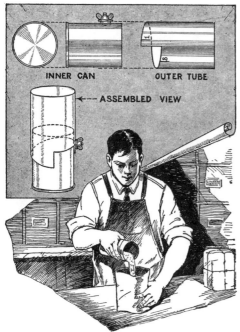

INNER CAN   OUTER TUBE

←-- ASSEMBLED VIEW

Adjustable Measuring Can for the Shop Eliminates
Guessing and Weighing of Small Material

Adjustable Measure for the Shop

Factory stockroom workers who issue materials by weight can save a lot of time by using the adjustable measuring can shown in the illustration. One of these, kept in a barrel of material for which it is to be used, can be quickly adjusted to measure any quantity within its capacity, and so save the trouble of guessing or weighing it. Two lengths of tubing of convenient size are required, one to slide within the other. The inner one is closed at one end by soldering a flat disk to it, and the edge of the outer tube is cut to a spiral, as indicated. Drill a hole in the inner tube for a screw and use two washers, one a little thinner than the tube and the other large enough to tighten on the outer tube when the wingnut is turned. Make a mark on the inner tube and graduate the outer tube, along the spiral, in sections to correspond with the weight contained in the can when the outer tube is turned to bring the marks in line. In use, the nut is loosened and the outer tube turned to one, two or three ounces, or pounds, as the case may be, the nut is tightened, the can filled to a heaped measure and leveled with a stick.

How to Cool a Hot Bearing

Some machine bearings continue to get very hot no matter how much ordinary oil or lubricant is applied. Even when mixtures of oil and graphite, powdered mica, soapstone, etc., fail to reduce the heat, there is one substance, namely coconut oil, that I have seen tried a number of times, and in every case the bearing, to which it was applied, cooled down and the machine was kept running without a shutdown. Even after the bearing gets very hot, the use of this oil will generally cool it in a short time. On bronze and brass bearings coconut oil seems to work like magic. In cool climates the oil may get too thick to be fed from an ordinary oilcan, but a little heat applied to the can will thin the oil. A bearing cooled by using coconut oil does not require flushing out after its use, as is necessary when mica, soapstone or some other "last-hope" remedy is tried.—James E. Noble, West Vancouver, Can.

Watering Trough for Hogs

Hogs like to wallow in mud and water, and will upset any ordinary trough. A Texas rancher made the circular concrete trough shown in the photo, which cannot be overturned. It has a float in the center which, when properly adjusted, keeps just

Circular Concrete Watering Trough for Hogs Cannot
Be Overturned

enough water in the trough for the hogs.
—L. A. Wilke, Fort Worth, Tex.

¶When filling nail holes in yellow pine, use beeswax instead of putty, as it matches the color well.

Maintenance of Concrete Silos

In the spring it is time to think of your silo, which, possibly, is in need of repairs. Silage juices, if not cleaned off cement walls, will continue their destructive action on the cement. Small pinholes enlarge rapidly during the hot summer days and in a short time the walls begin to crack and the silo will leak. To clean cement walls, use large-size wire brushes and hot water. It is advisable to dissolve about 1 lb. of coarse salt to each pail of water, which should be very hot. This application will kill the destructive germs of the silage juices. After drying, it is a good idea to cement-wash the walls as smooth as possible.—G. J. Issakoff, Sioux City, Iowa.

Wire Basket Helps Turn Eggs in Incubator Tray

Turning the eggs in an incubator is a rather slow and tedious task. Many poultrymen simplify and hasten the work by placing the egg tray on a convenient table and removing a row of eggs at one end so that the rest can be rolled in a mass toward that side. The turning is thus effected in a natural way and the eggs, which were removed, are replaced in the vacant end. While this method has its advantages, the removal of one row of eggs is slow and is accompanied by some danger of breakage. This can be eliminated by the use of a screen-wire basket, as shown in the illustration, one being provided for each tray. The basket is just large enough to accommodate a whole row of eggs.—G. E. Hendrickson, Argyle, Wis.

Wire Basket Holding One Row of Eggs Facilitates Egg-Turning Task in Incubators

Convenient Scaffold Which Is Portable and Adjustable to Various Heights

Adjustable Scaffold for Painters

The adjustable scaffold shown in the drawing will be found useful by painters. It consists of two right-angle brackets made of 2 by 4-in. material, two pairs of diagonal braces being nailed to each bracket to make it rigid and to permit the insertion of a 2 by 6-in. supporting plank, which in turn is prevented from slipping by means of stakes driven into the ground, as indicated. After the brackets have been set up against the side of the house, planks can be laid over them. Two or three pairs of supporting planks should be provided so that the scaffold can be set at various heights.—John Tobiason, Willis, Kans.

India Ink in Fountain Pen

India ink, used in fountain pens, dries out quickly and obstructs the flow through the feed line. This trouble can readily be remedied by plugging the small air holes in the cap. Moisten a bit of cotton batting with glycerine and push the wad into the end of the cap. After the pen has been filled with india ink, be sure to replace the cap as soon as you have finished writing, and every time you use it, or the precaution will be of no avail.—J. E. Noble, Hollyburn, Can.

Homemade Machine for Making Rope

By HAROLD JACKSON

HERE is a simple machine with which you can make rope for halter ties, straw slings, etc., from ordinary binder twine. It is made from a few pieces of 6-in. wood, some wire, about 3/16 in. in diameter, and a screen-door spring. The drawing shows the construction of the parts and the assembly.

The head of the machine is made from two pieces of 6-in. wood, nailed together to form a right angle, and braced as indicated. Three ¼-in. holes are drilled in the vertical piece about 4 in. apart and in the form of a triangle. Three cranks, made of the wire and shaped as shown, are placed in the three holes. The cranks should be about 3 in. long and all exactly alike in this respect. Make the crank block next. This is another piece of wood, 6-in. square, which is fitted with a wooden handle. Three holes are drilled in it to coincide with those in the head and fit over the horizontal crank ends. When

this block is moved by means of the handle, the cranks will all turn with it. The head assembly is nailed to a bench about 12 ft. long, or to the floor or hayrack, if a bench is not available.

The door spring is held by a nail driven into the bench some distance from the head. If you wish to make a halter rope that is to be 7 ft. long, fasten the spring so that there will be 8½ ft. between the head and the near end of the spring. The twisting of the strands shortens the finished length of the rope considerably. It takes 36 strands of twine, 12 on each crank hook, to make a ⅝-in. rope. This is a good size for halters. All the strands are then attached to the hook at the end of the spring. Draw the strands tight so they will not sag, and the winding will then be easy. Now turn the crank slowly. This will twist the strands separately. Twist them very tight, for the tighter they are, the stronger the rope will be. Keep the three strands separate until firmly twisted. Now unhook the spring and hold the strands with your hand. You will find that they have a strong tendency to twist in your hand. Allow them to do so, but keep them taut enough to prevent sagging. The strands will then roll up tight, forming the finished rope.

When finished, unhook the rope from

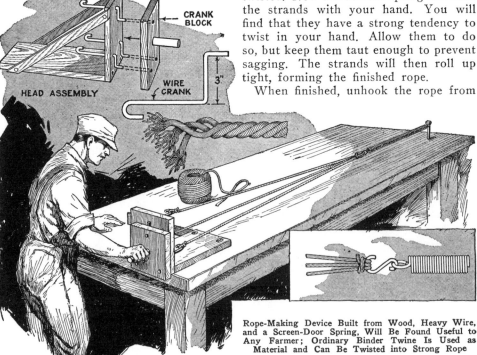

CRANK BLOCK

HEAD ASSEMBLY

WIRE CRANK

3"

Rope-Making Device Built from Wood, Heavy Wire, and a Screen-Door Spring, Will Be Found Useful to Any Farmer; Ordinary Binder Twine Is Used as Material and Can Be Twisted into Strong Rope

the head of the machine and it will be ready for use. If you are going to use the rope on a halter or want to put a ring or snap on one end, you can best do so by making a noose on the end. This may be done by running one end of the rope through the loops of the twine that were placed over the hooks on the machine. This forms a neat connection. A hog ring should be pinched onto the other end to prevent unraveling.

Cementing Gear-Shift-Lever Ball

After having several beautiful onyx gear-shift-lever balls stolen, the writer hit upon the idea of cementing one on to prevent its theft. Get about 6 oz. of fresh litharge, making sure that it is reasonably fresh, as it becomes "slacked" when exposed to the air and will not set. To a teaspoonful of litharge add glycerine until the mixture reaches the consistency of a very thick cream, and apply this to the threads both on the lever and in the ball. Then screw the ball down as tightly as possible. After a day or so, it will be impossible to remove the ball by hand.—G. T. Fowler, Bakersfield, Calif.

Dividers with Bent Points for Marking Centers

Ordinary straight-pointed dividers are often unsuitable for laying off hole centers when there is an obstruction such as a boss, shoulder or other raised part between the two points. To mark off center-to-center positions under such conditions, make a pair of dividers with bent points, as shown. With these you can get around most obstructions that would interfere with the ordinary tool. These dividers are made of flat metal with a caliper joint and are used as indicated.

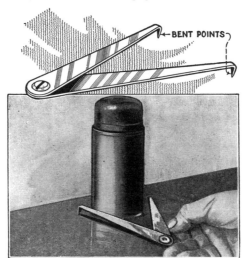

Laying Off Measurements over Obstructions with Bent-Pointed Dividers

Heavy Barrels Can Be Moved About Single-Handed by Means of This Truck

Truck for Carrying Heavy Barrels

The manager of a large oil station made a barrel-carrying truck that will prove of interest to garage and gas-station attendants generally, and also to orchardists, farmers and gardeners, as it allows one man to lift and convey a filled barrel. The truck consists of a U-shaped axle made by welding sections of two buggy axles together, and suspension hooks that engage the chines of the barrel. When the handles are pushed down to the position most convenient for moving the truck, the barrel will be raised 4 or 5 in. above the ground. Narrower trucks of similar construction can be used by ice-cream manufacturers, by making the suspension hooks shorter so that they will engage with the handles of the ice-cream tubs and hold them upright. —G. E. Hendrickson, Argyle, Wis.

Tail Holder Made from Battery Clips and Wire Prevents Cow from Switching

Preventing the Cow from Switching

When being milked in the summer months, cows are often annoyed by flies and switch their tails to the discomfort of the milker. To avoid this trouble one dairyman provides his milkers with the tail holders shown. Each is made from a pair of battery clips, to which a length of wire is attached. In use, one clip is attached to the knee portion of the milker's trousers, and, as he seats himself to do the milking, the other clip is attached to the brush of the cow's tail.—G. E. Hendrickson, Argyle, Wis.

Spring Center for the Lathe

Many jobs that are held in the lathe chuck are first laid out in order to determine the exact location of the part to be turned, bored or drilled. The spring center shown has been found of great help in locating the central point of the layout before closing the chuck jaws upon the work. The device is first

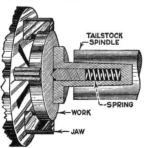

entered into the center mark of the layout, while the work is held firmly up against the flanged face of the center holder. It is then approximately in the correct position to be held in the chuck, after which the center is moved out of the way. If a more accurate setting is desired, it can be accomplished by using an indicator.—Chas. Homewood, Hollywood, Calif.

Jug Makes Good Bee Trap

Swarming wild bees often settle in very inconvenient places about the farm buildings, such as between partitions, under floors and other out-of-the way corners, where they can hardly be caught by ordinary methods. On a Wisconsin farm, a swarm collected between the lining and outside boxing of the barn, annoying both the farm folks and the live stock. At length, on the advice of a neighbor, the farmer suspended an open jug just beneath the opening in the building where the bees had entered, doing this work after nightfall. A piece of cardboard, rolled up to form a tube, was inserted several inches into the mouth of the jug. By the following evening practically the entire swarm was trapped. The secret of the trick, it is claimed, lies in the fact that in the slightest breeze, a low hum, very similar to that made by industrious bees at work inside of the hive, is produced in the open jug. The wild bees enter the jug to

pilfer but cannot easily find their way out again.—D. R. Van Horn, Lincoln, Nebr.

Steam-Boiling Liquids in Vats

In one workshop there are a number of large vats full of liquid, which must be kept boiling for several hours every day. The method formerly used to do this was to turn steam into each vat. As an experiment, the vats were fitted with light metal covers and just enough steam turned on to keep the liquids boiling slowly. The result was satisfactory as it effected a saving of more than 20 per cent in steam. There are many factories where live steam is still used to boil liquids in uncovered vats. Even when exhaust steam is used in closed coils, much of the steam can be saved and used in some other way if all the vats are provided with covers, especially if the vats are located in unheated rooms during the cold season.—James E. Noble, West Vancouver, Can.

Washing Photographic Prints in the Kitchen Sink

To be efficient a photo-print washer should have two features: The water should be kept in motion and the drain should be located at the bottom so that it will carry off the hypo, which is heavier than water and hence settles at the bottom. Both of these conditions are met in an ordinary kitchen sink if arranged as shown in the illustration. All that is necessary to use is a length of hose and two short pieces of pipe. The hose is attached to the faucet and held toward one side, as indicated, by means of a cord tied to the other faucet. This makes the water rotate freely in the sink. Remove the strainer from the drain and insert one of the pieces of pipe, which should fit into the drain snugly and rise 2 or 3 in. above the bottom of the sink, depending on the depth of water maintained during the washing. The other pipe, longer and of larger diameter, is notched in the bottom edge to permit the passage of water and placed over the first, as indicated. The water at the bottom, which contains the hypo, is forced out by the pressure and the swirling motion of the whole body of water.—J. G. Pratt, Washington, D. C.

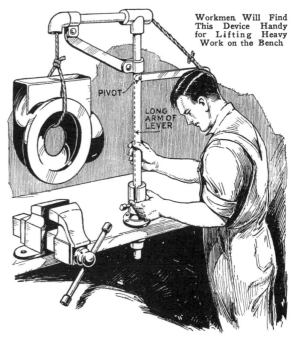

Workmen Will Find This Device Handy for Lifting Heavy Work on the Bench

PIVOT

LONG ARM OF LEVER

Device for Lifting Heavy Work on Bench

Often it is a rather difficult task to place a heavy piece of work in a vise single-handed, especially if the work is of awkward form. To facilitate the job, a special lifting tackle will be found useful. That shown herewith was made up of pipe and fittings, a lever of flat stock, a length of wire rope and a lock collar. The method of assembly is clearly shown, and it is used in the following way: The work is first placed on the bench, or on a truck of the same height, and the rope and hook are attached. It is then lifted by means of the lever and swung over the vise. If necessary, the lever can be locked in this position by the slotted collar as indicated. After the vise jaws are opened, the work can be let down with one hand on the lever, while, with the other, the vise is tightened. When through, the device is stowed away.

Kitchen Sink Makes a Good Print Washer for the Home Photographer Who Does His Own Work

Gluing Ivories on Piano Keys

By F. R. RODGERS

ALTHOUGH usually a troublesome job, re-gluing of the ivory tops on piano keys, when they have come off for some reason or other, can be done effectively by the following method: First, the front of the keyboard should be removed. It may be necessary also to take out the screws holding the pivots, which should be done so the complete keys can be lifted from the action. When several of the ivories have come off, or are loosened, care should be taken to keep the right ivory for its particular key, for in some cases they will not interchange. Scrape all the old glue from both key and ivory with a knife.

When one simply tries to lay a block on top of the ivory and clamp with a

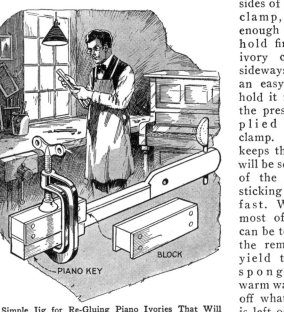

A Simple Jig for Re-Gluing Piano Ivories That Will Insure a Good Job

thumbscrew in order to glue the ivory in place, it will almost invariably slip, causing part of the ivory to extend outside of the key while exposing the raw wood on the other side. To avoid this, make special blocks as follows: Rip a piece of board and plane square to the exact width of the key; the thickness is immaterial. Saw off blocks just as long as the wide part of the key, since it is usually the wide part that comes off. Cut off some pieces of thin wood as long as the blocks, and fasten, with brads or small-head nails, one on each side of the block. These side-pieces will form a groove into which the key will fit. The same result can be obtained by plowing a groove the width of the key in a suitable length of wood and then cutting it into pieces as long as the keys, although the first method is easier and just as good.

Use hot glue and warm the blocks,

which will prevent the glue from chilling and setting too quickly. Spread an even coat of glue on the key, lay the ivory on it and cover with a strip of thin paper, allowing the paper to come over the sides of the key; then push the block down over the sides of the key and clamp, with just enough pressure to hold firmly. The ivory cannot slip sideways, and it is an easy matter to hold it forward, as the pressure is applied with the clamp. The paper keeps the glue that will be squeezed out of the joint from sticking the block fast. When dry, most of the paper can be torn off, and the remainder will yield to a little sponging with warm water. Scrape off what little glue is left on the edges of the key and replace it in the piano. The result will prove very satisfactory.

A word as to the glue may not be amiss. No doubt any glue will do, but the old-fashioned hot glue is best and the white kind is better than the dark, since with the white glue there is no danger of discoloring the ivory. Cook it in a regular double gluepot and do not have it too thick, as all the surplus glue must be squeezed from the joint. The glue should flow freely when hot, with about the same body as varnish. The white glue usually will not set as quickly as the general run of dark glue, although having the clamping blocks good and hot will prevent the glue from setting before the ivory can be properly fastened in them If hot glue seems too troublesome to use, or no glue-pot is available, select any good prepared glue that is rather light in color, and warm it by placing in a pan of hot water.

Making Attractive "Ballotini" Lampshades

By H. C. McKAY

A SHORT time ago, floor and bridge lamps were used for one purpose, namely, to give light. They were sufficiently ornamental not to look out of place in a well-furnished living room, but there the decoration stopped. The parchment lampshade brought into being a new era. The shade was accepted as an ornament in itself, and then began the development of the modern floor lamp.

Two Steps in Making the "Ballotini" Shades: Sewing the Cotton Sheeting to the Shade Frame; Above, Painting the "Sea" to Meet the Transfer Pattern

There is no one development which has furthered its value as much as has the "ballotini" shade. For the benefit of those readers who have not yet had the opportunity of seeing such a shade upon a lighted lamp, it may be

Below, Applying the Ballotini to the Shellacked Panel, and at the Right, the Completed Shade

ing; transfer designs; transparent photo oil color; one tube plastic embroidery compound; one jar non-spread fluid; one jar best white shellac; vials of ballotini of the proper shades for the design, and the necessary braid and trimming.

said that the ballotini resembles nothing so much as a beautiful opalescent crystal shade, with soft colorful designs apparently cast in the glass. No stained-glass shade could be more beautiful, yet it may be made in a few hours, and in addition to this, the design may be applied by anyone, regardless of artistic ability.

The ballotini shade is made upon a foundation of a closely woven white sheeting of good grade. The best quality pillow-slip material makes a very good material. This is sewed to the usual wire frame, and stretched as tightly as possible. The design is then painted or transferred onto the shade and finally the ballotini is applied, changing the shade from a rough, crudely decorated, amateurish article to a thing of enduring beauty.

The materials needed are: wire shade frame; one yard finest white-cotton sheet-

The ballotini is nothing but tiny, round glass beads in various colors, and transparent. These beads are sold in sprinkler-top vials.

The cloth is applied to the shade as usual in making any cloth shade. In this description the details of the shade illustrated will be given, but these may be changed to suit any design in hand.

The cloth is given a coating of the non-spread fluid, which, as its name implies, prevents excessive spreading of the color. This is allowed to dry. Then, in the center of each panel, a transfer design of a ship is placed. These transfers may be obtained from any paint, art or ten-cent store. They are given a thin coating of glue and fastened to the shade. The colored side is placed down, the side with the outlined design outward. This is allowed to dry for a half hour. Then the transfers are soaked with lukewarm water and the paper backing slid off. This leaves the design, a ship in full color, firmly attached to the cloth.

Conventional wave designs are now roughly sketched to meet the waves of the transfer design. Then cloud forms are marked irregularly in the sky. The waves and clouds are outlined in "plastic embroidery." This is a compound like thin putty, sold in a collapsible tube with a long spout point. It should be allowed to dry for four or five hours.

Now, in transparent photo oil color, the sea is given a coat of bluish-green, thinned in turpentine. Upon this, rough, jagged strokes of dark green are drawn carelessly. The upper part of the sky is given a dark-blue coat and the lower sky a coating of light blue, which is blended out to the white cloth about 1 in. above the waves. The white space between waves and sky is now filled with a mixed red and yellow blended-stripe design to simulate sunset. The red and yellow are placed on fairly strongly. The clouds are tinged on the underside with red or pink, and the tops left white. This color is allowed to dry. Do not get discouraged at this time, though the color is garish and the design rough.

When the color is thoroughly dry, the shade is ready for the ballotini. This is applied a panel at a time. The sea of the first panel is given a good coat of shellac and the ballotini (green) is sprinkled upon the wet shellac until it appears dry, showing that the shellac will take up no more. Shake the excess off and go to the next panel. When the green ballotini has been applied to the sea of all six panels, start with number one again and coat the clouds with shellac and cover this with cashmere ballotini. Cashmere is the name given a mixture of pastel shades which is very delicate yet effective. When the clouds are completed, start again, and this time coat the entire sky with light-blue ballotini. In this step, do not coat the ship, but leave the transfer uncoated. The shade is allowed to dry for 24 hours.

The shade is now lined with the usual lampshade material, and the trimming applied. The ribs of the frame are covered with a double-edged braid. The top and bottom edges are covered with tinsel-ruffled lampshade braid, and the decorative braid is applied to the lower edge.

Wallboard Disks Attached to the Flywheels of Printing Presses Insure Safety

Disks on Flywheels Protect Workers

In a printing establishment, it was found that large disks of wallboard attached to the flywheels of the presses helped to insure safety to the workmen. After cutting the board to fit the wheel, holes were made at a number of places so that the board could be laced to the spokes with wire. It is, of course, advisable to twist the ends of the wire together on the inside of the wheel so that the outside surface of the disk will be perfectly smooth.

Handy Method of Snipping Wire

When short pieces of wire are needed for pins, rivets, or other purposes, the usual method of cutting it without snips is to lay the wire over a sharp corner and

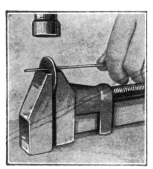

then crush it with a hammer. A better method is shown in the photo. Slip the wire through a small washer, lay the wire and washer over a monkey wrench as indicated, the jaws being set so that there is just enough space for the washer to slide between them. Hit the washer a smart blow with a hammer, and the wire will be sheared off squarely.

Workbench Drawer Which Can Be Opened and Closed Easily, No Matter How Heavily Loaded

Swinging Drawer for Workbench

It often happens that deep workbench drawers accumulate so many heavy items that they either stick or are hard to pull out. This difficulty can easily be overcome by providing a swinging drawer, as shown. A soap box, a length of 2 by 4-in. wood to stand vertically under the bench, two large spikes and a weight are all the materials needed. At the lower end of the two-by-four, a spike should be driven in permanently, after first drilling a guide hole a trifle smaller than the diameter of the spike, so that the wood will not split. The head should project about 1 in. Drill a hole in the floor, slightly larger than the head of the spike and about $\frac{3}{8}$ in. deep, preferably over a floor joist. It is well to drill a hole in the top of the workbench first so that the bottom hole can be located directly under it by a plumb line. The top spike should be a loose fit in the two-by-four, so it can be withdrawn when necessary. A diagonal brace, underneath the drawer, a weight to make it swing under the bench, and a stop complete the job.

Inasmuch as this type of drawer can always be opened with little exertion, no matter how heavy, it will be found a great convenience in the workshop.—H. Sibley, Pasadena, Calif.

Removing Sulphate from Storage-Battery Plates

Badly sulphated battery plates, which do not yield to the usual treatment of a long slow charge, may be saved from the scrap pile by the following means: Pour out the electrolyte, fill the cells with distilled water and allow them to stand until any acid in the plates has been soaked out. This may take several hours. Then the cells are emptied again and filled with a solution of pure sodium sulphate. The strength of this solution is not very important, although 7 oz. of the sulphate dissolved in 1 qt. of distilled water has been found satisfactory. The cells are now put on charge in the usual way and the sulphate will slowly disappear. Before refilling the cells with electrolyte, it is, of course, important to remove all traces of sodium sulphate by soaking the plates in water, one or two changes being needed before the process is complete. Then the electrolyte is replaced and the cells are connected for charging.

"Rumble Seat" for Dogs

A sort of rumble seat to provide comfortable transportation for dogs when they are taken for exhibition at shows, has been built on an auto by a dog fancier of Peekskill, N. Y. They are protected by a screen, and in bad weather the compartment can be covered.

Screen-Covered Compartment for Carrying Dogs on a Roadster

Household Bluing Helps Detect Punctures in Tire Tubes

Finding small punctures in an auto tube is sometimes rather difficult, even if the tube is immersed in water, as defects or small holes in the rubber frequently close up when the tube is only partly inflated. However, if ordinary household bluing of the powdered kind is placed in a new tube before it is put in use, by removing the valve and pouring about a tablespoonful of the powder into the tube through a small paper funnel, the bluing will sift out through the opening and leave an easily seen smudge when a puncture occurs.

Laying Off a Cam

In cases where strict accuracy is not required, a cam with a uniform rise can be laid off by the method illustrated. If the cam required is to have a rise of 2 in., take a piece of wood and turn it down until its circumference is 2 in. Then wind a length of string around it a few times and place it in the position indicated. A pencil

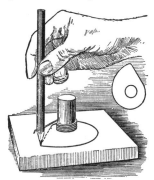

is slipped through a loop tied at the outer end of the string and is drawn over the material on which the cam is to be laid out, the string being unwound and the pencil held so that the string is taut.—Harry Moore, Rosemount, Can.

Measuring Voltage

Sometimes it is necessary to measure the potential of a power line, and the only voltmeters at hand are of too low a range to do the work. Then it is a good thing to know that two or three voltmeters may be hooked up in series, connected across the line, and the individual readings added to obtain the correct potential. For instance, two 110-volt voltmeters can be used in this manner to ascertain the exact voltage of 220-volt mains.

Road-Crossing Sidewalks Laid between Rails Are Fully Protected against Breakage

Protecting Concrete Sidewalk Crossings

In small towns having unpaved streets, one of the problems is to provide sidewalk crossings that will resist traffic shocks without breaking down. A good concrete crossing can be laid between two old railroad rails as shown. Earth or other road material should always be used to fill in level with the shoulders of crosswalks, in order to protect the concrete, but it is not unusual to see this precaution neglected in many towns. If rails are used as above, the concrete will be protected whether or not the earth fill is maintained.—W. F. Schaphorst, Newark, N. J.

Handle for Holding Small Blades

Small spokeshaves, cabinet scrapers, etc., can be conveniently held in the handle shown in the drawing. It is made from a piece of hardwood, cut down to the shape indicated. A slot is cut to admit the tool and two holes are drilled for

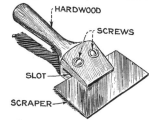

screws, which, when driven tight, compress the sides of the holder against the blade, keeping it securely in place.—J. A. Stevens, East Boothbay, Me.

Adjustable Staging Found Convenient

Adjustable Staging Used by Workers Engaged in Building Operations

Many workers will find the adjustable staging shown in the drawing convenient, as it can be set to any desired height. Each leg consists of two lengths of 2 by 4-in., or other suitably sized wood, slotted lengthwise and held together by means of bolts and wingnuts. Suitable braces are provided to keep the legs apart and to support the ridge piece. All the necessary constructional details are clearly shown.—Carlton Groat, Portland, Oreg.

Ball Mounting for Roll

A novel method of mounting a light roll so that it revolves with very little friction is shown in the illustration. This particular roll had to revolve by the action of paper passing over it and therefore must move very freely. Both ends are similarly mounted. A V-shaped center was machined in each end of the roll, which was supported by specially made brackets. These were drilled and tapped for small screws, also

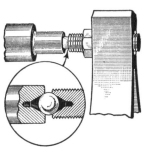

having V-centers. The screws were provided with pins for turning to obtain the correct adjustment, and nuts to lock them in position. A steel ball was inserted between the vees of the roll and the mounting screws, the latter being turned so that the ball had just a little play. The nut was then tightened.

Repair for a Broken Oilstone

To repair a broken oilstone assemble the parts on some piece of heavy steel metal or a stove lid. Apply heat until the parts are fairly warm and then coat the fractured ends with heavy shellac. Hold the parts together with a clamp and reheat them, allowing the stone to cool gradually. After cooling, the parts will adhere and the stone will be fit for further use.

Covering Prevents Dirt from Sticking to Tamp in Clayey Soil

Workmen tamping clayey soil are usually inconvenienced by a large amount of dirt sticking to the tamp, increasing its weight and making it ineffective. A remedy for the trouble is to tie a piece of canvas, burlap, or other heavy cloth, over the tamp as indicated in the drawing. One working crew used denim from discarded overalls. The reason for the effectiveness of this method is that the cloth sags down each time the tamp is lifted,

which causes the clay picked up to crack and fall off.—H. E. Benson, Denver, Colo.

Darkened Brooders Stimulate Chickens' Growth

A Wisconsin poultry man has proved by repeated tests, that the growth of brooder chicks is stimulated approximately 25 per cent if the brooder is darkened a few minutes several times each day. This method is followed naturally by the mother hen, who calls her chicks to her from time to time for the same purpose. The reason for the increased growth of the chicks when this is done, is that the temporary darkness induces them to nap and doze, which, it seems, helps to digest food previously eaten. It was formerly thought that a brooding hen did this to provide warmth for the flock but the same instinct seems to rule in hot weather.

Burning Out Carbon

Carbon is usually burned out by blowing oxygen into the spark-plug openings. A quicker way is to draw the oxygen into the cylinders while the motor is running. Attach the hose from the oxygen tank to the intake manifold by unfastening the tube to the vacuum tank and connecting the oxygen hose to the fitting of the vacuum-tank lead. Ordinarily the tank will hold sufficient gasoline to run the motor during the oxidation. Be sure that the radiator is full of water. Start the motor and run it slightly faster than idling speed. Turn on the oxygen gradually and at the same time close the choke slowly. Adjust the oxygen valve until the motor receives so rich a mixture that it will miss. Then let the motor run for ten minutes. The surplus oxygen combines with the carbon in the combustion chamber. Not only is the combustion chamber thoroughly cleaned in this way, but also the exhaust ports and valve stems, and the spark plugs.—R. P. Cole, Paterson, N. J.

Small Waterwheel Installed in a Brook Operates a Pump Which Raises Water to a Near-By Reservoir

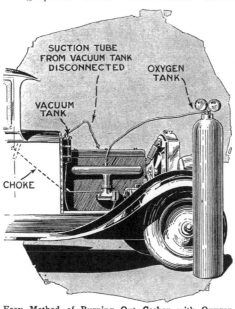

Easy Method of Burning Out Carbon with Oxygen While the Motor Is Running

Small Waterwheel Provides Farm with Water

In the hill country near San Antonio, Tex., there is a small waterwheel which pumps water from a brook to a near-by farm house. The installation consists of an ordinary paddle wheel placed in the stream so that the current causes it to revolve. The wheel operates a walking beam to which a pump is connected, as shown. The pump forces the water through a pipe line to a reservoir. There is a constant flow of water in the brook, which insures the continuous operation of the wheel. It has supplied water for the farm house and garden for several years and needs no other attention than an occasional oiling.

Easy Access to Well Pit

A Trapdoor and Stairway Which Provide Easy Access to the Well Pit

Many farmers use their well pit as a cooling room. Although convenient for this purpose, it is rather troublesome to raise the boards of the platform. An access which has been found handy is shown in the drawing. It is merely a trapdoor and a stairway, leading down into the pit. The arrangement is also useful during the winter when it is often necessary to wrap the pump pipe in order to prevent freezing. Obviously, it is easier to get at the pipe for this purpose, and for occasional inspection, through the trapdoor than through the platform.—Geo. R. Harrison, Council Bluffs, Iowa.

Loosening Rear-Axle Nut of Truck

It frequently happens that the nut which holds the rear wheel on a motor-truck axle shaft of the semi-floating type, becomes rusted or otherwise jammed so that it can neither be loosened nor tightened by ordinary methods. When such a condition exists, a sure relief will be found and much time saved, by setting the regular wrench in place on the nut, and attaching a chain between its outer end and the frame or body of the truck as indicated. The truck is then run backward a few feet. The nut will be held securely by the wrench but will be loosened by the turning of the axle shaft and wheel. To tighten a nut that cannot be run up snugly by hand, place the wrench on the nut with the handle to the left, attach the chain as before and run the truck forward as far as necessary. Many expensive axle shafts are ruined by being run loose in the rear-wheel hub and "wallowing" the keyway, and in most cases this results from the fact that a nut has been fitted improperly.—G. C. Douglas, Raleigh, N. C.

Self-Opening and Closing Cover

For a can containing a fluid that must be kept inclosed at all times, except when pouring, the cover shown in the drawing will be found convenient. Instead of the usual lid closing the entire top, a semicircular piece, with two loops for a pin, was soldered in place, and another piece, shaped as indicated, hinged to it. To make the lid open and close automatically a small weight is attached to the central strip of the lid, which is bent down at right an-

gles. When the can is tipped to pour, the weight swings forward and opens the lid, and when the can is set upright it closes.

¶When dismantling a machine having hardened parts it is often necessary to mark the various parts to assist in reassembling them; this can be done by applying a copper-sulphate solution to form a coppered surface on which a mark can be made with a scriber.

Attractive Wooden Trim for Cabinetwork

By CLAUDE WEST

WOODEN hinges, handles and escutcheons, worked out along artistic lines, are very pleasing as ornamental parts for cabinetwork, and afford an unlimited field for design. Such parts are especially attractive on pieces that otherwise are rather plain. Besides, they provide an excellent means of expressing individuality, and a touch of distinction may be given to a piece of furniture, which in every other way would be like innumerable others. With proper designing and finishing, pieces may be made to have an antique appearance, or at least suggestive enough of it to render them suitable to be used with period furniture. On the other hand, they may be designed and finished to suggest the most modern creation of the cabinetmaker's skill.

The cabinet shown in the photo, a semi-Priscilla design, is merely used as an example, and no dimensions or details for its construction are given except for parts to be mentioned later, which are shown in Figs. 1 to 9. The hinges should be made of sound, straight-grained

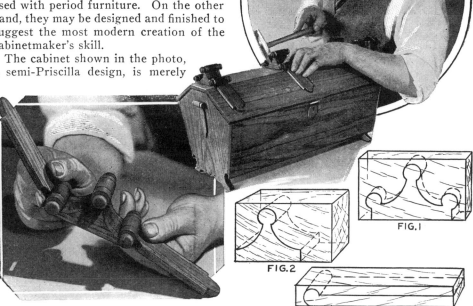

FIG.1

FIG.2

FIG.3

Ornamental Wooden Hinges of Many Designs Can Be Made by Cutting the Pieces Out with a Coping Saw and Gluing Them Together

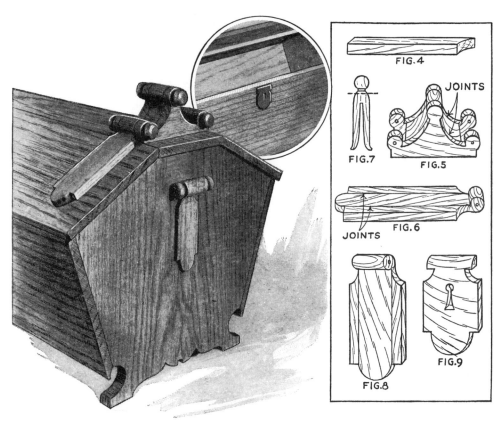

Figs. 1 to 9 Show the Patterns for the Various Parts of the Fittings on the Box Shown in the Photos

hardwood and the handles and escutcheons should match. In cases where it is possible to do the work on a bandsaw, the parts may be cut from solid stock of a thickness equal to the width of a hinge, and no gluing is necessary. However, as the work will be done by hand in most cases, the method illustrated shows how to cut out the pieces with a coping saw, and, as thinner stock must be used, the pieces will have to be glued together afterward. The drawings show a double hinge having one middle section and two end sections, each section being made of three pieces glued together. Pieces of the same thickness may be used so that their combined thickness equals the width of the hinge, but in this cabinet the middle piece is as thick as the outside pieces together. Fig. 1 gives a side view of these pieces of the middle section, two of them being required. The lines indicate the pattern laid out on the wood ready to be cut out. Fig. 2 shows the single center piece of the mid-

dle section, and Fig. 3 shows the center piece for the end section, two of these pieces being needed, one for each of the two sections. The material used for the latter should be of the same width as the material used for the piece shown in Fig. 2. Fig. 4 shows the outside pieces for the end sections, four pieces being required, two for each section. The material should be of the same thickness as that used for the piece shown in Fig. 1.

When the patterns have been laid out on the stock, as indicated by the lines, the cutting can be done with a coping saw. The stock should be long enough to be held down firmly on top of a bench or table, while the pattern being cut out projects over the edge to permit sawing. The saw should be held as nearly as possible at a right angle to the stock, so that the cutting will be done squarely, and the sawing must be done slowly and carefully, the pattern being followed just outside the lines. Any irregularities can then be smoothed out later. When the pieces have been cut out, they should be glued together as shown in Figs. 5 and 6, the former showing the middle section and the latter the end sections. The gluing must be done with care, so as to be sure that each piece is exactly in its proper position. After the glue has set thoroughly, scrape off any surplus and work out all the irregularities with a wood rasp or with coarse sandpaper. Then drill the holes for the hinge pins, for which small nails with the heads cut off will serve. Put the hinges together and finish smoothing and sandpapering, using fine sandpaper. The knobs, which appear to be the heads of the hinge pins, are simply glued in place, the pins being cut slightly shorter than the width of the hinge, to prevent interference. The knobs used for the hinges shown in the photo were clothespin heads, cut off as indicated by the dotted line in Fig. 7. The handles in Fig. 8 are made up of three pieces, cut out according to the pattern shown in Fig. 3. After being glued up, they are cut out as shown in Fig. 8. The escutcheons are shown in Fig. 9. They should be made of stock about ⅛ in. thick.

These examples are intended only as guides to the method of making up the pieces, and are capable of endless variation. The design, of course, should harmonize with the piece to which the trim is to be applied; therefore, in the cabinet illustrated, they are rather plain. For more elaborate work, the trim can be scrollsawed, carved or decorated in any manner desired.

Inexpensive Farm Tractor for Light Work

The principal parts of the tractor shown in the photos are a Ford chassis and a light three-speed transmission. The front end of the extra transmission was milled to fit the rear end of the Ford universal joint, a piece was cut from the front end of the Ford drive shaft, and the remainder was milled to fit the rear end of the transmission. The rear spring was removed and the frame was bolted to the rear-axle housing. An extra rim was bolted to each wheel and the rear wheels were fitted with wooden lugs. A farm-implement seat was added and a few minor changes and additions were made, which made the cost of the completed tractor about $17 besides the chassis, which the farmer had on hand. The two transmissions, working together, give this tractor a very wide range of power and speed, and it will pull a plow, harrow, pulverizer, roller or any other farm implement of about the same size.

Two Views of a Light Farm Tractor, Consisting of a Ford Auto Chassis Equipped with an Extra Transmission of the Three-Speed Type; This Arrangement Gives a Wide Range of Power

By raising the rear end of the tractor, the large rear wheels may serve as pulleys in running belt machinery.—Leland A. Dye, Boston, N. Y.

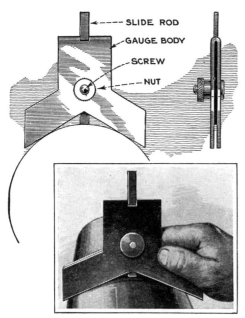

SLIDE ROD
GAUGE BODY
SCREW
NUT

Handy Gauge for Duplicating Diameters Where Regular Calipers Cannot Be Used

Gauge for Duplicating Diameters Takes Place of Caliper

An unusual type of gauge that I have found handy on repair work is shown in the photo. It is not always possible to caliper a size when duplicating a piece, owing to obstructions caused by the piece being in place on a machine, or perhaps an auxiliary part fitted to it after it was turned. If I cannot get the calipers on a job, I use this gauge. It is made by bending a piece of sheet metal double and cutting it a V-shape on the contact end. A slot is then filed on the top to take a sliding rod, which is made of the same stock. A nut and screw, similar to those used on a depth gauge, complete it. For duplicating a diameter, the gauge is placed on the old piece and the slide rod is pressed down until it touches the surface; then the nut is tightened to hold

the rod immovable and the new piece is turned until the gauge fits it in the same way.—Harry Moore, Montreal, Can.

Cleaning Terra Cotta

In cleaning terra cotta the bureau of standards has found that sodium hydrosulphite is effective and does not corrode the glaze. Fluo-silicic acid also cleans the material satisfactorily but attacks the glaze slightly. Trisodium phosphate is a good cleaner on standard finishes but unsatisfactory for glazed finishes. Soap powder cleans slowly and has a tendency to scour, thereby roughening the glazed surface, and hydrochloric acid, which is also a fair cleaner, has a slight corrosive effect on the glaze. Hydrofluoric acid should never be used on terra cotta.

Reading the Incubator Thermometer

Incubators are often located in places where darkness makes it almost impossible to read the thermometer without opening the machine and withdrawing the egg tray. As this is likely to chill the eggs, one poultryman devised a simple fixture by which the thermometer is held in place over the center of the egg tray, or can be swung into plain view against the glass at the front of the machine without opening the door. The holder consists of a stout wire, bent at right angles and inserted through a small hole in the top of the incubator. A loop at the end of the perpendicular arm rests on the top of the machine, and supports the bracket, so that the thermometer, attached at the end of the horizontal arm, is suspended at the proper distance above the eggs. Turning the loop at the top of the machine swings the thermometer against the glass of the door and after it has been read, it is swung back to its former position.— G. E. Hendrickson, Argyle, Wis.

Thermometer Read in Incubator with This Swinging Holder

THERMOMETER

Your Boy Will Like This Liner

By HI SIBLEY

THE toy-boat builder, having worked out ingenious designs in craft powered by clockwork, rubber bands and electric motors, will find a real steamer a fascinating novelty. Only a fraction of the countless ships that sail the seven seas are powered with anything besides steam, and a toy steamer affords a great thrill, for it has the action and sound of a full-size ship. There are no difficulties in making one, but if the young shipbuilder has a small upright steam engine among his toys, half the job is done.

Use white pine for the hull, which is made up of three pieces—bottom, main-hull block and deck. Lay out your outlines on the central block, which is 30 in. long, 6½ in. wide and 3 in. deep, and, after boring four holes at the corners of the hold, saw out the inside piece with a

the boiler. These can be bought at a very reasonable price; in fact, the engine used in the original of this model cost only eighty-five cents and is an exceptionally capable performer.

Set the engine amidships with quite a tilt aft so that the crankshaft will be nearly in line with the propeller-shaft position. Locate the engine, but do not fasten it. Now bore a hole through the stern just large enough to receive a brass tube of ⅜-in. inside diameter. This should line up with the center of the flywheel.

Cut a length of stiff brass wire for the propeller shaft and straighten it. The propeller can be cut from a tin-can lid or, better, a sheet of brass; solder it to the brass wire. Make two lead bearings, or plugs, for the ends of the propeller-shaft tube by pouring molten lead or babbitt, the latter being preferable, into a hole bored in a block of wood having a nail, of the same diameter as the shaft, in the center. When cold, the nail is easily pulled out, leaving a hole for the pro-

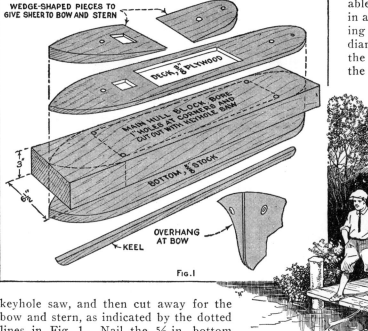

WEDGE-SHAPED PIECES TO GIVE SHEER TO BOW AND STERN

DECK, ⅜" PLYWOOD

MAIN HULL BLOCK BORE 1" HOLES AT CORNERS AND CUT OUT WITH KEYHOLE SAW

3"

6½"

BOTTOM, ⅝" STOCK

KEEL

OVERHANG AT BOW

Fig. 1

keyhole saw, and then cut away for the bow and stern, as indicated by the dotted lines in Fig. 1. Nail the ⅝-in. bottom board firmly to the main block, and you are ready to install your power plant.

The steam engine best adapted to this model is a small upright type, in which the crankshaft runs through the center of

peller shaft. File the plugs to a taper, so that they can be driven into the ends of the brass tube. The plug at the propeller end can be driven in permanently, but that at the other end should be loose enough to be taken out when assembling the various parts. Some sort of thrust washer, which may be a battery nut, for example, should be used between propeller and bearing.

It is almost impossible to line up an engine with a long propeller shaft accurately enough so that it will not bind, without using a universal joint. The latter, however, is simply made and permits the shaft to turn very freely at all times. Two brass or tin strips are cut, perforated and bent as shown, one for the flywheel and the other for the inner end of the propeller shaft. They are connected by means of a brass-wire "spider," shown in Fig. 2.

Most cheap steam engines have a lead flywheel and hub, and the latter can be drilled a short depth to receive the small brass screw that holds the universal arm. A drop of solder will fasten it more securely. Having assembled your propeller shaft, bearings, etc., in the boat, you can solder the universal arm to the inner end of the shaft and insert the spider. When all turns freely, fasten the engine securely to the bottom of the boat with screws. At this point, you can test the boat out in the water, first having given the hull a coat of paint on the outside to prevent water soaking in. Also it would be well to set a tin shield around the engine, as high as the universal and open in front, so that the wood will not scorch.

Tin, lined with asbestos, such as is used in pipes for hot-air furnaces, is excellent material for this shield. Fasten the upper end of the propeller shaft tube to a notched crossbar so that it will not vibrate.

Assuming that your newly launched liner meets the "engineer's" specifications and expected performance, finish up with the deck and cabins. The main cabin, directly over the engine, is made of ⅜ or ¼-in. stuff, and lined with tin and asbestos. The roof is also of tin, asbestos-lined, with a large funnel soldered over the opening for the top of the engine. This funnel

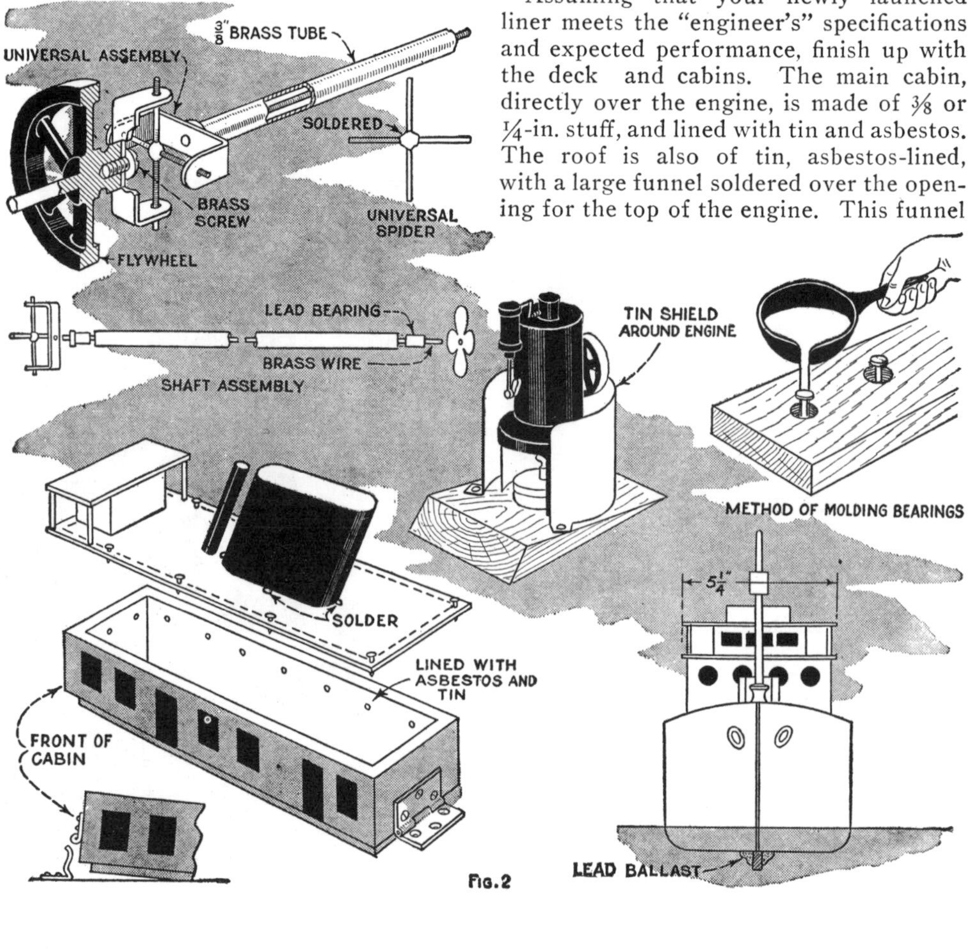

⅜" BRASS TUBE

UNIVERSAL ASSEMBLY

SOLDERED

BRASS SCREW

UNIVERSAL SPIDER

FLYWHEEL

LEAD BEARING

BRASS WIRE

SHAFT ASSEMBLY

TIN SHIELD AROUND ENGINE

METHOD OF MOLDING BEARINGS

SOLDER

LINED WITH ASBESTOS AND TIN

FRONT OF CABIN

5¼"

LEAD BALLAST

FIG. 2

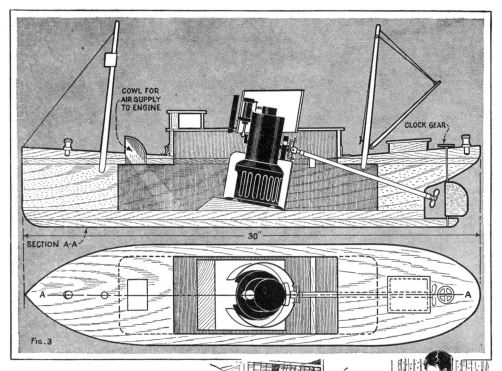

COWL FOR AIR SUPPLY TO ENGINE

CLOCK GEAR

SECTION A-A

30"

A — A

FIG. 3

must be of generous proportions, so that it can carry off the heat without danger of setting the boat on fire. The entire cabin is hinged at the back so that it may be tilted up when refueling or filling up the boiler. The catch at the front end can be made of tin or sheet brass. A solid block of wood will serve for the wheelhouse and also for the after cabin or hatch, which has no function except for appearance.

The rudder is of galvanized sheet iron or brass, with a large clock gear at the top of the rudder post for turning it. Masts, capstans, crow's-nest, etc., are made as indicated in Fig 3. An important item is the lead ballast, two triangular strips of lead, on the sides of the keel.

Paint the hull a bright red below the water line, black above, and deckhouses cream, with doors, windows and portholes outlined in green. Varnish the decks, and give the funnel a red band at the top.

Rubber Gasket for High Pressures

Even the best grades of sheet-rubber packing for use with high-pressure steam work will sometimes blow out under pressures of 150 or 200 lb., while the cheaper grades are seldom satisfactory for pressures over 100 lb. But the latter can be used for high-pressure work if it is prepared in the following way: Cut out the gasket or washer in the usual way and give one side an application of fairly thick liquid shellac. Have ready some cuttings made by using a coarse rasp on a piece of babbitt. Lead raspings will do in most cases, but the babbitt is better. Sprinkle the raspings freely over the sticky surface. Install the gasket in the usual way and tighten well after the joint is heated up with steam. So prepared, a gasket will seldom leak, nor will it blow out any quicker than those made of the more expensive material.—James E. Noble, Toronto, Can.

Device Helps to Reline Brake Bands

When relining auto brake bands, the jig shown in the drawing will be found of great assistance. It is made of ¼ by 2-in. flat-iron stock, bent double as shown. A small pin to fit the rivet holes in the bands is welded on as indicated, and a hole the size of the diameter of the pin, and exactly in line with it, is drilled in the opposite side of the jig. In use, the brake band and lining are held in the jig, which is clamped in the vise. The hole in the jig guides the worker in drilling holes through the lining, the pin fitting in the hole of the band directly underneath.—A. C. Cole, Chicago, Ill.

Laying Out Angles Accurately

Dividing a circle into equal parts represented by degrees, and the further subdivision of these degrees into minutes, is a task that few mechanics accomplish accurately. However, here is a simple method of laying out angles by making use of the 18-hole and 27-hole index plates that are provided with a universal milling-machine dividing head. This method is based on the fact that 40 turns of the index crank are necessary to cause the work to make a complete revolution. Hence it is obvious that each turn advances the work an angle of 360 divided by 40, or 9°. To subdivide this angle, use an index plate having a number of holes being an even multiple of nine. With an 18-hole plate a turn from one hole to the next represents ½°, or 30 min., and to the second 1°. By using the 27-hole plate, the movement from one hole to the next equals ⅓°, or 20 min. As an example, suppose you want to scratch two lines that

make an angle with each other of 20° 20 min. Proceed as follows: Set the work up in the dividing head and, with the 27-hole plate set on the index crankshaft, scribe a center line with the surface gauge. Two complete turns of the crank give 18°, and a turn equal to 7 times the distance from hole to hole (or 7 holes) is ⅞°, or 2° 20 min. By following this method, any angle can be laid out quickly and accurately. If you have to lay out an odd number of minutes, the following will be of help. It gives the number of minutes that a one-hole movement in the different standard index plates makes: 15-hole plate, 36 min.; 16-hole plate, 33.75 min.; 17-hole plate, 31.76 min.; 19-hole plate, 28.42 min.; 20-hole plate, 27.00 min.; 21-hole plate, 25.71 min.; 23-hole plate, 23.47 min.; 29-hole plate, 18.62 min.; 31-hole plate, 17.41 min.; 33-hole plate, 16.36 min.; 37-hole plate, 14.59 min.; 39-hole plate, 13.84 min.; 41-hole plate, 13.17 min.; 47-hole plate, 11.48 min., and 49-hole plate, 11.02 minutes.

Holder Prevents Soiling of Blueprints

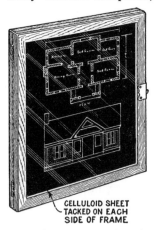

CELLULOID SHEET TACKED ON EACH SIDE OF FRAME

A Wisconsin builder, noticing that his workmen soiled and eventually ruined many valuable blueprints, devised a simple holder to protect them. It consists of two wood frames, hinged together and covered with celluloid sheets, obtained at a near-by auto-accessory store. The blueprints were inserted in the frame so that two floor plans or two elevations were exposed to view at either side. A latch was provided to hold the frames together and facilitate the removal or replacement of the prints.—G. E. Hendrickson, Argyle, Wis.

¶Stain putty to match the finish before applying it on high-grade work.

Prevention of Scale When Hardening Steel

One of the things to watch out for when hardening steel is the scale or oxide that forms on it. This is a matter for consideration when the piece must be true to size after hardening, because scraping off the scale usually makes it undersize. To avoid this, proceed as follows: Instead of placing the piece to be hardened in an open fire, as is usually done, put it in a container made from a length of pipe, threaded at each end for a cap or plug to shut out the air, and place the container in the fire. No scale can form because no air reaches the piece to be hardened. As a matter of fact, any sealed metal container can be used, depending on what is at hand. It is brought to the required heat in the usual way and quenched in water or brine.—James McIntyre, Hartford, Conn.

Counterboring Washers

Some washers, about ⅛ in. thick, had to be thinned down to 1/32 in. The only way to do this was by counterboring,

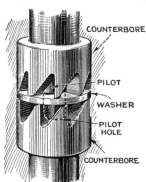

which involved the problem of holding the washers securely. I obtained duplicate counterbores and removed the pilot from one. This I held in a chuck bolted to the machine table. The one with the pilot still in place was held in the drill-press spindle. With this set-up I laid a washer on top of the pilotless counterbore, and brought the other one down until the pilot passed through the washer and into the pilot hole of the stationary counterbore. A glance at the set-up will show that one of the counterbores will cut. If the washer turns around with the moving counterbore, the stationary one will cut, and if the washer bites into the stationary counterbore, the moving one will cut.—Harry Moore, Hamilton, Can.

A Strong and Convenient Strap Holder Is a Timesaver for the Harness Repair Man

Clamp for the Harness Repair Man

Belt makers, harness repair men and other tradesmen who have to work with leather, rubber or fabric strips on a bench, will find the illustrated spring clamp very useful. The leaf of a discarded auto spring is bolted to the underside of the workbench at the end most convenient, and, through the eye of the spring, is fastened a double hook made from a length of ⅜-in. round steel with the ends sharpened. When splitting or trimming a belt or strap, it is placed flush with the end of the bench, as shown, the hooks being raised and then released to hold the strip securely at the far end, while the other is kept immovable by the left hand.

Handy Pocket Saw

Nearly every mechanical device used around the home seems to be assembled with screws. When tightening or loosening them one is apt to spoil the slot in the head, but the slot can readily be deepened by means of a short piece of

hacksaw blade. It will be found handy to keep such a piece on one's keyring.

Wire Mesh, Replacing One Wall of Storage Shed for Seed Corn, Permits Proper Ventilation

Storage Shed for Seed Corn

Seed corn should have plenty of ventilation and also be adequately protected from chickens, mice and rats. A good storage shed which meets these requirements has been constructed by an Indiana farmer, and is shown in the accompanying photograph. The corn is held on a number of wooden racks near one end, the wall at this end of the shed being replaced with wire mesh. This permits plenty of air and sunlight. The foundation and floor are well fitted to prevent the entrance of rodents.—J. C. Allen, Lafayette, Ind.

Stop for Reaming with Drill Press

In the manufacture of certain interchangeable machine parts using a taper pin, difficulty was experienced in getting all the machine-reamed holes exactly the same depth. Various stops were tried on the drill-press spindle, but they always slipped and it took too long to set them up. Finally the operator hit upon the idea of drilling a hole of the correct depth in a parallel on which the piece was taper-reamed. The reamer cuts through the piece and the end comes against the bottom of the drilled hole in the parallel, which gives a positive stop. This method eliminates all worry about the reamer slid-ing up into the chuck or the collar on the spindle slipping, and, of course, the time required for setting up is reduced to a minimum.—Arthur F. Parker, Philipsburg, Pennsylvania.

Tinning Cast Iron

To solder cast iron or fill a hole or crack in it is difficult, because the surface cannot be tinned readily. Grinding, filing or polishing does very little good, and a really satisfactory job of soldering is seldom obtained. However, a railroad shopman accidentally discovered that the surface could be effectively prepared for tinning by sandblasting. This method is especially adapted to the tinning of bearings that are to be babbitted. The sandblasting cuts away the carbon in the cast iron, but has little effect on the metal itself, except that it leaves it bright and clean. The solder clings to this clean surface almost as readily at is does to steel or tin plate. Sandblasting greatly assists in obtaining a good welding job with a gas torch. When tinning the sandblasted surface, regular soldering flux is used.—Avery E. Granville, LaGrange, Ill.

Milk-Can Rack for Auto Truck

One farmer who delivered milk to a neighboring town with a truck, was unable to load it with feed and other products on his return trip, because the empty cans, although light in weight, required all the space. To overcome this difficulty, the farmer built special racks on the sides of the truck to hold the empty cans, as shown in the photo. This left plenty of space for whatever extra load he wished to carry back home.

Racks Built on Sides of Auto Truck Hold Empty Milk Cans

Designing Radiator Furniture

By THOS. W. BENSON

THE USUAL steam or hot-water radiators are seldom things of beauty and when making furniture to improve their appearance, it is well to remember that the inclosure will influence the effectiveness of the heating system. Practically all the heat from the radiator is dissipated by convection, that is, by having the heat carried off by the air flowing over and through the radiator. Radiator inclosures sometimes increase, but too often decrease, the flow of air and thus lower the heating effect of the radiator.

In the accompanying illustration six general types of inclosures are shown diagrammatically. The following paragraphs

rate of flow and improves the heating. A change in proportions will usually result in reduced efficiency and the arrangement shown is possibly the best from the heating standpoint. Such an inclosure, on the other hand, does not prevent smudging of the wall and is not very decorative.

If screens are added, as in Fig. 2, with the opening B as in the previous case and A equal to R, the screens reduce the air flow and the arrangement is but 5 per cent better than the plain radiator.

In order to prevent smudging of the wall by dust carried up by the rising stream of warm air, it is necessary to use a solid top and discharge the warm air

will enable one to select furniture that is in keeping with conditions met with in his particular heating plant.

In Fig. 1, when dimension B is equal to R, the radiator will be 10 per cent more effective than before. This is due to the solid screen forming a well-defined path for the air circulation, which increases the

from the front of the radiator. To retain full effectiveness, the inclosure must have openings proportioned as shown in Fig. 3, where D is equal to R and C is twice B. The structure is rather high but any lessening of the discharge opening will reduce the flow of warm air and the radiator becomes that much less effective.

The practice of mounting a shelf over a radiator for flowers or books, as in Fig. 4, is a very poor one, and affects heat radiation to a greater extent than would seem possible. When the width of the shelf E is but half of dimension A in Fig. 1, there is a drop of 10 per cent in heat radiation. When E equals A, the reduction is 20 per cent and, in extreme cases, where E is one and a half times A, the loss is 35 per cent. Putting a screen in front, as in Fig. 5, with the solid top E equal to A, results in a 30-per-cent loss, but an all-screen inclosure, as in Fig. 6, reduces the effectiveness only 5 per cent.

Summing up, it is apparent that any attempt to use a solid-top radiator inclosure, except when it is arranged as in Fig. 3, will reduce the heat thrown off by the radiator. It is possible to disguise the radiator with open or screen-top inclosures, while still retaining heating efficiency, but the disadvantage of smudging the walls is still present. Loss of effectiveness of the radiators can be offset by carrying higher temperatures in hot-water systems and higher pressures in steam-heating systems, but the forcing of the heater leads to coal losses. Other alternatives are the use of larger radiators, or fans to circulate the air faster. It is for the individual to decide whether his heating plant will permit the use of radiator furniture, and these facts will aid in an intelligent decision.

Fitting Linoleum Snugly against Raised Concrete Border

Cutting linoleum to fit snugly against a raised concrete border is a task that re-

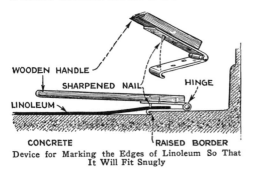

Device for Marking the Edges of Linoleum So That It Will Fit Snugly

quires considerable care, and the usual method of scribing is impractical in this particular case. The work is facilitated by the use of the simple tool shown in the illustration. It consists of a 4-in. strap hinge, screwed to a 12-ft. length of 1 by 2-in. board. The free portion of the hinge is bent over as indicated, and a sharpened nail or screw is driven into one of the holes in the other part, the point of the nail being directly over the bent edge and consequently directly in line with the edge of the raised border. In use, the loose leaf is fitted over the edge of the linoleum as shown, and the handle is depressed to make a punch mark, which indicates the exact point where the linoleum is to be cut to make a snug fit against the concrete border. The hinge is then slid along the edge and the operation repeated at 1-ft. intervals, leaving a row of punch marks that serve as a guide in scribing the cutting line. This device eliminates the frequent shifting of the linoleum necessary when scribing in the usual way.—Mary Gleeson, San Francisco, Calif.

Turning a Large Pulley in a Small Lathe

We had a number of 16-in. pulleys to turn down on a 14-in. lathe, a job which seemed impossible at first thought. However, the illustrated set-up shows how the work was done. A mandrel, on which the pulley made a running fit so that it could be rotated, was mounted 1¼ in. off center, as indicated. A lathe dog was attached to the mandrel near the tailstock, the dog being large enough to project beyond the ways of the lathe bed in order to prevent the mandrel from turning. A bolt was fastened to the faceplate to serve as a dog for driving the pulley.—C. Kugler, Philadelphia, Pa.

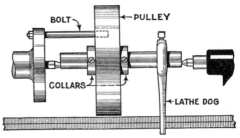

Set-Up Showing How a 16-In. Pulley Was Turned in a 14-In. Lathe

Sawdust Cakes for Kindling

Where a great deal of sawdust accumulates, as on the farm, good kindling cakes for the kitchen stove can be made as follows: Get a length of 3-in. tile and stand it on the fluted end on a smooth board. Make a plunger from a section of a small log and fit a handle to it on one end. Mix up sawdust with enough flour paste to make a crumbly but not too sticky mass. Throw some of this into the tile and tamp it down with the plunger. Then lift the tile off the cake and proceed to make another. When dry and hard, the cakes should be piled carefully in a dry place. One or two cakes will suffice to start the fire either by sprinkling with kerosene or placing them over lighted newspapers.—L. B. Robbins, Harwich, Mass.

How to Cut Duplicate Pieces on a Bandsaw

It is often necessary to cut out a number of duplicate pieces on a bandsaw. Sawing three or four at once means, of course, quite a timesaving, but the pieces must be securely held together during the operation. An easy means to this end is to cut two or more tapered slots, about 1 in. deep, in two adjacent edges of the material as indicated and then drive a small wedge into each slot. The wedges will hold the pieces together firmly and prevent their slipping apart while the sawing is done.—Neil Nelson, Kansas City, Mo.

WEDGE
SAW SLOT

¶ Aluminum castings may be ground on a disk grinder without filling the abrasive material, if a coat of paraffin is applied to the wheel.

Rack Constructed from Lengths of Pipe Facilitates the Draining and Airing of Milk Cans

Rack for Draining Milk Cans

An Alabama farmer has constructed a simple rack for draining and airing milk cans. It consists of two lengths of iron pipe, arranged along a fence as shown. One of them is held securely in place by crosspieces, which are nailed to the posts and have holes drilled through them for the pipe. The other length of pipe is held in a similar way in holes drilled through the posts. The milk cans are set on the lower pipe, upside down, and lean against the upper pipe. To remove them the handle is grasped and the cans are dislodged from the lower pipe.—J. C. Allen, Lafayette, Ind.

Accurate Measuring of Keyways and Grooves

When cutting keyways and grooves in machine parts, a very simple method of measuring them accurately is to use a pair of steel wedges, or an adjustable parallel with which every shop man is familiar. Place the wedges in the groove and slide them together until they are tight in the groove, letting the ends project. Then, by using the micrometer on the outside of the wedges, a true size can be obtained.

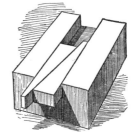

How to Handle Brass Pipe

By HORACE G. WOODWARD

I AM "right handy with tools" and do a great deal of repair work about our place. When preparing to make a new service connection with the city water main, I decided to have all pipes carrying water for the house of brass. Before starting the job, however, I made some inquiries about brass pipe and to get "kinks" of knowledge about such jobs. I am passing on some of the main points which may be useful to others doing similar jobs.

It is necessary to remember that brass, being an easier metal to work, does not require the force that would be applied to iron pipe, either in the vise or the wrench, or the stock and dies. Working in standard-iron-pipe-size brass pipe, it is desirable, for the vise, to split an iron-pipe coupling for such-size pipe with a hacksaw, lay a sheet of lead over each half and insert these on opposite sides of the brass pipe in the vise.

I was surprised to learn that threading may be done without any lubricant at all, but a characteristic squeak is then produced, which may be avoided by using soapy water or oil. The dies are the same as for iron pipe, but should have perfect teeth, and these in the best dies are shaped to advance in the work like a cultivator plow, lifting out the shaving. Experts say that the stock should not be jerked when cutting threads on brass pipe, but pulled with a steady movement in order to insure perfect threads, and I find this method gives fine results.

Another important thing in either brass or iron pipe is not to put too many deep threads on the pipe; six or seven perfect threads are sufficient, and more will simply weaken the pipe beyond the joint. Fittings should have a good reinforcing bead, and there is a fitting available that will extend upon the pipe beyond the perfect threads, giving great strength to the joint. The fittings should be of good quality brass, not iron.

Friction wrenches should be used on the pipe, and to turn elbows or tees, I use a monkey wrench, the jaws extending beside the part that projects sideways. A pipe wrench may be used on brass pipe, but has the same objection as on galvanized-iron pipe, cutting the pipe excessively if not carefully handled. Pipe wrenches should not be used at all on fittings. Powdered rosin, applied to the faces of the vise clamps or the friction faces of the wrench, will overcome the tendency to slip on the pipe.

The amateur worker, and many plumbers, may not realize the importance of reaming both iron and brass pipe to remove the burr at the ends. I have used a round file for this purpose with satisfactory results. I have observed in $\frac{1}{2}$-in. pipe a burr formed by a wheel cutter which reduced the capacity of the line fully one quarter. When pipe and fittings are accurately threaded no filling or dope is needed in the joints, but a paste of linseed oil and red lead is used by many plumbers to insure tight joints.

Brass pipe for laying in the ground should not be ordinary "yellow" brass, but annealed or otherwise suited to sustain settling strains.

Cementing Tool Tangs in Handles

A quick-setting cement for anchoring the tangs of small tools in wood or fiber handles can be made from pure shellac. Buy the dry shellac and dissolve it in just enough alcohol to make a paste, which is then put in a tin dish or can and ignited. Immediately after the flame has died down, and before the shellac has a chance to cool and harden, fill the handles with the cement thus made, and drive in the tangs, which should be heated. When cool, the cement will be found to be very strong and practically waterproof.

Holding Small Steel Articles for Photographing

When small steel or iron articles are to be photographed without showing any support, a magnet can be used to hold them as shown in the drawings. Fig. 1 shows the general arrangement. The background is a sheet of cardboard which is held to the base by triangular pieces of wood at each side. Behind the background and close to it, a strong permanent magnet is supported by a wooden rod, to which it is fastened with a few turns of copper wire. If the object is set against the cardboard, the magnet will hold it securely. When one item has been photographed it is simply lifted off and the next one placed in position. In this manner a great deal of time can be saved and retouching is reduced to a minimum because no support shows on the photo. A discarded magneto magnet is suitable for

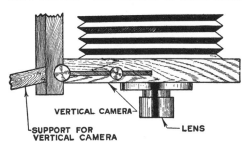

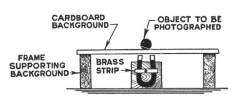

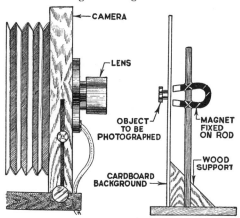

Permanent Magnet, Securely Supported on Rod, Holds Small Iron and Steel Objects for Photographing

this purpose and, for very heavy objects, several magnets may be placed side by side, or a small electromagnet may be used instead. The current is taken from

Spherical and Other Irregularly Shaped Pieces Can Be Held Securely on Flat Surfaces

a few dry cells, and as the current is only used for short periods of time, the batteries will last very long. Even with a vertical camera, a magnet support is sometimes valuable, especially if the object is irregular in shape or spherical, so that it may roll about or tip over during the process of photographing, particularly if some machinery is working close by, as in factories. The arrangement in this case is shown in Fig. 2. The magnet can be held by a block of wood, a strip of brass and a wood screw being used to fasten it to the block. Do not use a steel strip for this purpose as it will short-circuit the magnet.

This method is not confined to steel or iron objects. Many other articles can be held as suggested if a short iron pin can be inserted in them. For instance, if a smoker's pipe is to be photographed, an iron pin may be placed in the bore. The magnet will attract this and the object will cling to the background exactly like a solid steel body.—C. A. Oldroyd, Barrow-in-Furness, Lancs., England.

¶When the drawers in a chest, cabinet, or other storage place for tools, stick or are hard to pull, apply a little grease along the sides and other bearing surfaces.

Kinks on Accurate Drilling

I have been using a few kinks in laying out jig work for the drill press with great

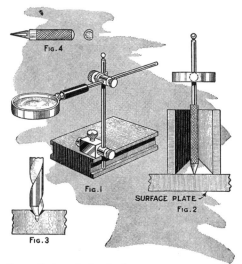

Sharp Tools and the Application of a Few Handy Kinks Will Help in Drilling Accurate Holes

success. A large magnifying glass, held by a clamp so that the worker's hands are free, is better than a small one. One method of holding the glass is shown in Fig. 1. It can be set to any angle. If no precision center punch is available, the surface gauge or a V-block can be used as in Fig. 2. This keeps the punch at right angles to the work. A flat scriber of the kind shown in Fig. 4 should be used, as a round one sometimes causes inaccurate work. The punch should be accurately ground to a sharp point, which will facilitate marking the work at the intersection of two lines. Use a center combination drill of a diameter smaller than that of the center-punch mark, and make the angle sharper. For instance, if the center punch has an angle of 60°, that of the drill should be about 70°. Then follow this up with a drill like the one shown in Fig. 3. This has a tendency to make the drill follow the hole. If dividers are used, keep them sharp at all times. Whenever possible, use a scale graduated in fiftieths or hundredths of an inch, because the lines on these scales are finer than those on more coarsely graduated rules. Such fine graduations enable you to set your dividers more accurately. If you are not sure of

the accuracy of a layout, drill small holes, that is, smaller than the finished size, insert the drill rod of the correct size and measure over all with a micrometer. If there is any error, use a round file to enlarge the holes so that the next-size drill corrects the error. I have found that it pays to blue the work, even though it costs more than rubbing bluestone on it, as this enables you to see the lines more clearly. If the above rules are strictly followed, and the tools are kept in good condition, no trouble will be experienced in drilling holes within limits from .003 to .005-in. center-to-center distance.—Charles Kugler, Philadelphia, Pa.

Spotting Wall Studs

The drawing shows how a carpenters' hammer may be used to space off for locating points in baseboards, hook strips, chair rails, etc., at which to nail them to the wall studs through the plaster. After finding one stud, by sounding or other methods, place the driving face of the hammer at this point and roll it forward over the claws, until the end of the handle strikes the surface of the board. The end has previously been scored, as shown, so that the mark comes exactly in line with the next stud, 16 in. from the first. This

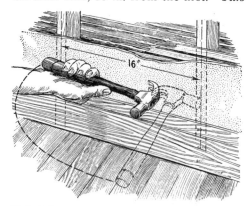

Marked Hammer Handle Enables Quick Measurement for Stud Nails in Baseboards and the Like

is an accurate and quicker method than sounding for each nail or using a rule.

❡Crude petroleum oil, diluted with gasoline, makes a good brown wood stain, resembling dark-oak finish.

SHOP NOTES

Two Tables in Art Moderne

By E. R. HAAN

INTERESTING, attractive furniture in ultra-modern style is the latest fad. Lamps, tables, stands, etc., in fantastic, bizarre color combinations, which make these items truly novel, can be seen and purchased at most art and many of the larger department stores. Although generally of simple construction, this type of

Bizarre, Colorful and Attractive Furniture, Executed in Art Moderne, Has Become Extremely Popular, Entire Rooms Being Furnished and Decorated in This Style

kind of veneer is satisfactory for making the table, as the surface is to be painted and beauty of the grain therefore need not be taken into account. Thirteen pieces of veneer, 16 in. wide, are used for making the end table. The dimensions of the various pieces are given in Fig. 2. As the method of joining these pieces together must not show on the finished product, 2-in. wood screws are used for this purpose, five of them being driven through adjoining sections, and spaced at equal intervals so that the strain will be well distributed. It is absolutely necessary to drill holes in both adjoining pieces to accommodate the screws. To drill these holes accurately, prick-punch a spot for the center hole, $\frac{7}{16}$ in. from the edge. Then prick-punch the centers of the two end holes and finally the remaining two, which must be located halfway between the center and the end holes. Drill the holes a trifle larger than the largest part of the screw shank, as in Fig. 1. Counterbore these holes in order to permit sinking the screw heads below the surface. After this has been

furniture is, at present, rather costly. Many admirers of the work, therefore, do not feel justified in purchasing it, but they may, with very little trouble and care, make it themselves at a fraction of the cost by following the instructions contained in this article. As small tables and stands undoubtedly have the widest range of usefulness and popular appeal, an occasional table and a davenport end table are herewith described and illustrated. Although the exact size, arrangement and color scheme of these items are given, it is permissible to construct them either smaller or larger, and the details may also be varied to suit the ideas of the builder.

The davenport end table is made of $\frac{7}{8}$-in. five-ply veneer, which is more expensive than ordinary wood, but has the advantage of being much stronger, and will not warp or crack through atmospheric changes. You can purchase the veneer already cut to specified sizes at most mills that handle this stock. The very cheapest

done, the drilled piece is placed on the piece to which it is to be attached, and holes, smaller than the threaded section of the screw, are drilled in the end of the second piece. These holes enable you to drive the screws into the wood easily, and without risk of cracking the wood. To reduce the friction of the screws entering the wood, smear soap or beeswax over the threads. When driving in the screws, care should be taken to avoid slipping of the screwdriver, as this may mar the surface and such marks are very difficult to cover when the table is being finished.

The use of a screwdriver bit in a carpenters' brace is recommended for driving the screws, although any ordinary screwdriver can be used. Fig. 3 shows part of the table joined in this way. When each piece is fitted to its neighbor, the outside edges must be perfectly flush and smooth. As the stock will not always fit exactly, it

surface is smoothed with fine sandpaper.

It must be remembered, however, that it is nearly impossible to apply the design, and to finish the surface properly after the table is completely assembled. Therefore, it has been found convenient to assemble the pieces into four separate sections, three of which are shown in Fig. 4. The remaining section consists of the top, the sides and the upper shelf. The four sections are finished on all sides, but not on the edges, before they are assembled. The finishing of the edges is done when the table is completely assembled, as they have to be planed down and sandpapered smooth to match each other; the table is therefore assembled temporarily, the edges carefully fitted, and the sections taken apart again for finishing.

Water putty or "plastic wood" is used to fill the counterbored holes into which the screw heads are sunk. Force the filler in firmly, allowing a small quantity to project above the surrounding surface. When it has thoroughly dried, which takes from 24 to 48 hours, use a sharp chisel to cut off the surplus neatly. Having done this, apply a coat of shellac all over. This application should be quite

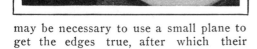

may be necessary to use a small plane to get the edges true, after which their

liberal on the edges where the crossgrain of the core of the veneer is exposed. Allow the first coat of shellac to dry overnight and then apply a second coat. When this is dried, rub the surface down with sandpaper held on a smooth block of wood. Steel wool can be used to remove particles of dust, which may have collected on the surface of the shellac while this was drying. The surface is cleaned thoroughly and a first coat of one of the new quick-drying enamels, or lacquer, is then applied. The entire surface of all the pieces is enameled or lacquered black.

At this point you may become rather anxious to hasten the process of applying successive coats of paint, but each coat must be allowed to dry thoroughly before it can be rubbed down and the next one applied. The enamel or lacquer may dry to the touch within a few moments and may seem hard after a few hours, but do not misjudge the true condition by these appearances. Wait at least 48 hours before you attempt rubbing down the ridges and removing the dust specks that are sure to be found on the dried surface. When painting, which can be done either with a brush or by means of a spray gun, the utmost care should be observed. First, the shop or room where the work is done should be clean, and the air should be as free from dust as possible. Therefore, do not sweep the floor, use a circular saw or a sander, or any other machinery, which is likely to raise dust, just before you apply the paint. Also, it is preferable to keep the windows and doors shut, especially on a windy day, when dust flies about everywhere. Your brush should be thoroughly clean. This is impossible if it is stirred in some old, exposed turpentine, or thinner, and then slapped against a wood surface. This is a dust-collecting rather than a dust-removing process. If the condition of a brush is doubtful, it should first be cleaned thoroughly in the solvent of the paint used, which is turpentine in case of ordinary paints and enamels, and thinner in case of lacquers. Thereafter, give it a thorough washing in clean, soapy water, rinse it well and set it away to dry. Dry brushes should be wrapped up in paper to keep out the dust. Before actually opening the lid of the paint can, raise it all around about ⅛ in., and blow the dust

away from the edge of the cover, for paint cans are often packed in sawdust, and some of the dust gets under the edge of the cover, dropping into the paint the moment the cover is removed. When the paint can is not in constant use, keep the cover on. Use a piece of cloth that leaves no lint, or a wide brush, to wipe off the surface just previous to applying the paint.

The precautions just mentioned may seem absurdly "fussy" but these seemingly insignificant details are really the things that count in doing good work, which, under ordinary slovenly methods, is entirely impossible. This is the secret of the beautiful finish which is usually credited only to experienced, capable painters. Brush the paint over the surface evenly, flowing on a moderate quantity, so that brush marks will even out. However, do not apply too much for this may take weeks or months to dry hard. Quick work is necessary when lacquer is used, as it cannot be brushed over a second time, but this must be done immediately after it is applied.

Rubbing down each coat, after it has dried thoroughly, is another trick for obtaining a flawless finish. Fine sandpaper, held on a block, may be used conservatively, that is, it should not be used too vigorously and should not be rubbed on one spot too long. It is much better to use the finest grade of garnet paper on a block, as shown in Fig. 6, keeping the surface well covered with water to prevent the accumulation of loose paint on the paper, which would ruin its effectiveness as an abrasive. After the surface has been cleaned and dried, the second coat of paint or lacquer may be applied. Three or four coats are necessary to permit a good rubdown to a perfect finish. Be sure to use the same kind of paint for each coat. The last coat is rubbed down with greater care than the preceding ones. After the garnet-paper rubdown with water, the surface is dried, and powdered rottenstone is used with rubbing oil to eliminate all the small scratches. A small piece of cloth, tightly wadded, is used to do this rubbing, which will result in a smooth, glasslike finish, rewarding you for your painstaking efforts. In the absence of rubbing oil, use ordinary sweet oil or crude oil.

The design is then applied. Modernistic furniture designs consist mainly of straight lines and arcs, combined to make simple geometrical forms. Fig. 7 shows a neat, attractive design, which may be followed. Overwrought, intricate designs in many colors are to be avoided for this is contrary to the

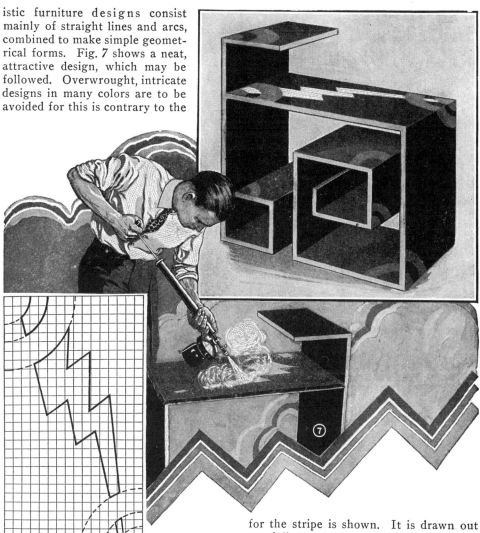

idea of simplicity, which modern art seeks to express. The design illustrated rendered in two colors, such as Chinese, mandarin or oriental red, with aluminum or silver, or a light gray on a black background, stands out in bold relief and is very distinctive. In this case the double quadrants were painted red, the irregular stripe or "lightning flash" aluminum, and all the edges aluminum. The designs can best be applied by means of stencils. This is comparatively easy and accurate results can be obtained. In the lower left-hand corner of Fig. 7, the template

for the stripe is shown. It is drawn out carefully on paper and is then cut out with a sharp razor blade. The small sections fit between the two bands of the quadrants. It is a good idea to cut the stencil for the quadrants at the same time, to be sure that the stencils fit together well. When the stencils are ready, get some rubber cement and apply a thin coat to the underside of the stencil, just around the edge of the cut-outs. Allow the cement to become apparently dry before pressing the stencil down on the surface on which the design is to be applied. The edges of the cut-outs must adhere to the surface securely, or the paint, upon being applied, will run under the stencil and ruin the work. A small hand spray gun of the kind shown in Fig. 7 has been found handy for applying the design, care being taken to thin the paint to the consistency most suitable for spraying and adjust the gun to the same end.

After the sections of the table have been completely finished, they are assembled and screwed together securely as described above. The remaining counterbored holes are filled, and several coats of paint are applied over the putty spots, each coat being rubbed down to match with the surrounding surface. The photo in the upper right-hand corner of Fig. 7 shows the davenport end table finished. Parts of the design are repeated at several corners.

Fig. 8 shows a useful occasional table,

top. Veneer, however, is necessary for the top, as it is of quite large size, and ordinary stock would have a tendency to warp, besides being more easily cracked and broken. All the other parts of this table consist of scrap pieces which anyone can find around the house or shop. They are cut carefully, planed and sandpapered smooth, and assembled as indicated. The color scheme in this case was jade green and oriental red on a black background, which was found very effective. The center-post braces are painted red, the post itself being black. The small square notches in the corners of the base are green, and the edges of the shelves may be painted either red or green, and similarly the edge of the top, although this does not show in the photo. The method of fastening the top to the center post is shown in the lower right-hand detail. The top may carry any suitable design.

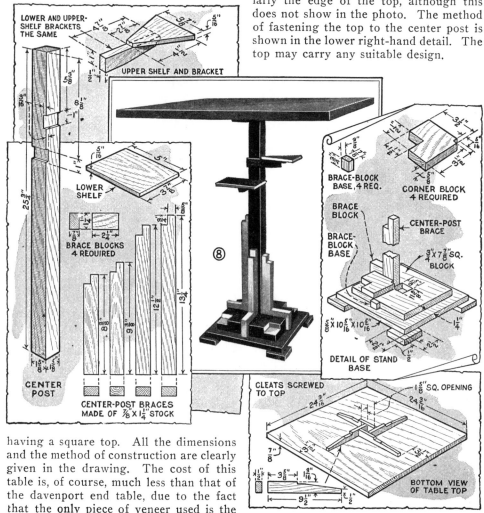

having a square top. All the dimensions and the method of construction are clearly given in the drawing. The cost of this table is, of course, much less than that of the davenport end table, due to the fact that the only piece of veneer used is the

A 6-in Bench Shaper
by J. V. Romig

THE VALUE of the shaper as a machine tool is appreciated by every mechanic, but the man in the small shop, much as he may appreciate the advantage of such a tool, is not always in a position to purchase it. Here, however, is a shaper that can be made in any small shop at a reasonable cost, and which, on work within its capacity, will rapidly pay for the labor and slight expense of building.

There are two types of shaper in general use, the push-cut and the draw-cut. Each has its advantages; the draw-cut shaper, for example, is the better for tool work, where profiling to a layout line is to be done, since the layout line faces the operator, and the tool, cutting on the back or draw stroke, cuts clean to the line. On work of this kind the push-cut shaper, cutting on the forward stroke, breaks off the edge of the work, and makes it much more difficult to work close to the line. In addition to this, the draw-cut type takes heavier cuts with less vibration, as the pressure on the slides and the work is toward the main frame. On the other hand, the push-cut type is better for work in which the tool must be carried at an angle, and it permits the use of gooseneck tools. The advantages of both types are combined in this shaper, by the simple expedient of employing two clapper boxes, one of the push-cut and the other of the draw-cut type, either of which can be used to suit the work in hand.

In addition, and by eliminating a few of the usual components of shaper construction, such as the slide on the ram, a more powerful and rigid tool is obtained. Vertical feed is secured by raising the cross-rail assembly, and angular work is machined by tilting the table. Horizontal movements are obtained in the usual manner, by sliding the table saddle on the cross rail by means of the feed screw.

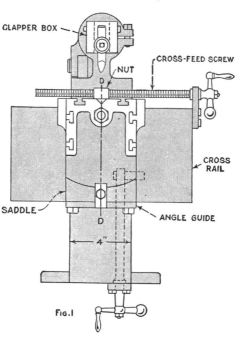

CLAPPER BOX

CROSS-FEED SCREW

NUT

CROSS RAIL

SADDLE

ANGLE GUIDE

D

4"

FIG. I

The main frame of this little shaper is a gray-iron casting, machined to the sizes given in the accompanying drawings. The pattern for the casting is made of white pine, and is quite easy to fashion, even for the amateur patternmaker. All the parts to the right of the frame are cast integral with it, while the parts to the left are separate, and positioned with pins. These portions are the part of the front slide and the base that overhang the center web of the machine, and the portion of the ram bearings at the top. The housings for the gear mechanism do not need any cores, as the shaft holes can be drilled from the solid. Patterns for the remainder of the parts should be made with sufficient allowance for the machining operations.

The ram is made from a length of cold-rolled steel, machined only on its front end for the clapper boxes. The bar should be tested with an indicator, in the lathe, and straightened. It may seem, at first glance, to be rather long, but this is an advantage, as many jobs that would take a longer stroke than 6 in. can still be done by taking two "hitches" of the ram; also, work that is too far from the front slide to be reached by the tool in normal position can be finished by moving the ram forward. The ram slides in two bearings in the main frame, and is kept from turning by the clamping member, which is also connected to the rocker arm below. On angular work, clearance for the tool on the return stroke is effected by turning the ram in the clamp the requisite amount. For all straight shaping or slotting work, the clapper

box is, of course, kept in a vertical position.

The clapper boxes are made of machine steel, to the drawings, and fastened to the ram with taper pins. The draw-cut box is held with two pins, and has an auxiliary toolholder swiveling on a taper pin. The setscrew that holds the tool tight is reached through the hole in the front of the box. The toolholder for the push-cut box is turned from a length of steel, and is held in the box by its lower flange, which fits in the counterbore in the rear of the box. A serrated tool-steel washer is used between the tool and the front. The tools are $\frac{1}{2}$ in. square, or $\frac{1}{2}$ by $\frac{3}{4}$ in.

When machining the main frame, care must be taken to get the ram-bearing holes square with the front slide, both vertically and horizontally. It is therefore best to machine the front slides first, to get a working surface for the subsequent operations. The ram bearings can be fitted with bronze bushings, although this is not essential. Compensation for wear is secured by splitting the bearings and adjusting with the clamping screws. Use oil cups or sight-feed lubricators on the bearings.

The ram is reciprocated by a crankpin on the main gear, the pin carrying a slide which fits the slot in the rocker arm. The crank may be clamped in any position on the gear, permitting

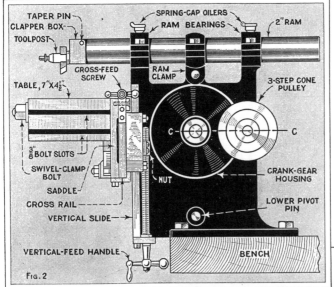

Fig. 2

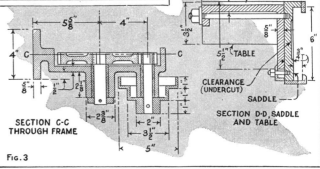

SECTION C-C THROUGH FRAME

SECTION D-D, SADDLE AND TABLE

Fig. 3

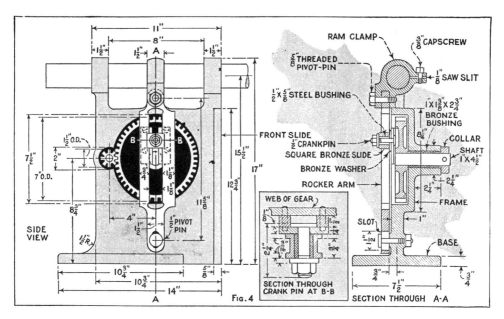

FIG. 4

any variation of stroke from zero to 6 in., the range of the machine. The rocker arm is fastened to the ram clamp with a screwed pin, and is pivoted on a pin at its lower end. The fit in the ram clamp should be snug, so as to eliminate play. Oil holes must be drilled and oil grooves cut to provide for the lubrication of all moving surfaces.

The gears are of No. 12 pitch, the smaller having 15 teeth and the larger 82, with a 1-in. face. The maker, of course, can use other ratios if he desires, but he must be careful to figure the center-to-center distance correctly. The large gear should have a solid-web center, so that it can be slotted for the crank-pin adjustment. Both gears are keyed to their shafts, and

should be a light press fit. The shafts run in bronze bushings. A collar is fitted and pinned to the large shaft, and a three-step cone pulley to the smaller one, as detailed.

The cross-rail assembly is built up of flat cold-rolled steel, as in the drawing. Four ⅜-in. flat-head screws connect the cross-rail proper to the guide pieces, and the holes for these screws are drilled ⅜ in. in all the parts except the ⅝-in. square spacing pieces, which are tapped to secure clamping action. The thin outer plates are fastened with nuts and should be fitted so as to allow free vertical movement, without any play, when they are drawn up tight. Brass shims, 1/16 in. thick, adjusted by ⅜-in. setscrews, regulate the side fit of the slide. All feed screws

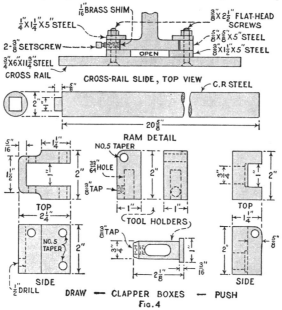

FIG. 4

are ½ in., 20 threads per in., fitted with ball-crank handles. All feed-screw nuts are of bronze, the one for the elevating screw being fitted to the rear right-hand slide plate, and the bearing for the cross-feed to the right-hand side of the rail.

The saddle is a casting, machined as in Fig. 3. It will be noted that the casting is wider at the top than at the bottom; this provision is made because there is greater wear and strain on the top slide than on the bottom one. The worktable

is also a casting, with the bolt slots cored in. It is machined square on all faces, and swiveled to the saddle on a ½-in. bolt near the top face, and clamped near the bottom. The lower edge of the table can be laid off in degrees to facilitate setting up angular work. The three faces of the table enable work of almost any shape to be handled from any angle.

When using the draw-cut clapper box, reverse the belt, so as to obtain slow motion on the return stroke.

Tool Carrier with Hingeless Cover Made from Common Wood Box

Any ordinary wooden box can be made into a serviceable tool box by using a length of rope for a handle. By arranging the rope as shown in the drawing, it

acts not only as a handle but also as a substitute for hinges, and enables one to press the lid on tightly while the box is carried from place to place. Drill a hole in each end of the box, in the center and near the top edge and two holes in the lid, all four being alined as shown. Pass the rope through the holes and splice or knot it. The length of the rope is determined by the size of the box and should be sufficient to allow the lid to be lifted and swung back out of the way when the box is opened. When carrying the box, the top part of the rope is held in the hand, and the weight of the contents causes the lower part of the rope to press down tightly on the top, so as to keep the lid securely in place.—Harry Moore, Hamilton, Can.

Handy Gate for the Farm

Always open to pedestrians but closed to stock, the gate shown in the drawing has been found both practical and con-

venient. The trouble of opening and closing the gate is eliminated and it cannot easily be left open by mistake. It consists of four posts set into the earth, about 3 ft. apart. The gate is hinged to one so that it swings between the two side posts as indicated by the dotted line. It is a good idea to arrange one of the side posts so that the gate will just clear it, but then it is necessary to hinge an extra piece of 2-in. stock to this post as shown. Unless it is swung back, this piece prevents the gate from being opened entirely. A hook and screweye are used to hold it in place securely. In this way the gate can be opened, when desired, to permit the passage of objects that are too bulky to get through the narrow opening, as, for instance, a wheelbarrow, or the live stock.— I. M. Wilson, Kansas City, Mo.

Hinged Gate for the Farm Is Convenient and Cannot Be Left Open by Mistake

Snowshoes of "Beaver" Pattern Made from Tennis Rackets

You can make a pair of "beaver" design snowshoes from a pair of old tennis awl about the edges of the leather foot-rest and the straps. Fasten the footrest into place with waxed thread or leather strips stitched through the holes around the

Tramping over Loose Snow Is Great Sport. These Snowshoes Were Made from Old Tennis Rackets and Anyone Handy in the Home Workshop Can Duplicate Them

rackets and two ash whips, bolted at the tail of the shoe and bound to the racket with rawhide strips. It doesn't matter if the tennis rackets are warped badly and have a few broken strings, for they can be replaced with strips of rawhide. Saw off the ends of the racket handles at a point 5 in. from the end. Whittle down two ash poles, each about ¾ in. in thickness, and dry them in the sun or by the fire. Each pole should be long enough to form a space about 3 in. wide about the tennis-racket rim. Then soak them in water until they can be bent into a loop without cracking. Whittle down the ends of each pole and drill two ¼-in. holes at each end, with a distance of about 4 in. between them. Drill two ¼-in. holes in the handle of the racket to correspond to the holes in the ash pole, and fasten the pole in place with a pair of small bolts through the handle. Replace any missing gut strings with lengths of leather. Cut a number of long strips from the side of a boot, each ½ in. wide, and bind the ash rim to the edge of the racket with an over-and-over stitch. Small and shallow notches should be made at intervals in the ash rim to keep the rawhide from slipping out. Cut out a leather footrest and a pair of straps long enough to stretch across the tennis racket. Make rows of holes with an edge. The rear strap should be fastened in the same way, save that a loop is formed over the footrest so that the toe of the boot can be slipped under it snugly. Give each snowshoe a generous coating of tallow or oil, to keep it from becoming water-soaked. You will have to practice to get on to the "gait." Every time you take a step you must swing the shoe around the other one before setting it down, and the first few steps will probably result in a spill or two. However, you will soon catch on to the step, and after a few trial tramps you will be able to cover considerable distances at good speed and without discomfort or weariness.—G. Everett Van Horn, Milton, Wis.

Securing Door with Loose-Pin Hinges

Loose-pin hinges on doors of cabinets and other similar constructions often permit intruders to gain entrance by removing the pins and lifting the hinge edge of the door outward. This may be overcome by fixing pins cut from a wire nail into the edge of the casing above the upper and below the lower hinges. Holes drilled into the edge of the door to fit the pins prevent the withdrawal of the door even after the pins are removed from the hinges.
—George Niederhoff, St. Louis, Mo.

Cambridge School-Teacher Who Glazed In the Space under His Back Porch to Make a Greenhouse

Back Porch Used as Small Greenhouse

Even in a city, where you have a very limited space, it is possible to provide a small greenhouse for pleasure or for extra earnings. A school-teacher of Cambridge, Mass., built the one shown in the photo, right under his back porch. It consists merely of a number of sash held in position securely on a suitable frame. Some of the sash are arranged to swing open to permit ventilation. The position of the porch is such that it receives considerable sunshine, and that is, of course, partly the reason why the porch could be used for this purpose.

Use for Modeling Clay in the Workshop

Modeling clay will often be found handy in the shop. A small quantity— 25 or 50 cents' worth —is enough for any ordinary job, and pays for itself many times over in saving of time. If a small screw or nut is lost in a maze of machinery, it can be quickly recovered by molding a ball of clay on the end of a stick or wire and lowering it to make contact with the lost object, which will stick to the clay and can then be lifted up without any trouble. The clay also helps to insert a screw in a tapped hole which is located in a recess of a machine so that one cannot get at it by hand. Fill the slot in the screw head with clay and then push the screwdriver blade into the slot. The screw will stick to the end of the screwdriver and thus be started in the thread. If a drawing is to be made of a casting having an irregularly shaped groove, its contour can be transferred to the drawing as follows: Fill a short space of the groove with clay, carefully remove it without distorting it and shave down a thin slice. This can be laid on the drawing and its profile traced. Imperfections in a model can be temporarily filled with clay while a casting is made in plaster of paris, and the clay can be reclaimed later.—L. B. Robbins, Harwich, Mass.

Stringing Barbed Wire Tightly

When stringing barbed-wire fences, many farmers use one-horse sleds of the kind shown in the drawing. If a fence is long, a reel often pays out so loosely that it is necessary to use a wire stretcher several times before the wire can be stapled to the posts. To overcome this trouble, one farmer fitted his sled with a simple brake. It consists of a long hook made of tire iron and is attached to the sled as indicated. When not in use, the barb of the hook rests in the end of the pipe axle of the reel, but when it is desired to brake the spool, to take up the slack in the wire, the hook is made to engage with the wire so that the reel cannot revolve.—G. E. Hendrickson, Argyle, Wis.

BRAKE

Simple Iron Brake on Sled Holds Reel from Revolving and Takes Up the Slack in the Wire

How to Make Rush or Fiber Seats

By L. DAY PERRY

WHILE the making or repairing of rush seating appears to be a very complicated process, it is in reality very simple and easy. The seat described here may be made by any careful boy in the home workshop. If well made, the finished piece of furniture will be very interesting, comfortable and serviceable. A working drawing of the seat which may be made by the amateur worker is shown in Figs. 1 and 2. The general dimensions as given are about right, it is well proportioned and may be easily transferred from place to place. However, the seat may be made square and either larger or smaller to suit the owner. The instructions for weaving the seat apply equally well, of course, either to new work or to the repair of old seats.

There are two kinds of serviceable material to use for wrapping the seat. One is the natural rush and the other is manufactured fiber. Both may be purchased from dealers in such supplies. If you wish to gather and prepare the rush you may readily do so. The ordinary swamp cat-tail is the plant, the leaves of which are used for rush seating. These leaves are cut in the fall, about the time the tips begin to turn brown, and dried slowly in the shade in basement, shed or loft. Before they are used, they should be soaked for several hours in water, and just before wrapping run through an ordinary clothes wringer to remove excess water.

Fiber is firmly twisted kraft paper procurable by the pound in indefinite length. For seating, it should be about ⅛ to 3⁄16 in. in diameter and preferably of natural-brown color. In every way fiber is easier to handle and quite as serviceable as rush.

Oak is probably the best wood for the construction of the frame, for it finishes well, tones in satisfactorily with the fiber, and will stand severe usage. Yellow poplar is also a wood that works well, takes stain beautifully, and is susceptible of fine polish. The worker need not hesitate to use this wood if he likes it.

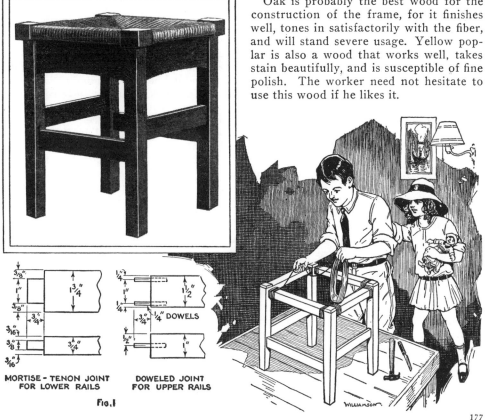

MORTISE - TENON JOINT
FOR LOWER RAILS

DOWELED JOINT
FOR UPPER RAILS

¼" DOWELS

FIG. 1

WILLIAMSON

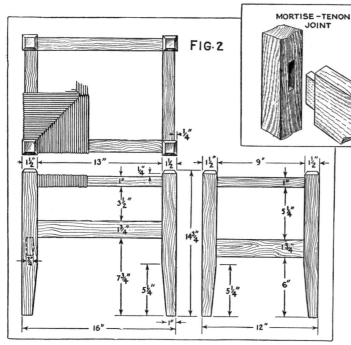

FIG. 2

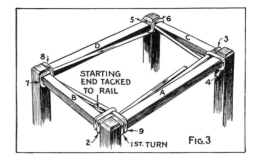

FIG. 3

In Fig. 2 are shown two kinds of joints commonly used in furniture construction. One is the mortise-and-tenon joint and the other the doweled joint. Either may be used. Both are used here. The size of each is given in Fig. 1. The doweled joint is used on the upper rails and the mortise-and-tenon on the lower ones. Certain trimming will need to be done where the dowels fit at right angles at the posts.

The holes for the dowel pins must be bored straight and accurate. A doweling jig is an excellent tool to use in centering and boring the holes. This tool is inexpensive and is a very fine one to have in the kit. A dowel bit should be used for boring, as it is a shade less in diameter than the regular bit and assures a tight fit and satisfactory joint. Be sure that each tenon fits into the mortise with a "driving" fit. Put the whole frame together to see that all points fit snugly, then finally assemble it with glue.

The method of wrapping the seat rails is shown in Fig. 3. This general scheme applies to any material which one may use for seating. The description to follow applies particularly to fiber, or fiber cord as it is commercially known. First wind about 25 ft. of the fiber into a coil. Do

this by wrapping it over your hand as you do a clothesline. Begin the operation by tacking one end of the strand on the inside of one of the rails. You may begin at any corner. As shown in the sketch, this is rail B. Next bring the strand over rail A, then down and up the inner corner, over the strand and rail B. The arrows on the sketch point the way. Continue down and under rail B, directly across the inner space to rail C. Wrap over and down rail C, up at the inner corner, then over the strand and rail A. Wrap the strand over and down rail A, then directly across the inner space to the top of rail D. This process is repeated at all corners. The sketch will make the process very clear, as the turns are numbered in the order in which they are made.

The strand of fiber should be pulled firm and tight at all times, and particular care should be taken at the corners, where the strands cross and the turns are made. Add

each new length of fiber by tying a square knot underneath the seat, or tacking the end of the old strand and the beginning of the new underneath one of the rails. The wrapping is continued until the two short rails are covered. Be sure that the strands are kept close together over the rails. A little tap with a block of wood and hammer will do the trick. When the short rails are filled, the wrapping is not yet complete, for there is an unfilled space on the two longer rails. Continue to wrap the fiber cord over and under these rails until the entire space is filled. Finally tack the end of the last strand under the proper rail. On a square seat, like the one in the photo, all rails are filled at about the same time, but on all rectangular seats the shorter rails fill first.

As the wrapping progresses, there are formed open spaces between the upper and lower strands. This space must be packed firmly with kraft paper such as may be purchased from the local store. Packing is necessary to build up the seat, to prevent sagging with use and to keep the fiber from breaking down at the inner corners of the rails.

If cat-tail leaves are used for the seating, first cut off the butt ends of the leaves as these are too coarse. Twist two or three leaves together to make a strand. Make a long twist and always in one direction. Add another leaf as the strand thins out, for there must be uniformity in thickness if the seat is to look neat and workmanlike. The butt ends are used for stuffing the seat. Aside from making the strand as the wrapping is done, the process for rush is the same as for the fiber cord.

The seat frame may be stained any desired color, and then filled with a paste wood filler. After thorough rubbing and drying, apply a coat of thin white shellac. Sand down the shellac with a fine grade of sandpaper. Apply several coats of good varnish to the fiber. Do not rub the varnish. Wax the frame or give it a coat of varnish and rub it down to a dull finish with pumicestone and water.

Tamper Made of Concrete

A tamper for use in the garden or in home concrete construction may be made as follows: Get a tomato can, about 4½ in. in diameter, and remove the top. Drive nails part way into the end of a broom-stick, or other round wooden rod, so as to form radiating projections. Insert the broomstick into the can and pour concrete around it. Care should be taken that the handle comes in the center of the can, and that its lower end does not touch the bottom while the concrete is being poured into place. Permit the mixture to harden, and a substantial tamper will result.—W. W. Baldwin, Washington, D. C.

Drawing Parallel Diagonal Lines

When a number of parallel lines have to be drawn at other angles than the ordinary

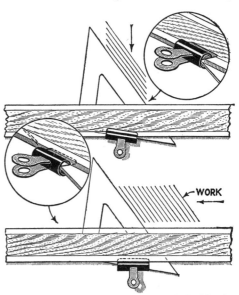

Using a Paper Clip to Hold a Triangle in Position for Drawing Parallel Diagonal Lines

triangles provide for, as in shading certain sections, the draftsman will find the use of a paper clip to be of considerable help in holding the triangles in the correct position. If the section to be shaded runs from top to bottom of the paper, the triangle is clipped to the T-square as indicated in the upper detail, and the square, carrying the triangle, is moved down the board as the lines are drawn. If, on the contrary, the shaded section runs horizontally, the clip is attached to the triangle as shown in the lower detail, and the triangle is then slid along under the T-square, with the clip bearing against the lower edge of the square.—W. G. Partin, Cleveland, Ohio.

Simple Jig Which
Facilitates Cutting
Tie Wires for Con-
crete Forms

Handy Jig for Cutting Tie Wire for Concrete Forms

A large number of tie wires, to hold concrete forms together, can be cut to the required length quickly and easily with the improvised device shown in the drawing. It consists of a plank laid across two ordinary sawhorses; a reel pivoted at one end of the plank to hold a roll of wire from which the tie wires are cut, and a tie-wire shaper, which is pivoted at the other end of the plank. The latter is made from a length of 2 by 4 or 2 by 6-in. stock, and a spike driven in at each end to hold the wire in the form of a flat coil, as indicated. The distance between the spikes must be equal to the length of one tie wire. After as much wire has been wound on the shaper as it will hold, or as much as desired, wrap the loose end around one end spike and then, with a large pair of wire cutters, cut through the coil of wire at the exact center between the end spikes. The number of U-shaped lengths of wire thus formed are then of the correct length and ready for use.— A. W. Burg, Lake View, Iowa.

Removing Battery Terminals

Battery terminals should always be tight. However, a terminal frequently becomes so tight that it is difficult to remove it when necessary. Strong-arm methods may injure the battery by loosening the post, allowing leakage and loss of the acid solution. Sometimes the post is even torn from the battery-plate assembly necessitating an expensive repair. For this reason, when detaching terminals from the posts, care should be observed to put as little strain on the post as possible. Special tools can be had for removing the different types of terminals.—Elmer Whittaker, Segregansett, Mass.

Quick-Tightening Grinding Chuck

A chuck with a novel method of tightening was made to hold some flanges while grinding out the taper hole. The flanges had four bolt holes, but instead of using bolts and nuts in the ordinary way, we threaded the chuck at the back and made a tightening sleeve that acted on four plain pins and secured the work by one movement of the sleeve. The pins have a groove cut in them a little wider than the thickness of the sleeve, and the face of the chuck and the sleeve are drilled to match the four bolt holes. The sleeve is also slotted at one side of each hole to suit the diameter at the bottom of the groove in the pins. In use, the four pins are pushed in place through the flange, chuck and sleeve. A bar is then inserted in the hole in the sleeve and this is turned, which causes the grooves in the pins to enter the slots and thus tightens all four pins equally and securely at the same time.— Harry Moore, Hamilton, Can.

❢ Marks at intervals of 6 in. on the handle of a post auger will aid in determining the depth of the hole.

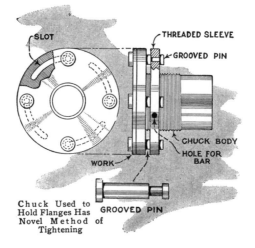

SLOT
THREADED SLEEVE
GROOVED PIN
CHUCK BODY
HOLE FOR BAR
WORK
GROOVED PIN

Chuck Used to
Hold Flanges Has
Novel Method of
Tightening

SHOP NOTES

Hints for Ship Modelers

By W. F. CROSBY

THE SHIP model builder who attempts to make his own blocks out of wood will probably find that he is up against a real problem, particularly if he tries to make these close to actual scale. In order to overcome the difficulty, the use of ordinary wire solder, as shown in Fig. 1, is about the best possible way of making non-splitting blocks. This solder may be obtained in several different diameters, it is soft enough to be drilled easily and may also be cut with a knife to the desired length. The groove for the strap is cut in easily and the hole for the running rigging cut at right angles to this.

Another method is to use small pellets of plastic wood slightly flattened out. A

thin wire strap may be worked around the pellet just before it is hard and a hole drilled without much difficulty for the line to pass through. This material will not split, and blocks may be made with great rapidity and with the utmost ease. The only thing to watch out for is that the

Fig. 3

BRASS SCREEN

WIRE

WIRE

TOP

SCREEN

WIRE

BULWARK

HAMMOCK BERTHING ON RAIL

Fig. 4

RAILS FOR SHIP MODELS

Fig. 5

of a skylight with a small drill, later finishing it smooth with a file. Windows may be made from old camera film, washed clean of emulsion.

On many of the old-time frigates, line-of-battle ships and other war vessels, the after side of each top was arranged with a small rail which was put there to keep the sharpshooters from falling overboard or to the deck. (See Fig. 4.) These rails quite often had a fine-mesh rope screen woven into them, and in making a small model, it is extremely difficult to do this. However, the difficulty has been solved by procuring some of the extremely fine copper or brass screening used in making and repairing gasoline filters on automobiles. A framework should be made of light copper wire and the screening fastened to it by sewing with fine thread or copper wire.

The same copper screening may be used for the hammock berthing along the main rail of most of these old naval-ship models, this screening also being supported by wire uprights set at appropriate distances.

More than half the charm of a ship model lies in the accuracy of the work, and in this respect it is essential that the rigging be of proper sizes. The stays of the various masts will usually be of the heaviest material, the lower shrouds of the next heaviest and the upper rigging somewhat lighter. The running rigging will be the lightest of all.

Since suitable cord is sometimes hard to get in the right sizes, it is somewhat easier to make up material which will be suitable by winding together several smaller cords to make one large "rope." This may be done by measuring the approximate distance that the line is to go and then allowing a few inches at each end for fastening. Take several such

blocks are all of exactly the same size.

The deck of the average sailing ship will be found to contain several gratings of fine "mesh" and also two or three skylights which may be extremely difficult to make of wood. Fiber of a thickness to suit the scale of the model will serve the purpose. This material will not split and may be worked and finished to look exactly like wood. For gratings, the size and shape should be secured and marked off into the desired mesh. The tang end of a small file should then be squared off and sharpened on a stone, and this may be used as a punch. The fiber is held over a narrow slot opening in the vise (Fig. 2) and the homemade punch driven through it by a quick blow of a light hammer. The entire surface may thus be worked into the desired number of square holes. If the fiber has a tendency to shred off on the underside, an old razor blade or sharp knife may be used for trimming off this excess material.

Fiber also may be used for rails and skylights, but in the heavier sizes it may be necessary to cut out the square holes

pieces and tie them to the workbench or fasten them in a vise (see Fig. 5) and then place the other ends in the chuck of a small hand drill, turning the handle toward you and winding until the different cords are securely twisted together. However, do not wind too tightly or the cord will be greatly shortened.

Such rigging must be kept tight or it will untwist and small clamps may be secured to each end until it is time to use it. A better and much more satisfactory way is to make up the rigging only as needed and then keep it taut until it is securely in place on the model.

One of the tedious jobs in completing an old-fashioned ship model is in the making and finishing of the many guns necessary. The guns themselves may be cast of lead or solder or, better yet, turned from hardwood on a small lathe. In the latter case, the material should be finished smooth and then painted either with bronze or black paint, depending upon the period of the ship.

The average frigate had carronades on deck and the heavier guns below and, in nine out of ten such models, the deck guns will be made incorrectly or mounted improperly. Carronades were considerably smaller than the other guns and had carriages which consisted of a flat piece with three little rollers on the underside. The carronade itself was mounted on a

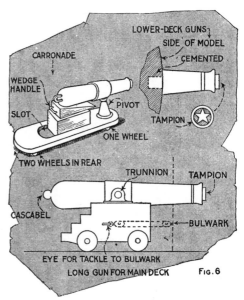

FIG. 6

swivel at the end nearest the rail, with a wedge arranged under the inboard end to depress or elevate the muzzle.

On the average model of this sort, the guns on the lower decks will simply be short pieces cemented into holes in the hull. These guns should be slightly greater in diameter and also slightly longer than the ones above. If long guns are to be made for the main deck, Fig. 6 will furnish a guide to the proper proportions for gun and carriage.

Curtain Rod Holds Surgeon's Tape

Rolls of adhesive tape of varying sizes are always convenient in the office of a police surgeon at San Diego, Calif. The rolls are held on a small curtain rod. Just below the rod, a piece of plate glass is

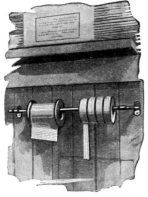

provided to permit attaching one end of the tape to it when it is necessary to pull a section of tape off the roll and cut it with the use of only one hand, as, for instance, in case the other hand is needed for holding the bandage on the patient.—Alpheus Lincoln, Los Angeles, Calif.

Acid Helps Remove Broken Tap

Mechanics often have trouble in removing a broken tap, especially if the tap is in tight and has broken below the surface. Before attempting to use any tools to remove it, fill the hole containing the broken part of the tap with muriatic acid or spirit of salt, taking care not to get it on the hands or clothing. Let the work stand for a few hours, which will give the acid time to dissolve some of the steel around the tap, so that the latter will be loosened sufficiently to be turned out. Sometimes the broken tap will become so loosened that it can even be lifted out.—James E. Noble, Toronto, Can.

Portable Truck Tracks, Made of Hardwood Slats Connected by Means of Chain, Prevent the Risk of Running Deep Ruts in Soft Lawns, besides Saving Considerable Time

Portable Tracks Save Lawns from Injury by Delivery Trucks

Portable tracks made of hardwood slats and connected by means of light chains have been found very useful in driving over soft lawns, to prevent ruining them. One truck owner who handles coal found sections 14 ft. in length most convenient. Each of these weighs about 70 lb., can be rolled up into a compact bundle and readily put on top of the load. This track saves the customer the extra charge for carrying the coal in baskets or bags, and the coal man a lot of time.—S. Merritt, Nyack, N. Y.

Facing Pipe Fittings

In our machine shop a job came in which made it necessary to face off pipe elbows so that the two ends would be at

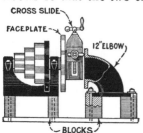

perfect right angles. To do this we blocked up the lathe and the elbow with parallel blocks as shown. The cross slide was fastened to the faceplate, with the cutting tool arranged to turn down the face of the elbow. The handle of the cross slide was given part of a turn at each revolution. After it was once set up, we made good time in this way.—C. Kugler, Philadelphia, Pa.

Repair for Broken Gear Tooth

It is occasionally necessary to replace a broken tooth of an iron gear, as this is not only much easier, but also less expensive than getting a new gear, especially if it is large. The repair described here is only intended for use on parts that are not subjected to

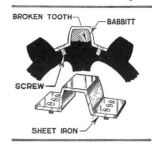

heavy loads. The gear face is ground down on each side of the broken tooth, and a piece of sheet metal is then used to make the shell of a new tooth. The sheet metal should be as heavy as can be conveniently worked. It is bent to shape over an adjacent tooth, one side being bent first and the top section bent back so that the tooth will not be too wide. The shell is securely fastened to the gear as shown and filled with babbitt.

¶Chalk rubbed on a file for use on steel prevents chips from sticking to the tool and scratching the work.

A Simple Rack for Draftsmen

At different times a draftsman needs a large number of tracings and blueprints for reference, when working on a single job, and unless he has them arranged in a systematic way, he loses a good deal of time in picking out each sheet as needed. In addition, he has little room to work if his table is covered with a pile of drawings, and his difficulties are seriously increased if he is engaged on the kind of map work in which one job is continued from sheet to sheet. A handy rack which takes up little room can be made out of a 2-in. plank, about 1 ft. square. Plane and sandpaper it, and drill sixteen 1-in. holes—four to a row—which should be enough for most purposes. Sandpaper the inside of the holes, varnish or stain the block as desired, and mark numbers neatly against the holes. The rolled drawings can then be placed in the holes, so that they will take up little room, and will be easy to pick out. Drawings usually have numbers assigned to them for classification on the drafting-room records, but for this purpose it will cause no confusion if temporary numbers are given to the different sheets, corresponding to the holes. The numbers can be written lightly in pencil on the backs of the sheets.

Handy Drawer for Double Bench

When a double-bench drawer can be pulled out from one side only it is annoying for men working on the other side, as they either have to walk around or ask someone on the drawer side to get the tools they need. One shop solved this difficulty in a simple manner: A drawer was made the full width of the bench with a handle at each end, and the tool-holding compartment was arranged to slide inside the drawer, on two runways.

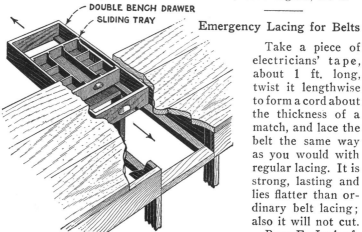

Handy Drawer for Double Workbench Can Be Pulled Out at Both Sides

Cutting Lips on Edge of an Old Valve Make It a Good Valve-Seating Tool

Valve-Seating Tool Made from Old Valve

A tool for cutting valve seats can be made from an old valve. The edge of the head is slotted with a saw in about eight places, as shown in the illustration. One side of each slot is relieved by filing in order to leave one cutting edge. The valve head is then hardened. An ordinary valve-grinding tool is used to rotate this cutter. In ordinary cases, only a few turns are necessary to true up and smooth a rough seat.—G. A. Luers, Washington, D. C.

Emergency Lacing for Belts

Take a piece of electricians' tape, about 1 ft. long, twist it lengthwise to form a cord about the thickness of a match, and lace the belt the same way as you would with regular lacing. It is strong, lasting and lies flatter than ordinary belt lacing; also it will not cut.
—Ben F. Imhof, Davenport, Iowa.

Cellar Doors Aid Work of Excavating Besides Protecting the Workers in the Pit

Cellar-Door Idea Employed in Foundation Digging

In sinking wells, 209 ft. deep, on the site of the Cleveland terminal, when the bucket carrying the excavated material came to the top, it was raised 6 or 7 ft. above the ground. Then the men slammed down two doors similar to cellar doors. As soon as they were down, the bucket was lowered onto them and dumped. Being on a sharp slant, the doors shot the excavated material onto a platform where it was picked up easily. The empty bucket was then lifted, the doors opened and the bucket lowered. The doors prevented any of the excavated material from dropping back into the well in the process of dumping. They were safety devices besides facilitating the work considerably.

To Prevent Radiator from Freezing

Autoists are often bothered in the winter by the freezing of the cold-water pipe leading from the bottom of the radiator to the lower part of the cylinder water jacket. If this pipe is frozen, and the engine is started, the water in the upper part of the radiator will soon boil, but as heat goes up, and not down, it will boil away before thawing out the frozen pipe. There is an easy method of remedying this, in a way that is entirely automatic. When the circulation is stopped, the boiling water is soon carried off in the small overflow pipe. If the lower end of this pipe is loosened from its fastening, and moved to a point directly at the base of the cold-water pipe, the heat of the steam will thaw out that pipe while the car is in motion. As soon as it has thawed out, the circulation, of course, will be resumed.

If the overflow pipe is so located that it cannot be moved, the autoist should carry a section of rubber tube to slip over the end of the pipe, and so direct steam to any cold part of the radiator he desires. The steam flow will cease as soon as circulation of the water through the piping is taking place again.

Fixture for Bending Structural Iron

For bending light structural iron of the kind often used in foundries for trolley tracks, the illustrated fixture has been found useful. It consists of two plates, A, bolted to a steel block, B, and to two spacing pieces at the ends. Two straps, E, are used to hold the device and the work together, and can be moved along the plates A to suit the work. Block B is threaded to receive a screw provided with a bar to turn it. The drawing shows an I-beam about to be bent,

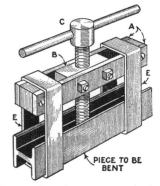

which is done by turning the screw against it.—C. Kugler, Philadelphia, Pa.

Combination Seat, Cabinet and Workbench

The illustrated combination seat, cabinet and workbench was exhibited at an exposition of the Berlin housewives' association, and shows what can be done along space-saving lines. It can be used as a hall chair if desired, although rather massive for this purpose. Sewing material can be stored in it, and when it is necessary to

Copyright, Henry Miller

Space-Saving Combination of Seat, Cabinet and Workbench; the Upper Photo Shows It as a Cabinet and the Lower, as a Workbench

have a large bench for cutting material, it can be set up quickly and without trouble by unfolding the double endpieces and the large top.

Working Glass in Machines

At one time we had an order for a lot of glass tubes, inside diameter ½ in., outside diameter ¾ in., and 10 in. long, to be threaded on each end with eight threads to the inch. The lathe was geared up for this thread, and a three-jaw universal chuck put on the spindle. The tubes were chucked with a piece of leather placed between the jaws and the glass. Near the other end of the glass tube the center rest was set, and a piece of leather

was folded over each end of the center-rest jaws and wired in place. The leather was used to prevent the glass surface from being scratched. Very little pressure was found needed to keep the work from turning. The tube was chucked and centered by running the tail center up and setting the jaws of the center rest. A 4-in. drum pulley was taken from the small tool grinder and put up over the lathe, and a tool-post grinder, which was carrying a properly beveled emery wheel, was set in the tool post instead of the threading tool. The tool-post grinder was belted to the 4-in. drum pulley, and the emery wheel set with a center gauge, whereupon the thread was cut as usual. We found that by using hard wheels, dressed to suit the work, or by using a combination of wheels, glass can be worked as easily as cold-rolled steel. This would apply to planer work as well. Glass should be worked at high speeds, and a dull surface will be the result. The emery wheel must be kept wet, either by using a centrifugal pump or by means of a tin can with a hole punched in the bottom.—J. B. Murphy, Plainfield, New Jersey.

HOW TO
YOUR OLD

The Popular Enamel Finish

off with clear water; the rinse-off being important, as any deposit of soap left on the surface is liable to prevent the new finish from drying or cause other trouble. Next wipe over the surface with a cloth dampened with gasoline, naphtha or benzine, to cut any greasy substance that may be present, from furniture polish or the handling a chair receives. Then sandpaper the surface lightly with No. 00 sandpaper, as in Fig. 1, to cut the gloss of the previous finish, and dust off all loose particles of sand.

That's all it is necessary to do in the way of preparatory work, unless there are digs, holes or cracks in the wood, in which event they should be filled with a plastic-wood preparation, such as is now sold for the purpose, or with a mixture of fine sawdust, liquid glue and whiting; sawdust, shellac and whiting, or

FURNITURE finishing, formerly an art for the professional only, has, with the vogue for color and the popularity of enamel and lacquer finishes, become a fascinating hobby of thousands of amateur painters throughout the country. It affords an opportunity, second to none of the home crafts, for the practical and profitable use of spare time, and is quite as interesting as fashioning things from wood or metal, when one knows how to go about it. Say, you have one of the old-fashioned golden-oak chairs (Fig. 2) with high-gloss varnish finish; it can be converted into an odd chair of as smart and professional appearance as any you see in the stores. (See Fig. 4.)

First, determine the color scheme. The charm of the odd chair lies in its beauty of color, and the use of the right colors to fit in with the decoration and furnishings of the room in which it will be placed. Have a definite location for the chair, and select colors that will look well in this particular place as well as in combination with each other.

Next, prepare the surface for refinishing. It is not necessary to remove the old coatings. Ordinarily, you can enamel previously finished surfaces by preparing them as follows: Simply wash the piece thoroughly with soap and water, and rinse

REFINISH FURNITURE

By
Berton Elliot

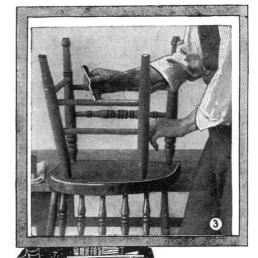

sawdust, lacquer and whiting, any of which is satisfactory, knifed well into the indenture, and, when dry, sandpapered down absolutely even with the surface. In the event, also, that the piece has previously been finished in mahogany stain, a coat of pure shellac should be applied after the clean-up work, to seal in the powerful stain and keep it from "bleeding" through the new finish. Of course, for the finest possible finish, the old coatings should be stripped off with paint and varnish remover, or sanded down to the bare wood, and the new finish built up from the wood, but a strictly first-class job can be produced over old coatings.

We are now ready to build up the enamel finish. Enamel is transparent by nature, and with the light, delicate shades especially, it is necessary to provide an even foundation of solid-covering flat paint, to hide the wood and surface imperfections. Regular enamel undercoater, sold by paint stores (usually in white only), is the simplest and most convenient form of flat material to use for the very light colors, but when enameling in the bright and strong colors, flat wall paint, in a color closely approximating the color of the finishing enamel coat, is usually a more satisfactory undercoater for the amateur.

When finishing in white or any of the light colors, such as ivory, cream, sand color, the delicate tones of blue, green, etc., a three-coat job will ordinarily produce a thoroughly satisfactory finish, when properly applied.

First, apply a coat of flat undercoater, in which a little varnish (about 10 to 15 per cent) has been incorporated, to help the coating adhere to the old varnished finish, without chipping off later on. Second, when dry, sandpaper lightly, to remove brush marks and level off the surface, dust clean, and apply a coat of half undercoater and half enamel mixed. Third, when dry, sandpaper lightly, dust off, and apply a finishing coat of full enamel.

The use of the right kind of brushes for enamel work is important. A soft-hair brush should be used, as it is next to impossible to lay on undercoaters and enamel with a stiff bristle brush, without leaving ridges or brush marks. It is also most important to keep dust from the surface. Particles from sandpapering should be dusted off, brushes should be perfectly clean, so that no dust or particles of grit will get into the work from them, and care should be taken that no dust is raised in the room until the enamel has dried dust-free. Work should be done as quickly as possible, as any brushing of the surface after the en-

If, owing to the condition of the surface or lack of experience in painting, a thoroughly satisfactory finish is not obtained with three coats, especially on large and conspicuous surfaces, sandpaper lightly again and apply another coat of full enamel. On the other hand, with the bright or dark colors, it is often possible to produce a first-class finish with two coats of straight enamel, preferably, however, mixing a little flat undercoater (about 25 per cent) with the first coat to give it a little more body and make a more solid covering. Enamel coats should be allowed to stand at least 48 hours before sandpapering and recoating; undercoaters may be sanded and recoated the next day. Only fine sandpaper should be used, never coarser than No. 00, and preferably No. 0000 or very fine wet-or-dry sandpaper or garnet paper for the enamel coats.

In applying enamel, first brush it onto the surface freely and quickly, with the grain of the wood. Then "cross over," without refilling the brush. This drags the enamel over any spots that may have been missed in applying the material and spreads it out into a uniformly even film. Then, with light strokes, brush over the surface again with the grain, without refilling the brush. This process gives a smooth, even, porcelainlike surface.

amel has commenced to set will result in a rough finish.

The final enamel coat can be left in full gloss, rubbed to a semi-dull finish, or polished to a highly brilliant "piano" finish. The rubbed effect is produced with pumicestone and oil in the following manner: Place some powdered pumicestone, which can be obtained at most paint stores or at a drug store, in a saucer or shallow dish. In another receptacle pour a little regular rubbing oil or good sewing-machine oil. Fold a soft cloth into a pad, or use a regular felt rubbing pad. Moisten the pad in the oil, then dip it into the powdered pumice, and rub over the surface, only about five or six times, and with not too heavy pressure, so as not to cut through.

Always rub with the grain, and as far as possible, rub the entire length of the surface with one stroke, to avoid a patchy appearance. Any carved or relief work can be reached by using a small vegetable brush, dipped into the oil and then into the pumicestone. When through, clean by wiping off the surface with a dry cloth, using a little cornstarch if necessary to help dry up the oil. Water is sometimes used instead of oil for rubbing. The rule is to use pumicestone and water wherever it is desired to rub undercoats, as oil rubbing leaves a greasy film on the surface which cannot be satisfactorily finished over. Oil is best for the finishing coat, as water rubbing cuts much faster and is likely to spoil the finish.

The high polish previously referred to is produced as follows: After the pumicestone rubbing and clean-up, wait until the following day, and rub the surface again, in a similar way, with powdered rottenstone and water, which imparts the handpolished effect seen on the finest furniture. The rubbing of a fine enamel finish calls for carefulness and considerable good judgment, and the amateur should be very cautious when first doing this work.

Unpainted furniture and novelty woodenware, now so popular, can be finished in the same way as previously finished

furniture, except that the first coat of flat undercoater should be thinned with turpentine to help penetrate into and satisfy the absorption demand of the wood; and, of course, the preliminary clean-up is unnecessary. The surface, however, should be sandpapered with fine sandpaper, with the grain, to plate smoothness, as ordinarily these pieces are only machine-sanded, and when examined will be found covered with tiny scratches which should be sanded out for a fine finish.

Auto Used as Tractor on Ice

Ice skating rinks throughout the country may profit from the experience of the skating pavilion in San Francisco, where

Old Auto Equipped with Grooved Cast-Iron Wheels Pulls Scraper over Ice

an old auto was fitted with grooved, cast-iron wheels so that it could be used as a tractor for pulling scrapers over the ice. This method is much better than the use of chains, which are not always effective and, besides, dig grooves in the ice, which cause extra labor.—C. W. Geiger, San Francisco, Calif.

Soldering Lead Joints

When making lead-to-lead joints, one of the main things to remember is to keep soldering acid or paste away from the cleaned lead surface, as any trace of this will make it very difficult to tin the lead. Finely powdered rosin mixed with alcohol makes a good non-tarnishing flux for lead. Neat's-foot oil is also good, this often being used in soldering the thin lead frames or "cames" on stained-glass windows.— James E. Noble, Toronto, Can.

Inclosure Prevents Frozen Pump

Although provided with drains below the surface for emptying the pipe above

Wooden Inclosure Lined with a 12-In. Straw Wall Prevents Pump from Freezing

the cylinder, some pumps freeze in cold weather, often when the supply is low or there is an urgent need for water. The owner of a mill-operated pump built a simple inclosure between the four tower legs, as shown in the illustration. On the inside, a straw wall and roof, about 12 in. thick, was held in place by woven wire. This insulation maintains an even temperature, keeping out the frost during the winter, and the extreme heat during summer. The door is on the south.—Dale R. Van Horn, Lincoln, Nebr.

Using a Large Planer for a Press

Some time ago we had several steel tubes, about 5 in. in diameter and 4 ft. long, which had to be a press fit over the piston rods they were to cover. Not having a press large enough to handle the job, we were stuck until the following idea was hit upon. There was about .003 in. left for a force fit. Both ends of each tube were capped and live steam turned into them, which enlarged them about the amount mentioned. The rods were bolted upon the platen of a 36 by 36-in. planer, and a solid backstop was erected just far

enough away to allow for starting the tube. When all was ready, the steam was turned off, the caps removed, and the tube lifted in position and shoved on by hand for about 8 in., when it began to go hard; then the planer was started very slowly, which pushed the tube home without further trouble. The whole scheme worked out very nicely and without much outlay. —A. Dane, Pottstown, Pa.

Rough-and-Finish Calipers

When calipers are set to a certain dimension, care is required to prevent the work from being made too small. However, with the calipers changed as shown, one can work quicker because the tool shows when one is near to the correct size, leaving enough stock for finishing. The calipers are made in the ordinary way, but with an auxiliary leg as shown, which is riveted to the short leg and a vee cut out on the top. The short leg is then tapped for a fine-thread screw, which is put in tight. Next a knurled nut is made with a plain part, which fits the vee of the auxiliary leg. In use, the calipers are set to the finished size of the work with the nut tightened. To measure the work down to the finishing cut, the nut is loosened to clear the vee. This allows the leg to rock to the extent of the difference between the plain part of the nut and the diameter of the screw. The nut, of course, is again tightened to lock the leg for the finished size. With the auxiliary leg unlocked,

work can be done rapidly, and if it does happen that too big a cut is taken off the work, it will usually be found that there is still sufficient stock for finishing, due to the difference allowed by the two settings on the caliper. —Harry Moore, Montreal, Can.

¶A stick wedged into the slot will sometimes aid in starting machine screws.

An Unusual Table Lamp

By H. F. WEATHERBY

THE TABLE lamp illustrated herewith is not only of a novel design, but it is in addition a most attractive and useful piece of furniture to add to one's living room or study. It gives a very restful and pleasing reading light and provides a space for one's favorite books, always at hand. If desired, the book shelf may be dispensed with, and a simple stretcher, as shown in one of the illustrations, may be substituted.

Most of the readers of Popular Mechanics have at least some small articles of shop equipment, and the construction of the lamp calls only for a coping or scroll saw, handsaw, brace and 3/4-in. bit, plane, half-round wood file, a hammer, and a vise in which to hold the work.

Go to the nearest cabinet shop or mill, where plywood can be bought, and get 1/4-in. material, from which the following pieces can be cut: Two pieces for shade, 6 by 14 in.; two pieces for ends, 7½ by 16¼ in.; one shelf piece, 3⅜ by 12½ in., and one 3 by 12½ in. Plywood is recommended because of its strength, and the chances are that scraps can be found, at little or no cost, large enough to make the above parts.

A cardboard pattern is laid out for the ends, as indicated, using 1-in. squares. Exact dimensions are not given on the drawing and the design may be changed to express one's individuality. Using this pattern as a template, mark around the two endpieces and saw them out with a coping, jig or band saw, if available. Smooth the rough edges, being careful to keep the plywood from splitting. The straight edges should, of course, be planed carefully.

The top pieces may also be cut out with a coping saw, but great care must be taken to keep the inside edges straight. If a circular saw is at hand, and you exercise care, the glass openings may be cut and rabbeted on this machine, as indicated by the left-hand section detail of frame; otherwise, if the work is done by hand, rabbeted blocks, as at the right, will prove easier to make and much more satisfactory. The shelf parts call for no explanation other than that they must be

An Attractive and Decidedly Unusual Table Lamp That Is Very Simple and Easily Made, and Will Give the Home Mechanic a Chance to Display His Skill

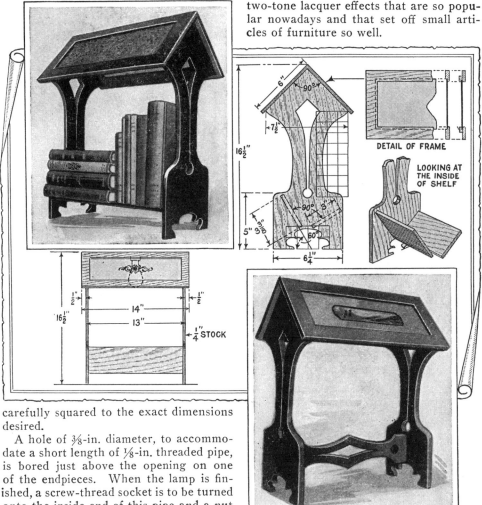

DETAIL OF FRAME

LOOKING AT
THE INSIDE
OF SHELF

two-tone lacquer effects that are so popular nowadays and that set off small articles of furniture so well.

carefully squared to the exact dimensions desired.

A hole of ⅜-in. diameter, to accommodate a short length of ⅛-in. threaded pipe, is bored just above the opening on one of the endpieces. When the lamp is finished, a screw-thread socket is to be turned onto the inside end of this pipe and a nut on the outside end to hold the socket.

The pipe may be extended to the center of the frame, and an ell and nipple used to make the bulb hang vertically, if desired, or two bulbs, one at each end, can be used instead of the single bulb at end or center, to suit the maker's taste. If the latter system is employed, it is suggested that long bulbs of the candle type be used. The wiring, of course, is very simple.

After careful sanding, nail the different parts together, and place ¼-in. square glue blocks on the underside of the shade, and under the shelf. None of these can be seen, but they will help greatly in adding sturdiness to the finished job. When these are dry, finish the lamp in any way desired. The writer suggests some of the

Colored art glass to match the finish is suggested for the shade, or simply a white ground or frosted glass which can be made most attractive by the addition of two of the transfers that are being used a great deal now. If the maker is sufficiently skilled, a design may be painted on the glass. The glass is held in place as indicated.

¶To sharpen the knives of meat-cutting machines, first rough-grind them, then set them up under a drill press so that the machine turns them backward, with the cutting side of the knife face down on a piece of plate glass on which valve-grinding compound is applied.

An Inexpensive Universal Joint

In light and medium-heavy machinery, a very cheap, durable and efficient universal joint may be made from three straight chain links of round section. In connecting this form of a joint, one end of each shaft, the driving and driven, must be slotted to receive the end link, and a bolt put through the shaft to prevent the link from pulling out. A reinforcing collar is shrunk over the end of the shaft to strengthen the slotted part. Such a joint will drive at almost right angles with very little friction. It is especially recommended for experimental and similar classes of machinery.

Hose on Street Protected by Pipe

When a length of hose is run across a street, where passing traffic is likely to cut or crush the hose, an inexpensive and effective protector can be made of pipe and fittings, as shown in the drawing. Take a piece of 2-in. pipe, about 10 or 12 ft. long, fit a tee at each end and screw a 1-ft. length of pipe into each tee to project in opposite directions, in order to prevent the pipe from rolling. For garden hose, 2-in. pipe has been found satisfactory, but for larger hose larger pipe should be provided. Such a protector is practically indestructible and can be carried from one job to another without even removing the hose.—G. C. Douglas, Raleigh, N. C.

Length of Pipe Makes a Good Protector for Hose Laid over Busy Street

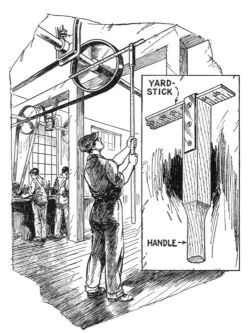

Yardstick Held at Right Angles to End of Pole for Taking Overhead Measurements

Measuring Overhead Pulleys

In making a survey of a large industrial plant, the writer found it necessary to measure a number of overhead pulleys, which were rather difficult to get at, so that a stepladder had to be carried along. To eliminate this encumbrance, I mounted a yardstick at the end of a long pole as shown. The end of the pole was planed square, and a strip of tin was bent to a U-shape permitting it to be screwed to the pole to hold the yardstick at right angles. Obviously, this device can be used for taking other overhead measurements.—L. G. Roller, Cedar Rapids, Iowa.

How to Make Wallpaper Washable

Ordinarily wallpaper cannot be washed but the following treatment will enable this: Dissolve borax, 2 parts, and shellac, 2 parts, in water, 24 parts. After mixing thoroughly strain through a fine cloth. With a brush or a sponge apply this to the surface of the paper, and when dry, polish it to a high gloss with a soft brush. Thus treated, the paper may be washed without fear of damaging the colors.—Edward Piranian, Philadelphia, Pa.

Useful Tire-Chain Repairing Tools

By G. A. LUERS

IN many garages and auto-service stations the repair of tire chains is an important task, especially during the winter months, when the streets and roads are icy and chains are frequently broken. However, as very few garages have proper equipment for removing, inserting and clinching the links, the tools described in this article will be of interest to owners of such establishments.

After mud and dirt are washed off the chains, prior to repairing them, they should be dipped in a bath of used crankcase oil and kerosene, in order to prevent rust. A steel drum is convenient for holding the mixture, and a number of hooks should be provided over the drum so that the chains can be hung up after the bath and the surplus oil drip back into the drum. A bench, about 10 ft. long, will provide plenty of room for extending the chains full length on the top and working on them. The bench also makes it easy to inspect the chains and avoids the inconvenience of laying them on the floor.

Close to the bench, a strip of wire mesh is tacked to the studs of the wall or to wooden cleats nailed there. This forms a simple holder for spare links for repairs. The links can be hooked to the wire mesh at almost any point, or, if desired, the links can be arranged in sections, according to their sizes, which may be marked on the wall above the mesh.

For opening or cutting out links there is a simple fixture at the left end of the bench. It is detailed at the top of the drawing and consists of a punch, held loosely in vertical position in a holder. This device is less tiresome to use than a pair of heavy pliers, tongs or hand cutters. Several chisel-shaped punches, of the same diameter, about ¾ in., so that they will all fit in the holder, are provided, some having sharp, hardened edges for cutting the links, and some with blunt, wedge-shaped ends for opening them. The holder is made of steel plate, cut, drilled and bent to shape and securely mounted on a steel base.

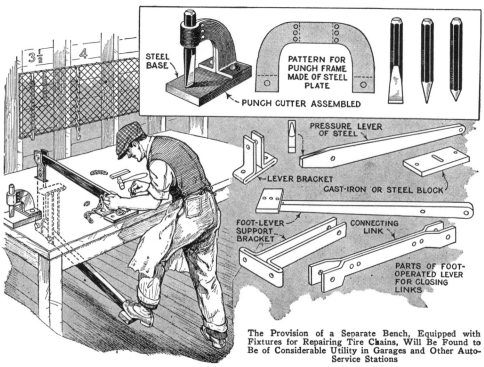

STEEL BASE

PATTERN FOR PUNCH FRAME MADE OF STEEL PLATE

PUNCH CUTTER ASSEMBLED

PRESSURE LEVER OF STEEL

LEVER BRACKET

CAST-IRON OR STEEL BLOCK

FOOT-LEVER SUPPORT BRACKET

CONNECTING LINK

PARTS OF FOOT-OPERATED LEVER FOR CLOSING LINKS

The Provision of a Separate Bench, Equipped with Fixtures for Repairing Tire Chains, Will Be Found to Be of Considerable Utility in Garages and Other Auto-Service Stations

For closing links, a foot-operated press, linked to exert heavy pressure when the foot is pushed down on the lower lever, permits the free use of both hands for assembling, setting and holding the links or chain sections under the jaw. It is mounted on the bench and consists of two levers, one forming the press jaw and the other the foot treadle. Two brackets support these levers, the rear ends being linked together to permit free movement of each, and a spring, not shown in the drawing, provided to hold the levers in an elevated position for working. A steel or cast-iron block is bolted to the bench under the jaw of the upper lever, which should be made of steel, while the lower one may be made of wood. The brackets are made of steel plate. With these tools and equipment, any shop is able to give quick service in the repair of tire chains.

Screw Holder Made from Clock Spring

Difficulty is often experienced in getting screws started in places where one cannot hold them with the fingers. Many methods and devices are resorted to for doing this, but the one shown in the photo has been found to be effective. Take two lengths of clock spring, about 3 or 4 in. long, put them to-

gether as indicated, insert the ends, which must be ground square, into the screw slot, and press the springs together at the other end. This will grip the screw securely so that it will not drop off, and can readily be inserted. Also, the curvature and the stiffness of the springs enable the worker to give the screw a considerable twist.

Oilcloth Cover Pulled Down over Bunch of Bananas Protects Them from Frost

Cover Keeps Frost from Bananas

When bunches of bananas are left suspended in a store window overnight during cold weather, they may sometimes be frost-bitten. To guard against this a Wisconsin fruit dealer improvised the effective protector shown in the illustration. It consists of a cylindrical cover, made from small barrel hoops and white oilcloth. To the top edge two equal lengths of stout cord are fastened. An old window-shade roller having a good spring is attached to the ceiling just above the bunch, and the free ends of the cord are tacked to the roller as indicated. The cover can then be raised and lowered in the same way as a window shade, and does not spoil the appearance of the window.

Refacing Old Oilstones

When hollows begin to appear in oilstones, it is time to reface them. This can be done by grinding the surface down on a marble slab, on which coarse emery and some water are applied. Slate can be used instead of marble if desired, or a piece of coarse emery cloth, tacked to a smooth board. Rub the oilstone over the abrasive with a circular motion.

Collapsible Benches for Pipe Fitters Are Rigid and Take Very Little Space When Folded

Collapsible Workbench Made of Pipe and Fittings

While passing a plumbing and pipe-fitting shop one day, I noticed a number of collapsible benches made of pipe and fittings. They were arranged so that, when set up, they would be rigid, which is usually not the case with collapsible benches, and when folded, they would take very little space in the truck. The supporting framework consists of a number of lengths of pipe, tees, elbows, flanges and couplings, arranged as shown in the drawing. U-bolts are used to hold the bench top securely to the frame, as indicated.—Irwin Chesterfield, Chicago, Ill.

Cover Keeps Steering Wheels Clean

Garage mechanics may unintentionally soil the steering wheels of autos with  greasy hands, when moving the cars about. To avoid this, one garage owner provided covers to fit tightly over the wheel, entirely inclosing it. They are made of circular pieces of canvas. A hem is sewed all around the edge to receive a length of elastic tape, which keeps the cover firmly in place. A large cloth is also placed over the driver's seat so that the mechanic will not soil it.

Burlap Used on Poultry-House Nests and Roosts

By covering the fronts of poultry nests with burlap curtains, the nests are made dark, and therefore more attractive to the hens. They are also a protection against egg-eating, since the hens will not eat eggs lying in darkened nests. If they already have the habit, they can be broken of it by providing the nests with the burlap curtains. These curtains should fall to within 3 in. of the bottom of the nests, and each should have a V-shaped piece, 4 by 5 in. in size, cut out for air and a small amount of light. For nests used by sitting hens, the curtain should be made to cover the whole nest, a diamond-shaped piece being cut out for air and light. The curtains should be fastened with hooks, so that the hen may be released twice a day for food, water and exercise.

Weighted File Handle Prevents Breakage

A ball-shaped handle is often the most convenient kind for small, light files, and if the handle is weighted it will serve the further purpose of preventing the file from being easily broken, especially on jobs where ordinary and comparatively heavy tools are used. If, in a moment of forgetfulness, a heavy tool is dropped on the file, it will  probably be broken, but a weighted ball handle prevents this, as it holds the file in a vertical position as shown. No matter how it is laid down, it assumes this position automatically. The handle is made in two sections, one of metal and the other of wood, being joined by means of a screw, and afterward ground to an approximate ball shape. The file shank is stuck into the wooden part.—Harry Moore, Montreal, Que., Can.

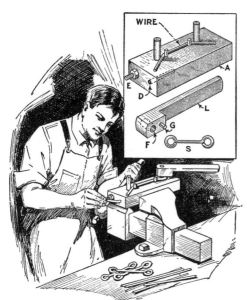

A Simple Jig Which Will Facilitate the Making of Links of Equal Size

Fixture for Forming Wire Links

An inexpensive fixture for forming eyes or loops in wire links is shown in the accompanying illustration. It is designed to be held in a bench vise and consists of a block, A, into which are fitted two pins, the distance between their centers being equal to the distance between the centers of the loops or eyes to be formed. Two smaller pins, also driven into the block, locate the preformed wire centrally with the eyes. A hole, D, equal in depth to the length of the wire forming the eye, is drilled in the end of the block, and an adjustable stop, E, is tapped into the end as shown, and locked by a nut. The lever L, which is used for forming the link eyes around the pins, has a pin, G, and it is drilled at F to fit the link-forming pins.

The process of making wire links is as follows: First cut off the wire to the developed length of the links. Next insert one end of the wire in hole D and bend it until it touches stop E. Repeat this bending operation at the opposite end of the wire, being careful to keep the bends in the same plane, so that the partly formed link will lie flat in the fixture. At this stage of the forming operation the link is shaped as shown in the detail. The lever L is placed in position on one of the pins so that pin G engages the wire

and the eye is then formed by rotating the lever about the pins, after which the forming operation is repeated at the other end of the wire, producing the complete link as shown in detail S.—Leonard Keiser, Jr., Hawthorne, N. J.

Double Doors for One-Way Passage

Almost everyone at some time or other has experienced the annoyance of having a door pushed in his face just as he was about to open it. Here is a method of arranging double doors which make such accidents impossible. The doors can be made in any design to suit the builder, but the hinges must be put on opposite sides, so that each will work one way only. This is further assured by arranging latches as shown. These are made from rods, formed into a handle at one end and bent to a right angle at the other end, which rests against the wall when the door is shut. The latches are held to the door with two straps. The only way to open the door is to grasp the handle and pull it up to a horizontal position. Thus, although most people keep to the right, the

Self-Locking Handles on Double Doors Allow One-Way Passage Only

doors are made proof against the few who persist in doing the wrong thing.—Harry Moore, Rosemount, Can.

¶In the process of hardening, the fine cutting edges of a tool should never be exposed to the hottest place in the fire; heat the heavy part first, allowing the heat to run to the thin edge.

HOW TO MAKE THINGS

Fascinating to any boy, yet practical enough for men with technical skill, the four books of the NEW BOY MECHANIC LIBRARY have been recognized as the most useful books in any home. Their interest to the whole family lies in the fact that devices are described that are of use about the home, in the garden, shop, and in outdoor sports and games of all kinds.

What You Will Find to Interest You in

THE NEW BOY MECHANIC LIBRARY

3,849 Ideas　　　　Four Beautiful Volumes　　　　3,917 Illustrations

A faint idea of the world of useful articles in these books may be had from the following list of the main subjects treated. Look over this list. Any one or two articles that interest you may make the books worth much more than their small cost.

Electrical devices	Hammocks	Toboggans	Tents	Decorative leather work
Photography	Sleds	Wind wagons	Skiis and skiing	Gymnasium
Carpentry	Wood working	Dog cart	Indian snowshoes	Iceboats
Automobile	Motor sleds	Water sports	Power devices	Skating
Household helps				

Toys
Painting
Boats
House decoration
Camping
Drafting
China painting
Decorative metal work
Fishing
Furniture
Farming
Gardening
Poultry
Fruit growing
Laboratory helps
Models
Magic
Entertainments
Music
Outdoor games
Outdoor winter sports
Stoves
Radio
Wireless
Furnaces
Tricks
Puzzles
Bicycle
Flowers
Hunting
Trapping
Library helps
Metal working tools
Secret locks
Indoor games
Kites
Parachutes
Plumbing
Sheet metal work
Pets
Swings

SEND NO MONEY Simply send your name on the attached coupon and indicate whether you want the complete library at the special price of $7 or a selection of individual books at $2 each. There are four books in the library and you will be pleased with your purchase if you take them all. However, you may already have one or more of the volumes, and will want to complete the set by ordering the rest. Book 4 is brand new. It contains the latest articles on radio as well as over 3,000 other articles. Send No Money. Simply sign and mail the coupon. The books will be sent to you at once. When the postman delivers them, hand him the price of the books plus the few cents postage. That is all. If you want the books sent direct to a friend, it will be necessary for you to send the cash with the order.

The Four Books

$7

MAIL THE COUPON TODAY

POPULAR MECHANICS PRESS
Popular Mechanics Building, Room 712　　　　CHICAGO, ILLINOIS

POPULAR MECHANICS PRESS
Popular Mechanics Building, Room 712, Chicago, Ill.

Please send me at once C. O. D. the Boy Mechanic Library at $7. ☐ (Put a cross in the square); (or—the individual books you want). ☐ Book 1, $2; ☐ Book 2, $2; ☐ Book 3, $2; ☐ Book 4, $2.

Name ....

City ....

Street .... State ....

INDEX TO VOLUME 25

NOTES

NOTES

NOTES